ANTIQUE DENTAL INSTRUMENTS

ANTIQUE DENTAL INSTRUMENTS

Elisabeth Bennion

SOTHEBY'S PUBLICATIONS

First published 1986 for Sotheby's Publications by
Philip Wilson Publishers Ltd
Russell Chambers, Covent Garden, London WC2E 8AA
and in the USA by Sotheby's Publications
Harper & Row, Publishers, Inc
10 East 53rd Street New York NY 10022

ISBN 0 85667 310 2
Library of Congress Catalog Number 86-050085

Designed by Christopher Matthews

Phototypeset by Tradespools Ltd, Frome, Somerset
Printed by BAS Printers Ltd, Over Wallop, Hampshire
and bound by Dorstel Press Ltd, Harlow, Essex

Contents

List of colour plates

Foreword

The reasons for the changes that have occurred in all aspects of dentistry in the last two decades are far too many fully to enumerate here. However, it may be said that the work of members of the dental profession is changing from its age-old struggle to remedy and repair the ravages of the two most widespread irreversible ills of mankind, dental caries and periodontal disease, to the application of methods of prevention and the supervision of their effectiveness. Dental scientists have made it possible to understand the causes and effects of dental disease as never before. Dental health education has advanced dramatically and has proved successful worldwide in the reduction of dental disease in children. For several years, observant clinicians in many countries had gained an impression of improvements in the dental health of their patients and, particularly, of the falling caries levels in children; the epidemiologists brought the solid, supporting evidence later.

At such a time of change within the profession and in its service to the community, Elisabeth Bennion's conspectus of dentistry of the past deserves the warmest of welcomes. At all times dentists have been quick to adopt advances in scientific, technical and medical fields whenever they have seen them to have any application to their clinical practice, adopting them to improve their service to their patients as well as for their own advantage and convenience. By her comprehensive exploration of the origins and development of the instruments that the practitioner used, supported by picture, fact and anecdote, Elisabeth Bennion has made the clinical aspects of bygone dentistry the core of her study and produced a fascinating story.

G. L. Daley OBE LDS
President, British Dental Association

Acknowledgements

The writing of this book has been very much helped and encouraged by the kindness of so many people. First among them are Maurice Freeman and Arthur Kauffmann, whose interest and support have never flagged and to whom I am most affectionately grateful. I must thank all the museum curators I have consulted who have been so generous in giving me their time and advice, particularly Mr Archie Donaldson of the British Dental Association, whose expert knowledge has been invaluable. I am, not least, grateful for the patience, courtesy and interest of the staff of my own local library in Wimbledon who have never failed to obtain for me the most obscure books from the most unlikely sources, and to my dear friends John and Margaret Begent in whose flat at Dover so much of this book was written. It gives me pleasure to put the last word to it this ninth day of February, the Feast of St Apollonia.

Elisabeth Bennion

'For there was never yet philosopher
That could endure the toothache patiently'

Much Ado About Nothing

1 Introduction

The place of the tooth in life and folklore

The peaks of civilization have seen the worst teeth, but the very progress in culture and science such peaks have produced has provided the means of treating them. Between the peaks, however, have been wide sloughs when methods of treatment have remained static, not to say fallen into desuetude. What has remained consistently strong has been the wealth of folklore associated with the tooth and the important place in life that it has held.

In earliest times the tooth was seen as immortal. It remained the same when taken from the body and, when the flesh decayed and the bones crumbled, the tooth survived. Early man saw teeth as endowed with a special force to withstand the changes of time. Teeth were in effect supernatural; indispensable to life and surviving beyond it. They were long associated with the sun, which has always represented everlasting life for primitive societies, rising and setting with an inevitable regularity which was central to their lives, a symbol of vitality and immortality and thus related to the tooth. The tooth, then, was regarded as being divine and under the special protection of the sun. It is no small coincidence that evergreens, connected with sun worship for obvious reasons, have been high among cures for dental disease. Paeony seeds and roots, related to the sun by their name, which derives from 'Apollo', are other popular ingredients of ancient cures.

Different food, habits and environment have produced considerable changes in the teeth of modern man compared to those of his primitive ancestors, not least in size. In ancient societies the tooth was not merely used in mastication: it was a weapon of defence, used in speech, as a tool, a charm, an adornment; an instrument of ire, an aid to digestion, a secondary sexual weapon and displayed in pleasure. In modern times it has become a means of identification. Many of our most common and time-honoured expressions relate to the tooth: 'to grit one's teeth' is interpreted as a sign of bravery or, at least, resignation; 'to show one's teeth' is a sign of aggression; 'to cut one's teeth' is seen to mean a time of severe test and stress through which one will progress; to have one's teeth 'set on edge' may indicate a state of severe irritation. Hercules, who was believed to have had three rows of teeth, is no doubt the origin of the expression 'hard-bitten', indicative of large, strong teeth and a mean, aggressive nature. 'Long in the tooth' is naturally associated with age.

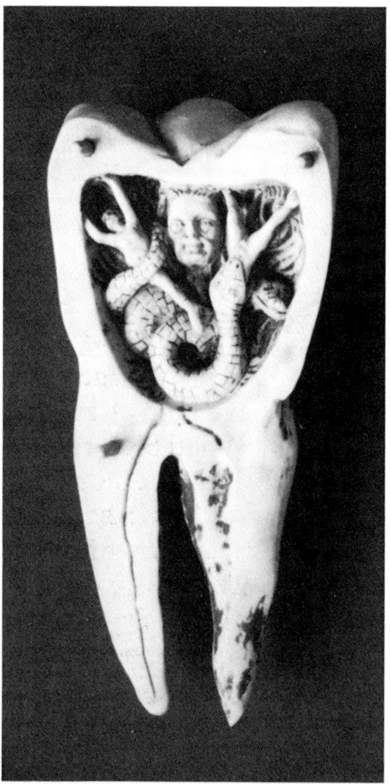

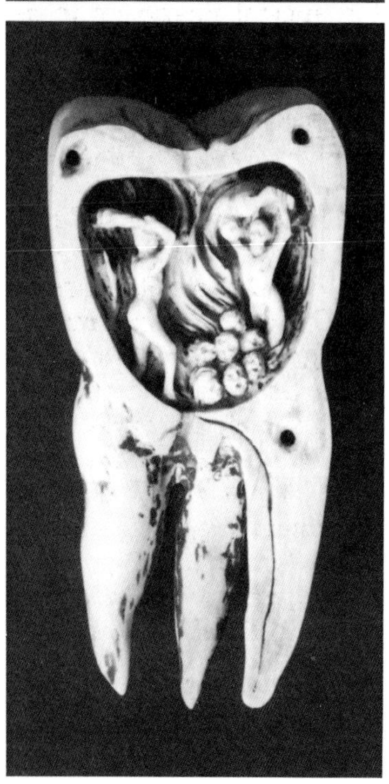

1 *French ivory carving showing the toothworm as one of the Tormentors of Hell, c.1750. (Museum of the History of Dentistry, Cologne)*

In primitive societies the tooth, as the token of vitality, was worn by witch doctors – those who sought to bring healing and therefore the likelihood of life. It represented qualities more desirable than the physical or chemical kinds already possessed, wherever and whenever faith was expressed in primitive ritual, rite and ceremony. It was only slowly that tooth care took the place of tooth worship.

The loss of teeth was associated with loss of virility, and for ancient man this usually meant death. What was seen as the indestructibility of the teeth gave rise to the belief that they held the secret of life, which they would take with them on leaving the body. The retained custom of throwing a child's first tooth into the fire is a direct link with returning the tooth to the sun. Since the tooth was protected by the sun, the diseases that attacked it were seen as the enemies of the sun, and therefore caused by a serpent, a snake or more often a worm, all of them regarded as evil.

It was a commonly-held belief that pain and suffering were afflictions from the gods and that, were the gods appeased, the torments would cease. Toothache is suffered at some time by everyone, and from early times man has made an effort to treat his dental problems and cure one of the worst pains to be experienced, by extraction, counter-irritant and various medicaments. In the past, by far the most popular methods were incantations, charms and other appeals to the occult, some of which have persisted into this century. William Perkins in *A Discourse of the Damned Art of Witchcraft* of 1608 remarked, 'Charming is in as great request as physic and charmers more sought unto than physicians in time of need', an updated interpretation perhaps striking a chord of sympathy in those who still care for a touch of ordinary, old-fashioned bedside manner.

The two themes that survived from the ancient sun worship connection into the more accessible past are the attribution of dental suffering to the insidious worm, the enemy of the sun, and its treatment in various ways by the mouse, another relation of the sun. It is fairly easy to accept the worm as a likely cause of toothache; putrefaction was always seen to be accompanied by crawling, worm-like organisms. In some languages, e.g. Manx and Gaelic, there is a semantic connection between the worm and toothache. The earliest reference to a worm in the tooth would appear to be from a Babylonian tablet in the British Museum describing the Creation. When the creatures had been told their place the worm came, weeping, and asked where to go. It was told to live in dried figs and apricots but replied, what were those to a worm? It asked, 'Set me amid the teeth and let me dwell in the gums, that I might destroy the blood of the teeth and of the gums . . .' (See pl. 1.)

Toothworms were frequently fought, like with like, by preparations compounded of worms, maggots, caterpillars and other such creatures. In ancient Rome and on into the eighteenth century fumigations of henbane were very popular to 'kill maggots'. In tenth-century England a cure read, 'For toothworms take acorn meal and henbane seed and wax, of all equally much, mingle these together, work into a wax candle and burn it till it reek in the mouth. Put a black cloth under it, then the worms fall in it.' John of Gaddesden (1280–1361), one of the most renowned medieval surgeons, firmly believed in the presence of toothworms. Jacques Houllier (1498–1562), author of *Chirurgia* (1555), was the first person to doubt the practice of fumigating for worms. He was certain that some lodgement of maggots in the mouth or cheese-mites in the cavities of the teeth could have caused the belief that was seized upon as a cause of decay by simple or unscrupulous people. Few could have paid attention. In *Much Ado About Nothing* Don Pedro says, 'What! Sigh for the toothache?' to which Leonato rejoins, 'Where is but humour or a worm.' By the eighteenth century there are reports of an extracted tooth being put in a glass of water, upon which the worm was seen to emerge and swim away. It was possible that a split tooth might expose the nerve in worm-like pose. There were contemporary stories of quack tooth-drawers concealing minute scrolls of white paper in their finger-nails, which they left in the mouths of their patients who afterwards obligingly spat them out, confirming the existence of worms.

The mouse was considered by the ancient Egyptians to be under the direct protection of the sun and an antidote to death. After the subsidence of the Nile hosts of mice appeared in the mud, from which it was deduced they were directly created by the sun by spontaneous generation and were its creatures. The mouse, therefore, appears in many cures for toothache and halitosis and itself was seen to have particularly strong and fine teeth. The Egyptians used to split the body of a living mouse in half and lay it, warm, along the gums of a patient. Remains of undigested mice have been found in the bodies of children buried in Egypt 5,000–4,000 B.C. The value of the mouse spread to other cultures. The Roman writer Pliny mentioned mouse therapy and suggested that a mouse eaten twice a month would protect one from toothache. Cures involving mice still appeared in the early part of this century.

It was not just the old pagan religions that were involved with the tooth; the monotheist creeds had contributions to make on the subject as well. The Talmud shows understanding of the old connection between strength and the condition of the teeth; indeed, the loss of one or more teeth was sufficient to disqualify a rabbi from service in the Temple. It saw teeth as imperishable and advocated garlic, oil, fruit juices and the eggs of grasshoppers as a cure for toothache. The Mosaic Law considered the loss of a tooth as so important that, if a tooth were taken by violence, it could only be repaid in like kind, 'a tooth for a tooth'. Mohammed had advice for the care of teeth, and the medieval Christian Church, in that turgid area between religion and magic, was positively preoccupied with it.

As a rule, people in the past took a tough attitude to pain, but the obtrusive effect of toothache on them cannot be overestimated. People suffered in ways that are almost unimaginable today; a humble country person in agonizing pain might wait several months for the travelling tooth-drawer to appear at the next fair and give him relief, and one finds frequent reference to the anguish of such people. There is a medieval story of a weeping child bitten by a snake (again the snake appears) in which a passer-by says, 'Is that all? I thought you had the toothache.' And an old Hungarian proverb says, 'Adam hath eaten the apple and our teeth ache from it.' (See pl. 2.)

While there are about 93 saints related to medicine, there are very few for dentistry. Bruno Floria suggests this is because dental pain was often so acute there was not sufficient time for the sufferer to sink to his knees and pray. It is St Apollonia – and we must note her sun-related name – who became the patron saint of dentists and all who suffer from toothache. A native of Alexandria, she was martyred in A.D. 248 by having her jaws broken and her teeth knocked out prior to being burned (the details differ a little from place to place). Medieval pilgrimages were made to shrines where her teeth are still preserved; her mouth was apparently so divine it must have contained far more than 32. The Bohemians alleged that if one fasted on her feast day of 9th February one would not suffer toothache for the rest of the year. In Bavaria the following popular prayer bears testimony to the anguish of unremitting toothache and again suggests it may have resulted from offence given:

St Apollonia
A poor sinner I stand here,
My teeth are very bad.
Please be soon reconciled
And give me rest in my bones
That I forget the toothache soon.

Apollonia, Apollonia
Though the holy saint in heaven
See my pain in yourself,
Free me from evil pain
For my toothache may torture me to death.

Apollonia of Bayerland,
I raise to thee my right hand
And promise thee ten candles
If thou takest my toothache from me.

2 *Medieval stone capital in the south transept of Wells Cathedral showing the importance of toothache in contemporary life. (Dean and Chapter, Wells Cathedral)*

3 *St Geneviève and St Apollonia holding forceps and tooth. Lucas Cranach the Elder, 1506. (Loyd Trustees, National Gallery, London)*

Pictures of St Apollonia (pls. 3 and 4) in medieval art show dentistry as very much a matter of instruments rather than potions, though that is not borne out in the customs recorded. Charms and incantations, occasionally accompanied by blood-letting, were the usual resort. A charm in Hereford Cathedral reads as follows:

> *Mary was seated upon a stone, weeping. Jesus came to her and said: 'O, my mother who art so sorrowful, why dost thou sit here?' She replied, 'My son, my teeth ache so badly that I can neither sleep nor wake.' Jesus said, 'Arise and come. Neither thou nor any man shall suffer pain if these words are carried on you.'*

There was widespread belief in the medieval world that if some particular object were put in a bag and worn round the neck, as it decayed so would the toothache wane. This persisted, apparently, well into this century; in Yorkshire it was a piece of raw meat, in Norfolk a piece of bread. Many charms, called 'toothache slips', were sealed pieces of paper to be worn about the person and never unsealed. Contagious magic was popular too: an animal tooth was worn as an amulet in many parts of the world and today an Arab may hang a hyena's tooth round his camel's neck for strength. Children's cast teeth were put near mouse holes that the new teeth might be strong as a rodent's. In the reign of Queen Anne there appeared a newspaper advertisement: 'Lost – About two months ago, a ring with a tooth set in it. Whoever will bring it to Mr. Green, Goldsmith in the Minories, shall have the value of it.' Possibly the tooth was the first shed tooth of a child, believed to preserve a mother from uterine pain.

Vestiges of the ancient belief in the immortality of the tooth can be found in customs treating toothache with items associated with the dead, for example a nail from a coffin, a tooth from a corpse, moss from the head of a corpse. The eighteenth-century Spanish painter Goya said, 'Teeth from the hanged are singularly effective in the art of witchcraft, as without these one cannot make anything rational.' One of his pictures shows a woman holding a scarf over her averted face and reaching up to the gallows to pull teeth from the mouth of the hanged man. Another belief involved transferring pain to an inanimate object. Nailing pain to a tree was a very popular and ancient custom reported by the Roman historian Livy. In Friedrichshagen sufferers touched and walked round a pear-tree three times repeating an incantation; an animal might be made the recipient for pain – spit into a frog's mouth, for example, and tell it to go off with the pain. In Brunswick one wrote upon one's door a message to the toothache to go away, one was not at home. Many incantations were addressed to the moon, presumably as the obverse of the sun.

Other customs were more intimately connected with the Church. If the newly baptised child had its mouth rinsed out with holy water from the font it would be safeguarded from teething

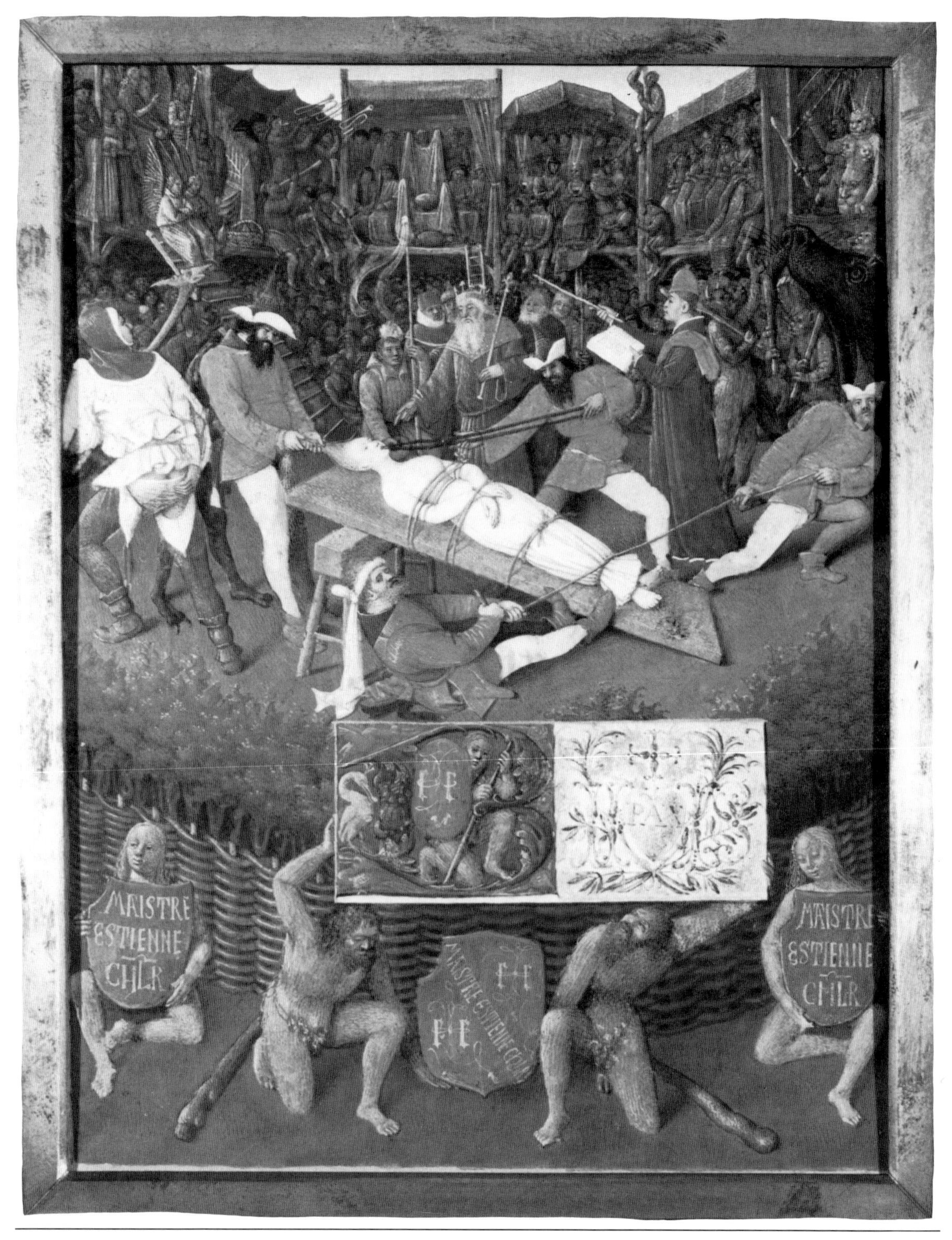

4 *The Martyrdom of St Apollonia from* Heures d'Etienne Chevalier *by Jean Fouquet, c.1455. (Musée Condé, Chantilly. Photograph Lauros-Giraudon)*

troubles; for the same reason the mother should return from her churching and breathe into the infant's mouth. In Switzerland babies were fed a pap made of linden sprouts, cut on Good Friday at 12 o'clock. A more secular recommendation held that a wet-nurse with blonde hair – i.e. sun-coloured – was likely to give the infant trouble-free teething.

Aberrations in the normal course of dentition were viewed with alarm; any other than the norm was wrong, and wrong meant ill-fated. A child born with teeth was seen as a threat to the family and often drowned or otherwise killed. Such children might become sorcerers, witches or vampires, and Shakespeare's description of Richard III – 'That dog, that had his teeth before his eyes' – no doubt reflected contemporary opinion. Shakespeare's source appears to be the *History of England* by John Rous, the fifteenth-century antiquary of Warwick. Whether or not it was true that the king had been born with a full set of teeth – and one of the so-called witnesses was blind – it was clearly used as a way of depicting him as a demonic ogre. Pliny, alone in his opinion it would seem, felt that a child born with teeth was a favoured child, who might well turn out to be a genius. Nearer our own time it is the sense of ill-fortune that lingers, and even today early teething is associated with early death in some places. A Spanish proverb says, 'When a child cuts its teeth, death is on the watch.' At the other extreme there is a tombstone in the churchyard at Gayton-le-Marsh, Lincolnshire, of 'Elizabeth Cook, a poor woman who never had a tooth in her mouth, June 11th 1798.'

Were teeth well spaced out, it was a sign of good luck; were they irregular, a sign of fickleness. Yellow teeth denoted insanity; broad and long teeth meant villains, traitors and jealousy; long front teeth suggested sensuality and bestiality. This type of dental fortune-telling was compounded in 1865 into the pseudo-science of odontological physiognomy, a short-lived enthusiasm.

Alongside these magic and quasi-religious beliefs were a number of remedies which, if to modern thinking no less fanciful, were devised from early medical study and formed the basis of serious dental treatment. It is easy to smile, but which of us has not slept with a milk-tooth beneath the pillow in the confident expectation of finding a coin replacing it on waking? The present writer, in the course of writing this book, was told it was to be hoped the book would not make her dream of teeth as that could only mean a death.

In the twentieth century the tooth has sunk from being the most highly prized organ, itself a deity, to being a degenerate and frequently neglected aggravation. Indeed, in the early part of the century it was recurrently blamed for any chronic bodily malady and removed as treatment. It has been said, 'Removing the teeth will cure something, including the foolish belief that removing the teeth will cure everything.'

A brief survey of the dental profession

Any study which can illuminate the emergence of dental surgery as a service to the public must have some interest and worth; while dental disease still flourishes this study can be associated with the present. Dental health, often thought to be excellent several centuries ago, was clearly not so. Badly-ground flour containing fragments of grit and sand, shells, hard seed and bones ground down the teeth excessively; gingivitis was even described by the Saxons. We have seen how the loosening of the teeth was perceived as a sign of waning strength; indeed the Greek philosopher Aristotle believed that those who had most teeth would be longest lived, though since he also believed – an opinion shared by Pliny – that women had fewer teeth than men, there would seem to be little logic in the argument. Despite such signs of ignorance, it is obvious that concern with various dental disorders and attempts to alleviate them have existed from the earliest times. There is an Egyptian hieroglyph for one who deals with teeth, found in the Ebers Manuscript of *c.* 1550 B.C., discovered at Thebes in 1872. There are references to care of the teeth found in the writings of Hippocrates, Galen, Oribasisus, Celsus, Aurelianus, Paul of Aegina among others, as well as from the Arab surgeons. These considerations were mostly regarding caries, maleruption and extraction. Dental art reached a pinnacle with Roman civilization but fell into decadence with it.

Ambrose Bierce (1842–1914) in *The Devil's Dictionary* defined a dentist thus: 'Dentist, n. A prestidigitator who, putting metal into your mouth, pulls coins out of your pocket.' One can only regret the truth that many would have agreed with him several centuries earlier, so often has dentistry been associated with money. The papal edict of 1215 separated the medical profession into physicians and surgeons, precluding the monks, who had hitherto handled all medical care, from drawing blood (see pl. 6). The monks then taught the barbers, who visited the monasteries professionally and were naturally used to handling knives, to undertake operations under their direction. The monks abandoned the tooth and its problems but they kept alive the traditions of Greek medicine through the Dark Ages. Those who remained to look after the fortunes of the tooth were the barber-surgeons who were essentially craftsmen, the travelling tooth-drawers who were probably the most experienced, and the charlatans of the market-place who were, necessarily, showmen. Dentistry became the province of these three groups and very little was ever written about it.

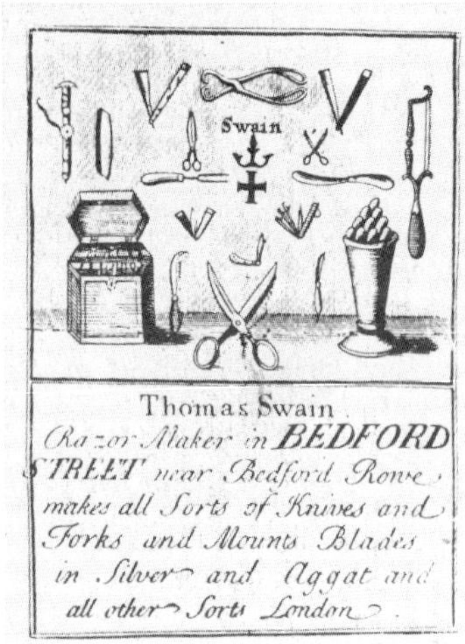

5 *Advertising bill for Thomas Swain, cutler, used as a receipt, c.1740. A dental pelican is in the top left-hand corner. (Museum of London)*

In the twelfth century a tooth-drawer might very well be a keeper of the public baths, and his job would include drawing the teeth of those who ate meat in Lent and forcing confessions from suspects in criminal cases. The popular image of the tooth-drawer was of a man in a pointed cap carrying the insignia of St Apollonia, wearing a necklace of extracted teeth and crying his

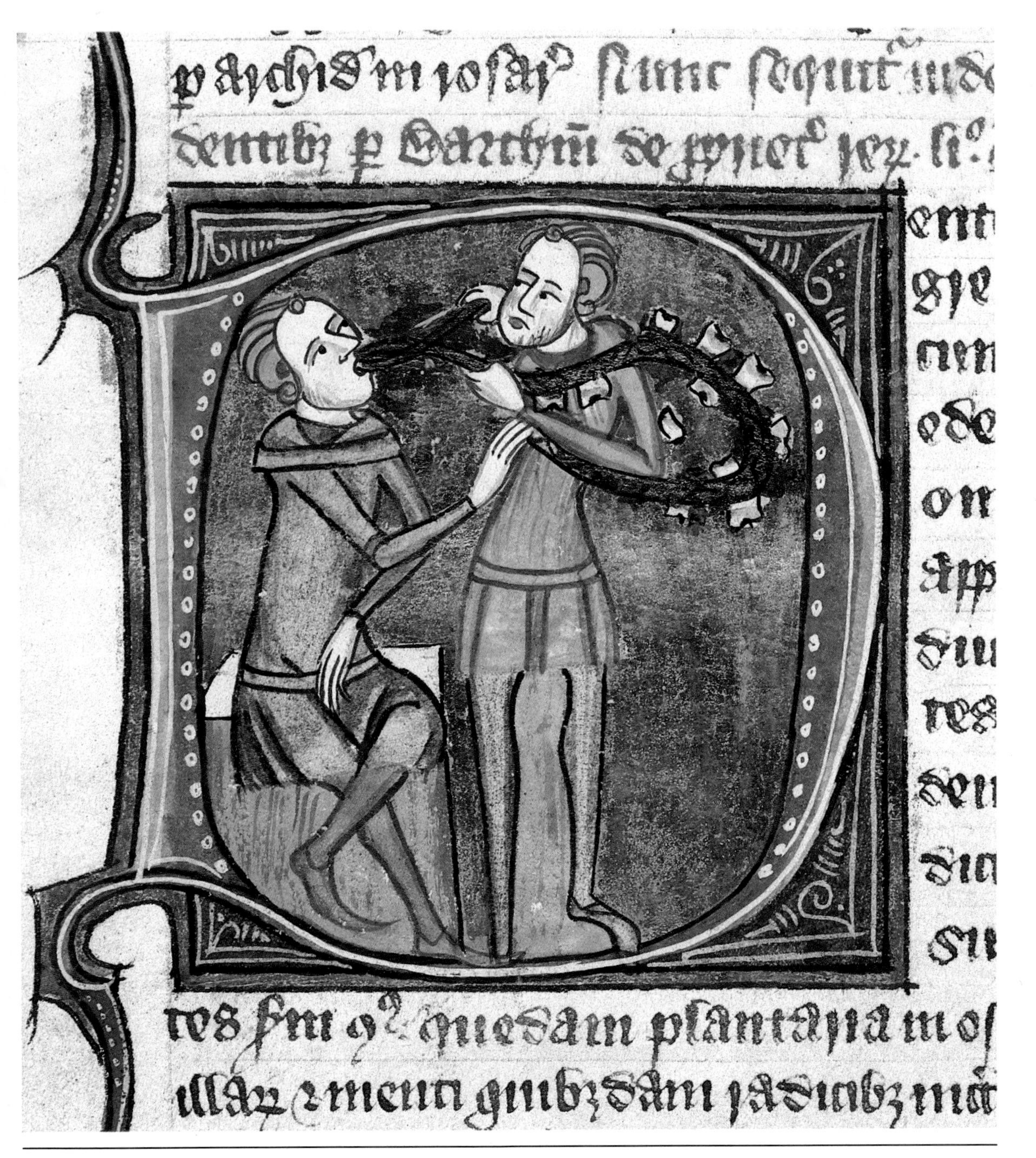

I *14th-century dental extraction; note the necklace of teeth. From the encyclopaedia of Jacobus the Englishman. Royal MS. 6E V1 f.503 verso. (The British Library, London)*

II *19th-century ceramic fairing showing the entertainment value of tooth-pulling. (Peter Goodwin, London)*

6 *Cauterization of the mouth, French manuscript, 13th century. (Trinity College, Cambridge)*

7 *Wooden panel showing an itinerant dentist and his family in all weathers, c.1840. Note the chair with head-rest. (Museum of the Baltimore College of Dental Surgery, Baltimore, Md.)*

skill as a painless operator – thereby giving rise to the French saying, 'He lies like a tooth-drawer.' The corresponding saying in Germany was, 'He shouts like a toothbreaker.' The fourteenth-century poet William Langland, in *Piers Plowman*, mentions 'porters, pickpurses, and peeled [i.e. bald] tooth-drawers', indicating the kind of company they might be expected to keep.

In 1415 there was a prohibition against quackery in England, and in every town members of the Barbers' Company were called before the mayor and aldermen for examination of their skill and practices. The masters were instructed to inspect all the instruments used and a fine of 40 pence in default was inflicted. In 1462 an application was made for a charter of incorporation, in which tooth-drawing was especially mentioned, and in 1540 Henry VIII finally granted the charter forming the United Company of Barbers and Surgeons.

The rise of the type of tooth-drawer we have seen has been considered as springing from the scarcity of people courageous enough to extract teeth. All writings have been so very full of descriptions of devices to avoid extraction – such as the fat of the green frog, which would cause the bad tooth just to fall out – that it is clear extraction was recognized as an extreme form of toothache remedy.

Between the Dark Ages and the Renaissance little development took place in the treatment of teeth. Guy de Chauliac (1300–68), chief among the luminaries of the Montpelier School, wrote a standard work, *Chirurgia Magna* (not printed until 1478), giving a detailed view of the state of dentistry but clearly showing little progress and suggesting barely any. He did, however, give a list of necessary instruments indicating knowledge was increasing among those who would operate them. In an earlier manuscript he used the word 'dentista' instead of 'dentator', expressing the evolution of the term for those specializing in the treatment of the teeth. The usage of the word in England was thought for some time to be a mere fashionable following of all things French. In 1530 a work devoted exclusively to the teeth, but in fact only collating ancient teaching in popular form, was published in Germany. The Belgian surgeon Andreas Vesalius (1514–64), a considerable anatomist, did much work on the formation and structure of the teeth. He was the first to make the distinction between molars and pre-molars and demonstrated the existence of the nerve chamber. He was again the first to maintain that women had as many teeth as men – a claim that was ignored by later writers, making one wonder how many surgeons looked in a woman's mouth. Vesalius was followed by Gabriele Fallopius (1523–62) and Bartholomeus Eustachius (1520–74), author of the first original treatise on teeth, *Libellus de Dentibus*, published in Venice in 1563.

By the late sixteenth century the term for a dentist had changed to 'operator for the teeth', and slightly more respectable aspects were suggested by this definition. The old-style tooth-drawer, still replete with necklaces of teeth and holy relics – and, by now, with a toothpick to denote good breeding (see Chapter 7) – had become a frequenter of fairs and market-places. All writers seem to refer to tooth-drawers in terms of approbation.

The separation of dental science from general medicine, which has been mentioned, was accentuated in the seventeenth century. Writings on dental subjects increased and they show the poor standard that pertained. It was still held that worms existed in the teeth and that toothache, so often combined with earache, might be treated by applications through the ear. Some claimed that a sure cure for toothache was phlebotomy and an aperient followed by blisters and plasters. Another school of thought held that the sweat from between the legs of a cat chased over a ploughed field would be equally efficacious.

The first book on dentistry written in English, published in Dublin in 1685, was Charles Allen's *Curious Observations on the Teeth* (later known as *The Operator for the Teeth*). It is interesting that at a time of interminable disasters this book should ever have been published in Ireland; presumably it was not thought controversial. There is an interesting and important point where Charles Allen was at variance with other dentists of the time: he felt it the duty 'of such as live under a Civil Government to contribute as much as he can (in his own station) to the publick Good'. Generally, there was a great reluctance in people with experience and knowledge to pass it on, and even when they did so their writing was not easily accessible to many.

At the turn of the seventeenth century dentistry reached a peak of development in Paris. Pierre Fauchard (1678–1761), it was said, raised dentistry from a 'handicraft of vagabonds' towards a learned profession. In 1699 an edict had been passed in France legalizing the position of dental surgeons as distinct from physicians, surgeons or barber-surgeons, but examinations in dentistry were still held by physicians and surgeons, much to Fauchard's disgust; he felt that they might be learned men in their own subject but not in his. In 1728 he published his long and important work *Le Chirurgien Dentiste*. A professional man, he had much to say against the tooth-drawer:

> *A man who has been bribed in advance appears when the market crier calls for a toothache. The swindler inserts a previously extracted tooth into his mouth, together with a bloody hen's membrane and soon the awed crowd sees the 'patient' spit out a fully grown and bloody tooth as a result of this painless extraction.*

The profitable side of dentistry was now perceived by many; Fauchard remarked drily, 'There will soon be more dentists than persons affected with dental disease.' One of those to disclaim the existence of worms in the teeth, he was a formative influence on the development of dentistry in the next 100 years.

Fauchard's teaching was tardy to cross the Channel, possibly due to language differences or politics or national chauvinism. In the United Kingdom matters progressed slowly, with little treatment other than extraction. With no restraints on advertising, this insertion by an early woman dentist in *Post Boy* of London in 1719 is no doubt typical:

> *The widow of the late Dr Povey, operator for the teeth, now follows the same business; she cleans teeth and puts in Artificial ones so easy, neat and firm that they need not be removed for years . . . and sells all his medicines . . . She hath a Cephalick, which certainly cures the toothache in a minute's time, beyond any person in England; and she stops hollow Teeth so that the pain will never return again.*

It was the work of John Hunter (1728–93) which, by placing dentistry on a scientific basis, became the threshold of a truer knowledge. In 1771 he published *Natural History of the Human Teeth*, followed in 1778 by *Pathology of the Teeth*. His studies were extensive and minute and the anatomical specimens he used are still preserved. He encouraged a serious approach to dental problems; for example, he was the first to assert that continuing pressure can change the position of the teeth, an early directive towards orthodontics.

Nevertheless, there was no organized course of study available, nor qualification for practice. An apprenticeship was the only way to learn the trade. In 1820 Levi Spear Parmly (1790–1859) – there were eighteen dentists in two generations of the Parmly family (pl. 9) – offered instruction in the art of dentistry for 100–200 guineas. Another dentist offered one day's teaching for £50. The terms of apprenticeship were harsh, and the boys who were taken on had to promise solemnly to keep secret what they learned. Appenticeships lasted between five and seven years, and during this period a boy could not marry, play at cards or dice or visit playhouses or taverns. He had to work faithfully at the tasks set and had to accept that such surgical knowledge as might drift his way would come only through the poor who came to be treated early in the morning. The premium for this might be as much as £500.

Since there is no record of the numbers of those in practice at one time, or any kind of journal devoted to dentistry, it is hard to form a complete picture. Those few who practised with any skill or success were probably qualified surgeons, but the vast majority were obviously uneducated and disreputable, jumping on what they saw as a highly lucrative band-wagon. It was said, 'The adage that any fool will do for a parson may be applied with still greater force and truth to the profession of a dentist.' The charlatan tooth-drawers and blacksmiths were still in the majority, however, drawing teeth at country fairs, the cries of the sufferers being drowned with raucous music, an entertainment described by Thomas Hardy as late as the end of the nineteenth

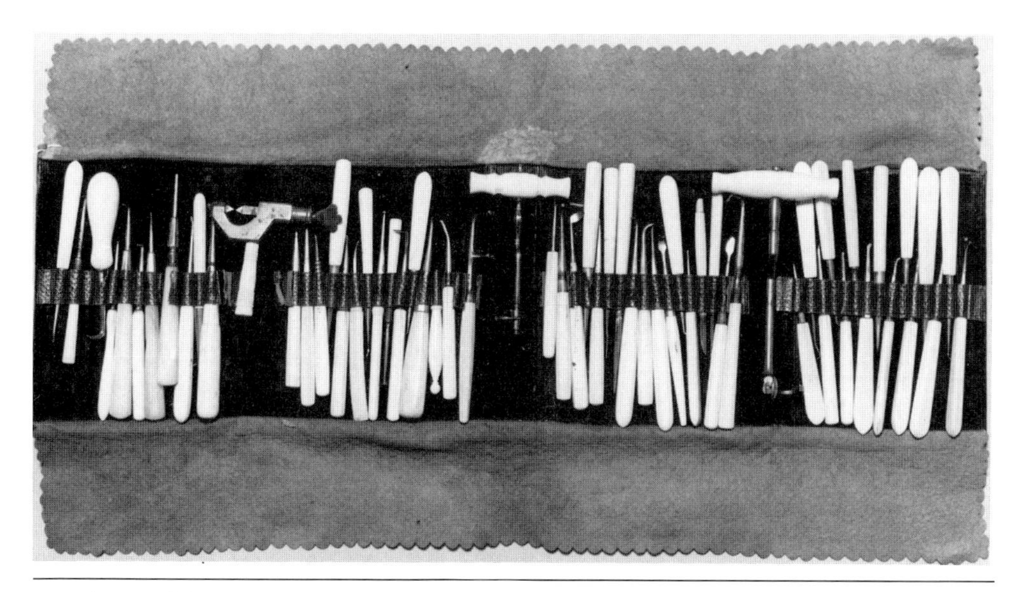

8 *Collection of dental instruments, early 19th century, each appox. 16 cm. (Howard Dittrick Museum of Historical Medicine, Cleveland, Ohio)*

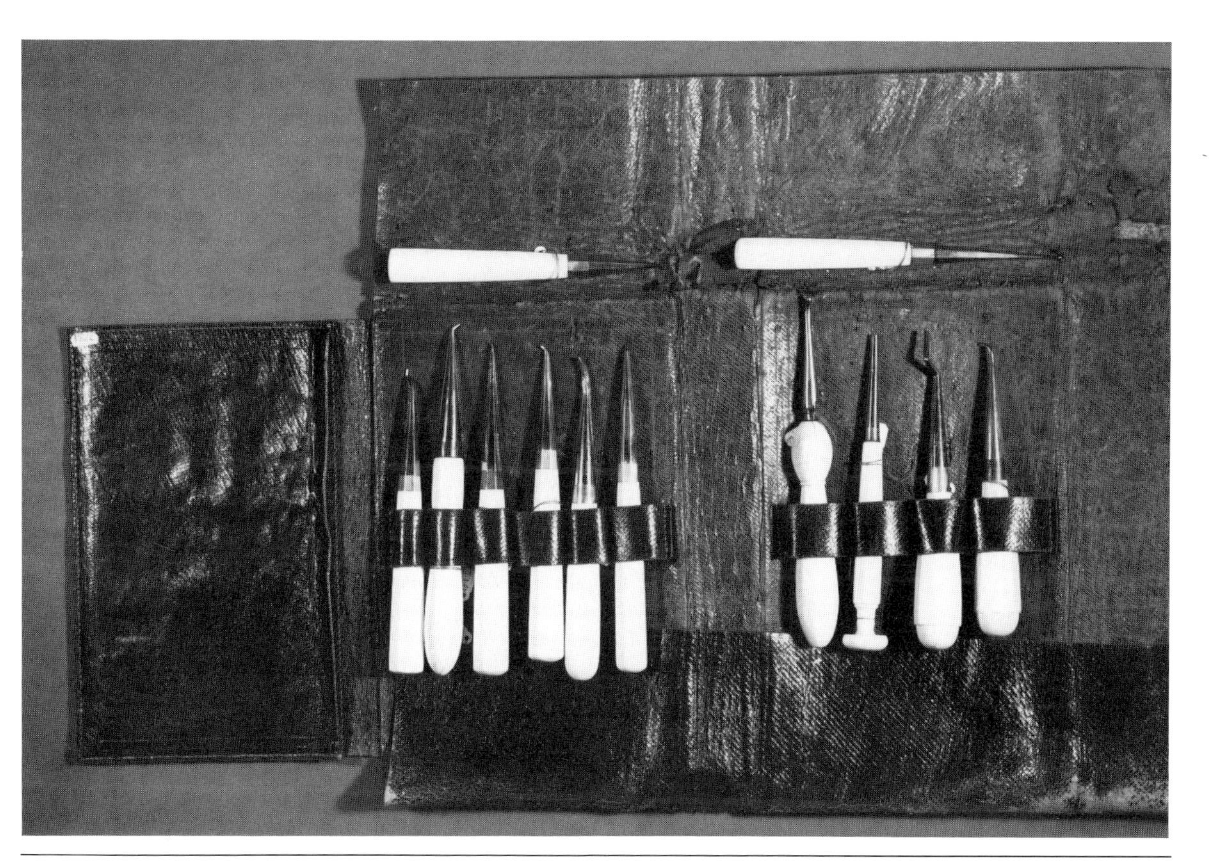

9 *Leather pouch of ivory-handled gold-foil pluggers, c.1850. Used by Dr Samuel and Dr Henry Parmly. Each approx. 14 cm. (American Dental Association, Chicago, Ill.)*

century (see col. pl. II). In France there were several pictures painted showing monkeys as dentists, reflecting the popular view of most practitioners. Much suffering was endured owing to lack of proper treatment. Apart from the absence of dental training few decent instruments or materials were available – an absolute essential to dental surgery – and it was not until the mid nineteenth century that real improvement was noticeable.

On the other side of the Atlantic things progressed a little differently. In 1749 Sieur Roguet from Paris was advertising in Boston, among many other things, that 'He deals only for ready money with the Quality and Members of Parliament.' John Hunter's great influence on British dentistry hardly touched America as it coincided with the War of Independence and few books were imported at the time. On the other hand some British dentists went to America themselves, among them Robert Wooffendale (1742–1828) in about 1766, Fendall (b. 1753), and, in 1767, John Baker (1732–96), who became one of the many dentists to George Washington. Baker took as a pupil the patriot and silversmith Paul Revere (1734/5–1818). Following the Battle of Bunker's Hill and the subsequent British withdrawal from Boston, he and two others set out to find the body of General Warren. Among the badly decomposed corpses Revere alone was able to identify the body positively – by the bridgework in the mouth, which he himself had constructed. The circumstance of a silversmith turning dentist was not unusual; in the early days of the Colonies dentistry was a sideline of men whose main occupation might range from ivory turner to wig-maker. The attraction to the profession of those who had these particular manual and technical skills was one factor which gave America pre-eminence in the complex restoration of the mouth. By 1770 Paul Revere was advertising in the *Boston Gazette* or *Country Journal* that he could treat teeth 'as well as any Surgeon-Dentist who ever came from London'. In fact, the majority of visiting British dentists went mostly to sell tooth-brushes and dentifrice and did not stay in one place long enough to impart whatever knowledge they may have had. One exception was Robert Cartland Skinner (d. 1834), who practised at the Dispensary of New York and wrote *Treatise on the Human Teeth* in 1801, the first such work to be printed in America. It was, however, America that now took the lead in dental progress.

The first dental society in the world, the Society of Surgeon-Dentists in the City and State of New York, was set up in 1834, and the first dental school in the world, the Baltimore College of Dental-Surgery, in 1839, with Dr John Harris (1798–1848) as the first American to give professional lectures. The college was started by private enterprise but was approved by the state; it not only gave instruction but issued a diploma of qualification. More dental schools were founded in America than anywhere else (see pl. 10). It was easier to institute schools there as there was less prejudice to contend with and no established medical schools

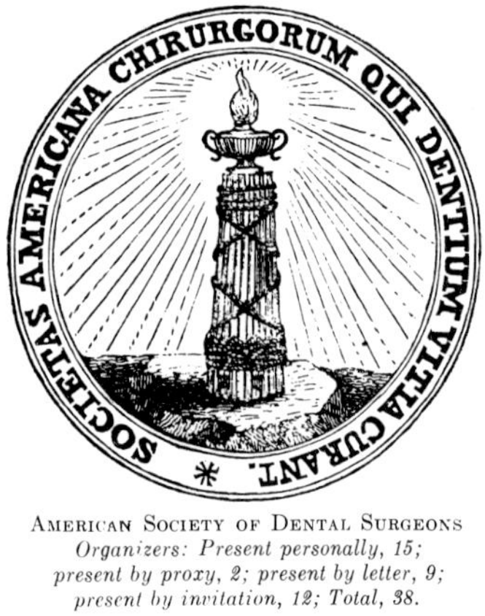

SOCIETAS AMERICANA CHIRURGORUM QUI DENTIUM VITIA CURANT.

AMERICAN SOCIETY OF DENTAL SURGEONS
Organizers: Present personally, 15; present by proxy, 2; present by letter, 9; present by invitation, 12; Total, 38.

10 *Seal of the first national dental society, the American Society of Dental Surgeons, 1839. (Museum of the Baltimore College of Dental Surgery, Baltimore, Md.)*

claiming rights to a study they had previously ignored or neglected. What was seen as a tripod, upon which the profession must be established, was formed, by first the school at Baltimore, secondly the American Dental Association for scientific study, discussion of knowledge and innovation and co-operation between members, and thirdly The Journal. *The American Journal of Dental Science* was founded in 1839 to disseminate knowledge and stimulate improvements in education. All this happened simultaneously whereas in the United Kingdom there was a very uneven growth of the same tripod.

In Britain John Hunter persuaded William Rae to give the first lectures on dentistry at his house in Leicester Square in 1782. One of his first pupils was Joseph Fox (1776–1816), who later lectured at Guy's Hospital in 1803. However, such scant instruction made little impact (see pl. 11). Grossly misleading advertising was rife, and a noticeable absence of ethics gave a general view of dental roguery. Dentists with well-furnished rooms in fashionable districts had immediate cachet compared to those at fairgrounds, and built up vast fortunes with blatant claims and hugely excessive fees. Even Samuel Cartwright (1789–1864), a highly respected practitioner who had served as mechanical assistant to a dentist while learning anatomy, saw 40–50 patients a day and was said by some to have earned £10,000 a year. Such great competition resulted in considerable secrecy about methods and discoveries.

After agitation by Alexander Nasmyth (d. 1848) and Sir John Tomes (1815–95), who did so much to promote English dentistry, the Odontological Society of London was set up in 1856 with Samuel Cartwright as President, and the *British Journal of Dental Science* published the society's transactions. Earlier the same year a meeting had been called to consider the feasibility of forming a College of Dentists, but acrimony arose over what were seen as private meetings between some members. Its eventual formation was beset with dissension, and in 1863 it and the Odontological Society amalgamated to form the Odontological Society of Great Britain. Meanwhile, in 1859 a dental hospital and school had been founded in Soho Square. A curriculum of study was drawn up but was hindered by a reluctance to recognize dentistry as a branch of surgery, and a sense of inferiority was felt by dentists. Renewed pleas for recognition were made to the Royal College of Surgeons in London, and the Charter was at last extended to include examination and licenses in dental surgery.

Punch, in May 1861, said it was

> *very much pleased to observe that the educated and honourable members of a profession which renders invaluable service to the public, have united for an effort to establish a broad line of demarcation between themselves and the quacks and snobs who have brought discredit upon the name of Dentist. It is true that no thinking person could confound the accomplished anatomical*

Young Practitioner. **"H'M, VERY ODD—I MUST HAVE MADE SOME MISTAKE; THERE'S NOTHING THE MATTER WITH *THIS* TOOTH. NEVER MIND, TRY AGAIN!"**

11 *Cartoon from* Punch, *1858. (Punch Library, London)* *scholar, whose treatment of the Mouth is based upon principles of science, with the vulgar and greedy creature whose only object is to make a lucrative job for himself and who is known wilfully to damage the teeth of unhappy victims for the sake of extorting larger fees; but then the world is not made up of thinking people . . .*

In 1859 the Medical Act had been amended to provide registration of dentists licensed under the Act, but this was opposed by non-professional dentists. The College of Dentists then tried to obtain a charter to become the Royal College of Dentists but failed. A second dental hospital was founded in London by James Robinson (1816–62), called the Metropolitan School of Dental Science, which eventually came under University College Hospital. Later, schools were founded in other cities, usually as part of existing medical schools. By 1880 a four-year course of study had been established (a curriculum not recognized in the – by now – United States for another 50 years). Nevertheless, in 1880, 4,000 had served an apprenticeship but only 500 held the Royal College of Surgeons Diploma.

In 1879 all dental practitioners had had to be registered with the newly-formed British Dental Association. In the process, the Association took the opportunity of excluding the more obvious and better-known quacks, for which purpose it had hastily to convert itself to a limited company under the Companies Act of 1865 in order to dodge any possible lawsuits with the peeved and precluded charlatans. Notwithstanding this, in 1919 a departmental committee appointed to examine the working of the Dentist's Act of 1878 found there was nothing to stop anyone, however ignorant, from practising dentistry and informing the public of the fact by advertising or other means. This resulted in the Dental Act of 1921, which made it unlawful for an individual who is not registered in the dentist's register and under the Medical Acts to carry on practice as a dentist.

In Canada the School of Dentistry of the Royal College of Dental Surgeons in Ontario was established in 1875 and affiliated to the University of Toronto in 1888. In other countries the formation of dental schools took longer, and in France, where dental education had first started, L'Ecole Dentaire was not founded until 1892.

By 1900, in the United States, there were about 60 dental schools, mostly privately owned and giving the practical side of training rather than teaching academic subjects. With the invention of the foot-drill in 1871, dentistry had become an even more financially attractive skill, and attitudes had changed enormously. Although there were some who were conscious of professional obligations, many practices were run on a profit-making basis, and concern was raised that dentistry would become more firmly entrenched as a trade than ever; the universities were exhorted to influence better standards of treatment. Despite the number of schools, in 1870 there were

10,000 dentists in the United States but only 1,000 were graduates of a school.

The social standing of the dentist has long been a difficult one. Just as the surgeon was not found as acceptable as the physician, so the dentist lagged behind the surgeon. Despite all the professional advances mentioned above, in 1878 the *British Medical Journal* could still say, 'Medicine is a profession, dentistry is largely a trade.' The journalist Peregrine Worsthorne recalls the difficulty experienced between the wars in deciding exactly where the dentist, calling at the house to look after his grandmother's teeth, should be given luncheon. It was unthinkable he should join the family in the dining room, yet the servants' hall did not seem quite right. A compromise was reached by his luncheon being served to him in the library alone.

The historian Lilian Lindsay has said that the seeds of the profession, sown in the nineteenth century, found a soil so barren and unpromising it was thought a miracle they took root. Increasingly, society has demanded good health, not least in its teeth, and aided, though tardily, by the recognition of anaesthesia as a necessity, dental patient and practitioner have united in a better relationship where prevention of disease is seen as the objective.

The account which follows attempts to portray the history of dentistry through its instruments. The earliest dental instrument makers were the armourers and blacksmiths, later superseded by the cutlers. Pieces of particular sophistication and refinement, for use on the most important clients, were made by the goldsmiths and silversmiths, while specialist instrument makers did not make their appearance until the eighteenth century; usually as a sideline of cutlers. All these men were such craftsmen they were incapable of making something useful without at the same time making it beautiful and their work thus provides us with a new key to the culture and humanity of their day. The study ends in the last quarter of the nineteenth century, when dentistry was poised to step forward into the modern age and when the new principle of antisepsis precluded the use of all the delicate materials and decorative detail so prevalent to this time. A certain amount of snobbery is directed against any study of mere objects, the implication being that it is the philosophy or ethics or sociology of dentistry which would be the worthier subjects. Without their instruments, however, the dental practitioners could have achieved nothing; their instruments were an extension not only of their bodies but of their ideas – symbols of man's ingenuity in his ceaseless endeavour to alleviate suffering and promote health.

2 Extracting instruments

In 1548 Thomas Vicary (d. 1561), Surgeon to Queen Elizabeth I, wrote *The Englishman's Treasure or the True Anatomy of Man's Body*. In it he said, 'To make an aking Tooth fall out of himselfe without any instruments or yren tooles . . . Take Wheat.' A century later Richard Baxter (1615–91) said in *Poetic Fragments*,

> *An aching tooth is better out than in,*
> *To loose a rotting member is a gain.*

When one considers the number of recommended methods for making a tooth fall out without using force that have been recorded over the centuries, it is curious that the longest chapter in this book should be devoted to extracting instruments. In the Ancient World and, indeed, throughout the Middle Ages extraction of teeth was seen as an extreme relief for toothache, only to be attempted when all else failed; on the other hand, it was one of the few surgical operations where it was known that the rest of the bodily functions would remain unaffected. After all, did a child not shed its teeth? And they might always grow again. Hippocrates (460–375 B.C.) only advocated extraction if the tooth were already loose, otherwise he would treat it with cauteries or masticatories. It is certain that the operation was not one to be considered lightly. Apart from the excruciating pain from the methods current there were other hazards to be considered: damage to the jaw, deep infection of the tissues and bloodstream, and even death was not unknown. As late as the sixteenth century Ambroise Paré (1510–90) cautions readers of his *Instrumenta Chirurgiae* not to be too vigorous in extraction or part of the jaw may be torn off as well.

In Elizabethan England there was constant allusion to toothache, rotten teeth and bad breath. The state of the Queen's teeth is well known; she had suffered from toothache as a child, supposedly caused by sugar, a commodity much prized when sugar-loaves were formal presentation pieces. In a play of 1659, a tooth-drawer speaks of 'rotten teeth with eating sugar-plums and sweetmeats at funerals'. It is small wonder that Queen Elizabeth was so frightened of having a tooth extracted, despite days and sleepless nights of unremitting toothache, that the Bishop of London allowed the surgeon to pull out one of his own – 'and she was hereby encouraged to submit to the Operation herself'. Her successor, James I, engaged in pulling out the teeth of others for his own amusement and paid 18s to anyone willing to let him, though most people found it all too important to retain their teeth, and not just for eating. For instance, for two centuries the dental requirement for the admission of infantrymen into the army was a sufficiency of incisors and canine teeth for biting off the tops of the cartridges (the automatic firing pin was not introduced until 1865).

Many an operator, in the Middle Ages and after, thought it tactless to proceed immediately to extraction; it was too like a common tooth-drawer. Better to try to cure the toothache, they thought, and the recipes were certainly ingenious. John of Gaddesden (1280–1361) tried the ubiquitous phlebotomy or an application of plasters to the gum and purgatives, he tells us in *Rosa Medicinae* (*c.* 1350). Every kind of excretal medication was advised: sparrow manure and sweet almond oil dropped in the ear – a popular orifice for a toothache remedy; fresh sage and one's own urine rubbed on the tooth; honey mixed with the faeces of a white dog and collected in March, with a little nutmeg, mixed to a compound. By the fifteenth century herbal mixtures were sometimes applied to aching teeth through a small metal funnel. John Josselyn (fl. 1630–75) in his *Account of Two Voyages to New England* wrote, 'for the Toothache I have found the following medicine very available. Brimstone and Gunpowder compounded with butter, rub the mandible with it, the outside being first warm'd.'

If the toothache persevered, the next step was to make the tooth fall out of its own accord. Pitch, mixed with raven or mouse manure, might be successful. Aulus Cornelius Celsus (25 B.C.–A.D. 50) said, 'a pepperberry freed of its skin, and inserted into the cavity will make the tooth split and fall out', and Pliny suggested juice from a plant grown in a human skull. John of Gaddesden favoured the fat of the green frog – a treatment still popular in the late eighteenth century – but he nevertheless needed extracting instruments. (Optimistically, he believed that the brains of a hare might make a tooth grow again.) In 1687 Charles Allen wrote that powdered red coral placed in the tooth would cause it to fall out. The loosening-up process so often referred to by the early writers was often accompanied by arsenical compounds which would have induced a necrosis of the bone and the eventual falling out of the tooth.

The earliest extracting instruments to have survived in illustrations are those in *Chirurgicorum omnium* by Albucasis (936–1013). Albucasis, when finally forced to proceed to extraction, was the first to detach the gum from the tooth with a scalpel. Then, the patient's head between the operator's knees, he rocked and shook the tooth until it came out, taking great care not to break it. His extracting instruments, like others of the Middle Ages, seem curiously ill-designed, with over-large jaws and very small handles. Five centuries later, a Dutch surgeon from Leyden, Anton Nuck (1650–92), seems to be the first writer to suggest that, to carry out a successful extraction, it is essential to have an adequate knowledge of anatomy and instruments that vary in size according to the tooth.

Extracting instruments fall into five main groups: pelicans, elevators and levers, screws, keys and forceps.

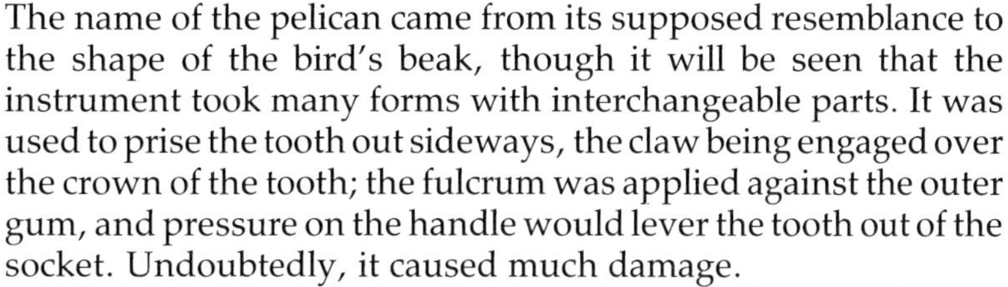

Pelicans

12 *Pelican, c.1650. (Museum of Swedish Dental Society, Stockholm)*

The name of the pelican came from its supposed resemblance to the shape of the bird's beak, though it will be seen that the instrument took many forms with interchangeable parts. It was used to prise the tooth out sideways, the claw being engaged over the crown of the tooth; the fulcrum was applied against the outer gum, and pressure on the handle would lever the tooth out of the socket. Undoubtedly, it caused much damage.

John of Gaddesden describes instruments of iron which were 'wide at the front and sharply cutting at the front and force the tooth down and it will thus fall out'. These may have been forms of pelican, but the first reference to one, as such, comes from Guy de Chauliac (1300–68) who based it on the coopers' tool used to force the last hoop onto a cask. The Venetian Andreas della Croce (1500–75) illustrated a very similar example in *Chirurgiae*, published in 1596. The first illustrations of a pelican appeared in 1460 in Giovanni d'Arcoli's (1412–84) *Practica*. These, though crude, give a good idea of the instrument at that time: a straight shaft with a single claw attached by a rivet and with a heavily notched bolster. Walter Ryff (1500–62) illustrated several in *Chirurgia Magna* (1545), by this time with two claws, each with a roughened inner edge, and of different lengths to accommodate different sizes of tooth. Ryff showed one example where the claw can be removed by a thumbscrew on the pivot. His bolsters were of amazing serration though we are told they were wrapped in a patch of leather in use. By the seventeenth century one sees ornamental round handles of steel, wood and ivory, heavily ornate, although simple handles still existed. In 1627, for instance, Gabriele Ferrara of Milan showed a pierced metal, spatulate handle and fan-shaped bolsters in his book on surgery.

Lorenz Heister (1683–1758) introduced an important advance by attaching a claw to an adjustable screw operated by the handle; three different claws could be attached, each having a differently angled head and curve to the shaft. The surgeon René-Jacques Garengeot (1688–1759) illustrated a pelican of this type in his book, *Traité des Opérations de Chirurgie* (1725) but, unlike Heister, he used a concave bolster and a straight claw-shaft. In *Descrizione degl'Instrumenti* of 1766 Mauro Soldo showed a whole series of pelicans with broad flat shafts, single claws and curiously short, turned handles, characteristic features of the eighteenth century. Antonio Campani (b. 1738), in his *Odontologia Ossia Trattato Sopra i Denti* of 1786, illustrated an open fitted bolster supported at either end by a branching shaft. Both Garengeot and the Berlin dentist Johann Jacob Joseph Serre (1759–1830) showed movable bolsters, which allowed more scope

13 *Pelican, c.1570, 13.5cm. (I. Freeman & Son, Simon Kaye Ltd, London)*

for adjustment, as did the endless screw, which reached from the end of the handle to the bolster. The endless screw was known in the mid eighteenth century and re-introduced by Jean-Baptiste Gariot in *Traités des Maladies de la Bouche* (1805).

A more complex pelican by Ryff was the double-ended type. This had two bolsters and two claws, and each shank had a semi-circular diversion to take the finger for a firmer grip (pl. 13). Francisco Martinez (1518–88) in his book of 1557, *Coloquia Breve*, illustrated a similar pelican but with concave bolsters. This double-ended form recurred occasionally over the years. John Woodall (1556–1643) showed his version in 1617 in *The Surgeon's Mate*; another forms part of the Prujean Collection of 1653, now in the Museum of London. Paré used two double-ended pelicans, both geometric in design. All the above occurred in a comparatively short space of time in four different countries so were apparently in general use. By the eighteenth century the shafts became thinner and more elegant, the convex bolsters had deep, even notches and the claws were fixed by a swivel joint. Double-ended pelicans with a single claw were illustrated by the maker Jean-Jacques Perret in his 1772 catalogue and by Antonio Campani in 1786, and both show a broad, flat shaft of double vase shape with slender claw-shafts.

An interesting development in the design of pelicans appeared in 1799 with the publication of *Recueil des Planches du Dictionnaire de Chirurgie*. This showed saddle-shaped bolsters screwed into the shaft, which made the relationship between the claw and the bolster variable. Even more adjustment was made possible by attaching the claw to an endless screw, described by Etienne Bourdet (1722–89) in *Researches and Observations* of 1757.

14 *Pelicans, each approx. 12 cm.*
(Musée Fauchard, Paris)

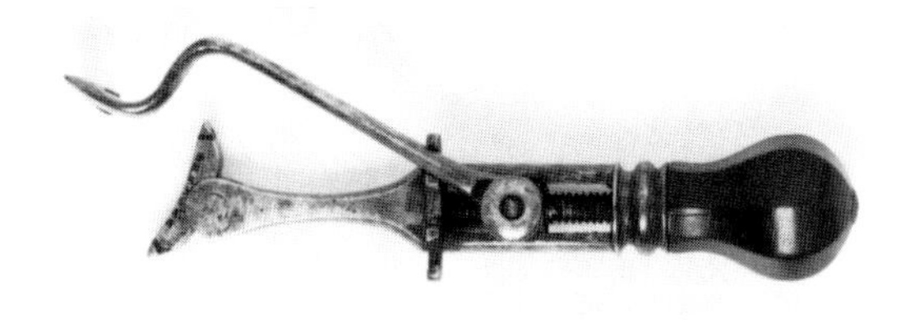

Concave bolster, single claw on screw, Brager, c.1775

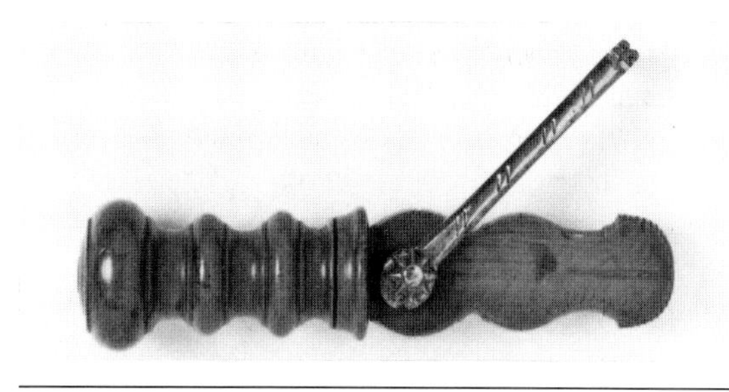

All wood with decorative metal claw, c.1770

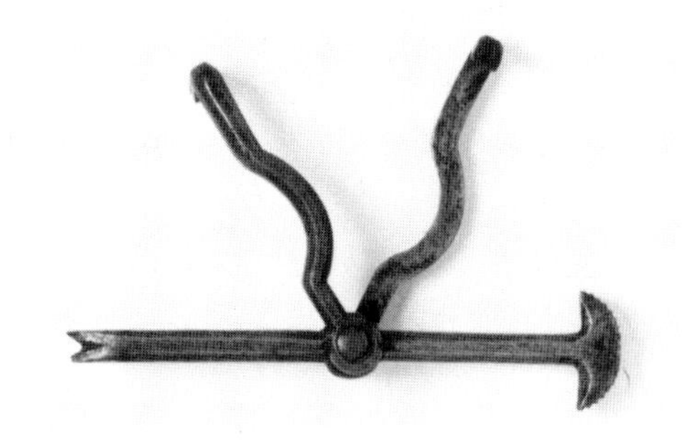

Two claws, and elevator at reverse end, c.1720

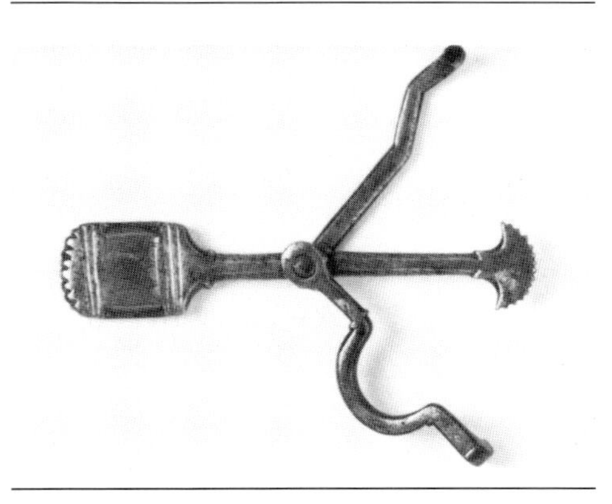

Two claws and extremely heavy handle, c.1600

15 *Pelicans, each approx. 12 cm.*
(Museum of the History of Dentistry, Cologne)

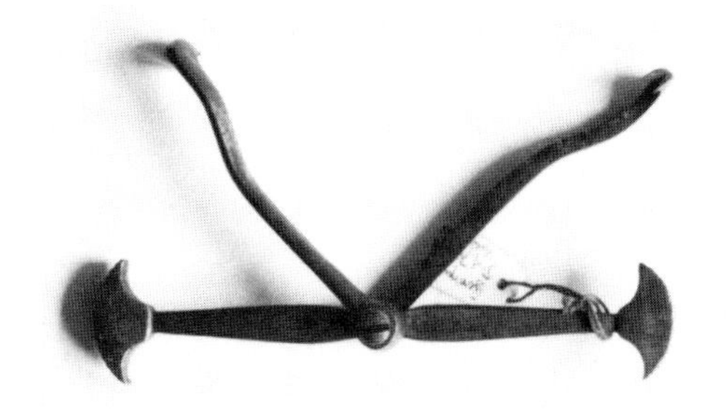

Double-ended type, c.1700

Forceps with screw, as Leber, 1770

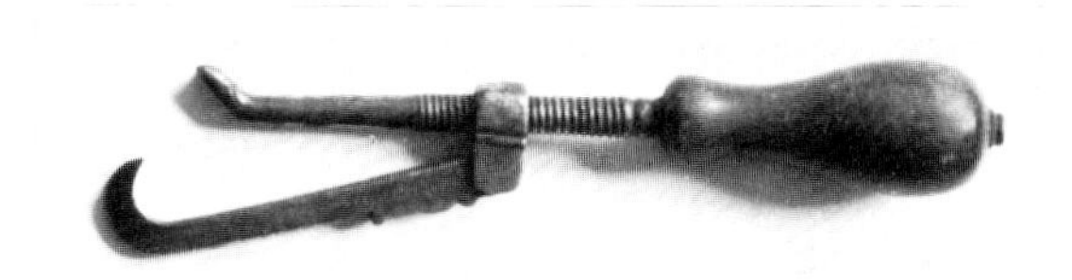

Pelican as Knaur, c.1796

Pelican, c.1730

16 *(Top) Pelican, c.1620, 12 cm; rare pelican with elevator, c.1730, 13.25 cm. (I. Freeman & Son, Simon Kaye Ltd, London)*

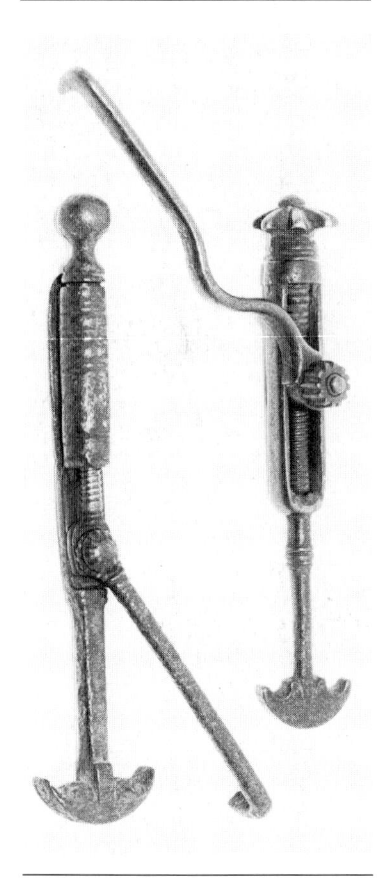

17 *Pelicans with screw mechanism, c.1750, 13 cm. (Museum of the History of Science, Oxford)*

In the 1686 edition of *Curious Observations on the Teeth*, Charles Allen gives a detailed account of the pelican '. . . so well-known by everybody. The polican [sic] is the best of extractors,' he says, describing an instrument with two bolsters and two claws. (He strongly advises against extraction whenever possible, however; even stumps in their sockets help to keep other teeth upright and should only be removed if there is danger of occasioning 'an ill habit in the Gums, that might be hurtful to the sound ones'.) A great favourite with operators was the pelican with deeply cleft bolster, as illustrated by Ryff and Paré, sometimes with the claw bent at a right angle. John Woodall says in *The Surgeon's Mate*, speaking of tooth extraction,

> *. . . by indiscreet drawing of a tooth either the jaw is broken, or some bad accident is provoked . . . and I esteeme him an unworthy Surgeon how high soever hee beares his head that can draw a tooth well, and will upon neede at sea scorn or deny to do it . . . If it bee the furthest tooth of the jaw either above or below, or that it be a stumpe, except it bee of the foremost teeth, the pullicans are the fittest instruments to draw with.*

A later modification was the forward-curving bolster with a corresponding curve to the claw, shown by Perret in his catalogue of 1771 and by Juan Alexand Brambilla (1728–1800) in his book, *Instrumentarium Chirurgicorum Viennense* of 1781 (pl. 50). This form of pelican became known as the *tire-toir* or *tirtoir*; it developed into the Douglas Lever, called after James Douglas, an army surgeon with the Welch Fusiliers in the early eighteenth century. It was illustrated by Alexander Monro (1697–1767) in *Medical Essays and Observations* in 1742, with the addition of an elevator at the reverse end. Brambilla had another pelican, in which the relation of the claw to the bolster could be varied by a series of notches on the claw-shaft and a hinge by which the position could be altered. Other methods of moving the position of the claw entailed sliding the base of the claw-shaft in a slot on the main shaft, securing it at the desired point by means of a screw. Ryff showed an adjustable claw-shaft, the base of which apparently rotated round the main shaft on a screw-thread. Heister showed this type with the addition of a hollowed bolster to take the shape of the tooth, as did Thomas Knaur in his book *Selectus Instrumentorum Chirurgicorum* (1796).

Charles Laforgue (1763–1823), author of *L'Art du Dentiste* (1802), introduced several types of pelican similar to forceps in that they had two handles to be held together. Probably the earliest example of this type was illustrated by Joseph Schmidt, in *Speculum Chirurgicum* of 1656. Pelicans with the shaft cut in an oblique direction were much used by Dubois, dentist to Louis XIV, and were highly regarded by him for being rigid. Benjamin Bell (1749–1806) illustrated pelicans in his *System of Surgery* (1782) but felt they had no particular advantage over keys, particularly

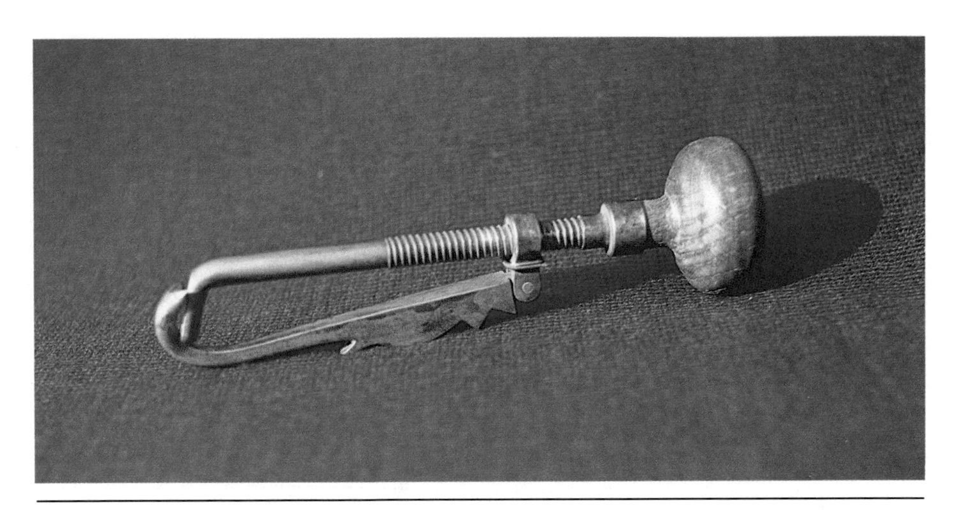

III *Pelican with screw mechanism, c.1720. (Museum of Medicine of the USSR, Kiev)*

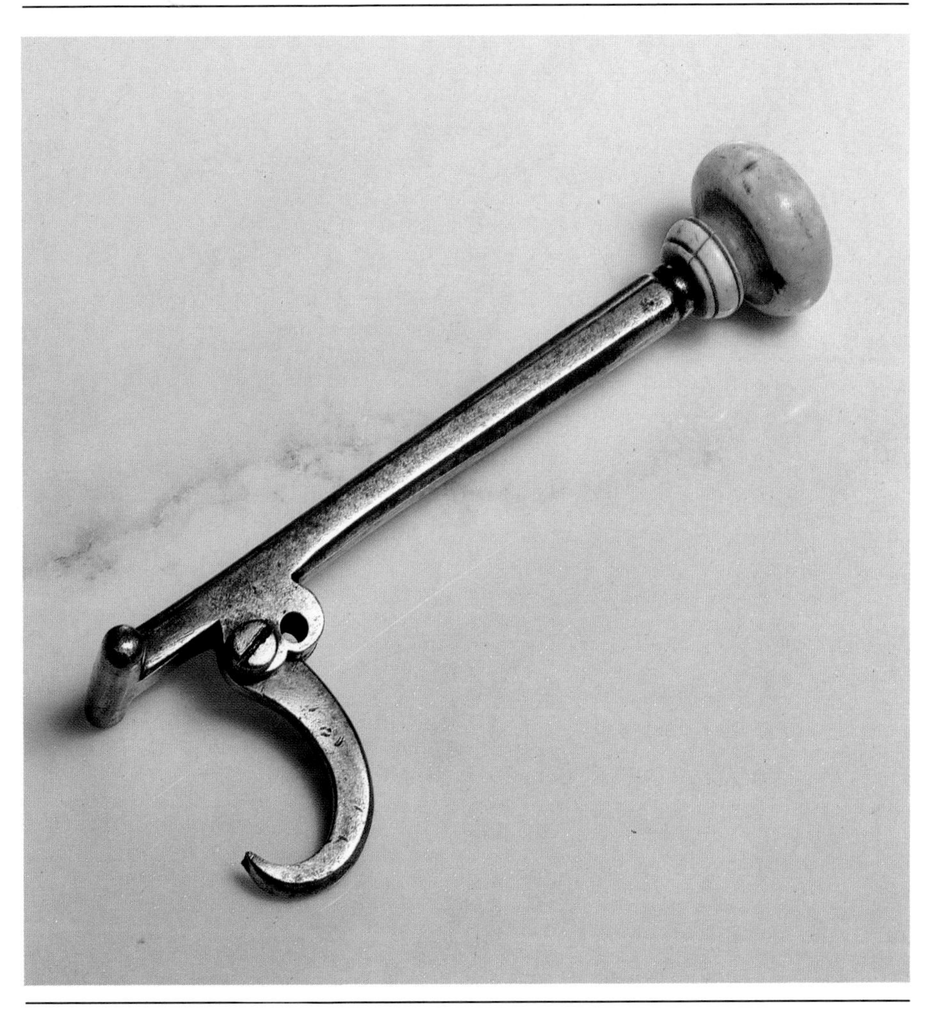

IV *Unusual pelican with transverse bar to act as fulcrum; the claw can be fixed in two positions, c.1780, 13.5 cm. (I. Freeman & Son, Simon Kaye Ltd, London)*

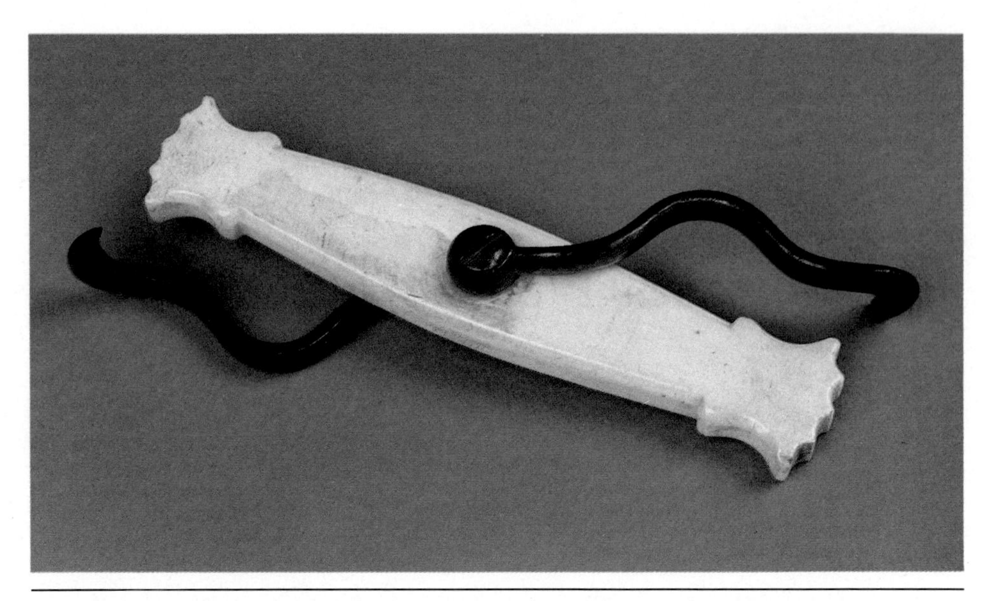

V *Ivory-bodied pelican, Charrière, c.1860. Probably one of the last made. 10 cm. (Private Collection, Dr Claude Rousseau, Paris)*

VI *Early toothkey, c.1750, 12 cm. (Private Collection, Dr Claude Rousseau, Paris)*

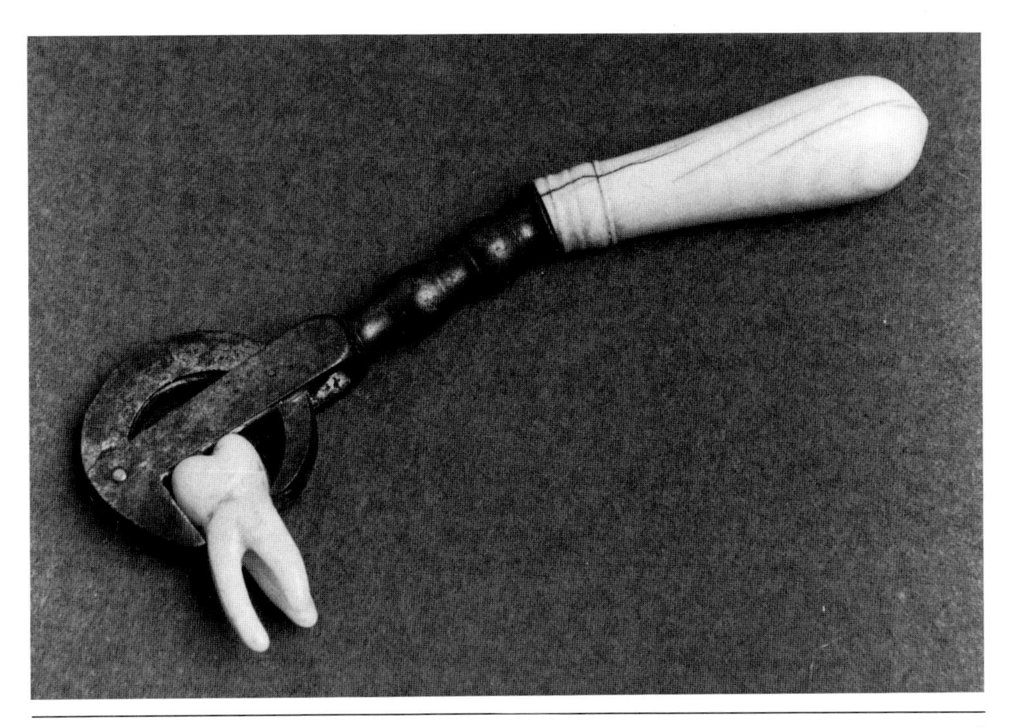

18 *Pelican in which the claw passes through the shaft, as designed by Jourdain, 1759; at one time used as a gavel in RADC HQ Mess. 14 cm. (Royal Army Dental Corps Historical Museum, Aldershot)*

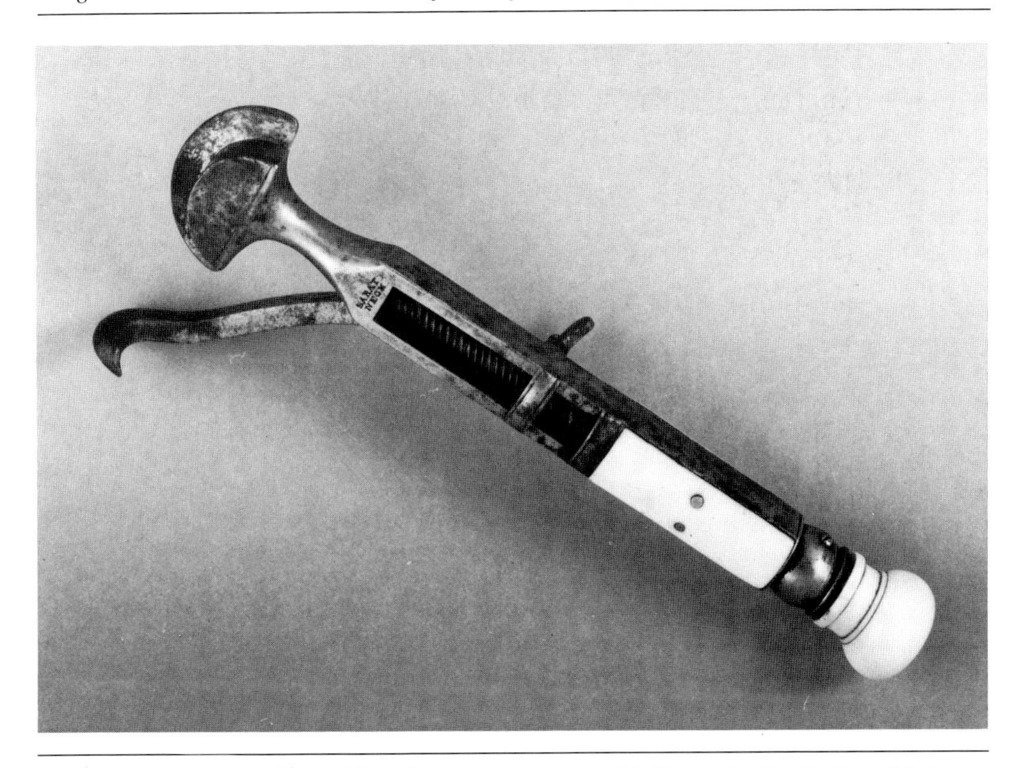

19 *An ivory-mounted pelican with endless screw, the recessed bolster for leather binding. Sabat Neck, c.1800, 12 cm. (Private Collection, London)*

where it was necessary to turn a tooth towards the inside of the mouth. Justus Christian Loder (1753–1832), who taught Goethe anatomy and tested all his instruments on corpses, was another who did not put his faith in pelicans.

Pierre Fauchard (1678–1761) was full of practical good sense on the subject of extraction as he was on all dental matters. 'There are certain cutlers who meddle with extraction of the tooth. Apparently the instruments which they make give them an itch to try them . . . In order not to frighten the patient caution must be had to hide the instrument.' Well might he feel this as his pelicans were far bolder and heavier than earlier versions, 'constructed in a way which has never been done before'. The body of the instrument should be of boxwood, he tells us, a fashion very popular in Italy and Spain, and it should be bound with two bands of iron or brass flush with the surface. The bolster, or bolsters, should be covered in soft leather and linen – even changed for the next patient – the covering of the convexity preventing damage to the gum. He goes on to describe the amazing variety of interchangeable attachments he makes it possible to assemble on the same body. He sometimes finds a concave bolster suitable so that several teeth then serve as a support for the action. With one of his pelicans Fauchard shows a strip of lead, bent to three sides of a square, with which he compresses the cavity after extraction.

An extremely complicated type of pelican with two handles was that designed by Eugene d'Estanque and patented by him in 1861. He illustrated it in *L'Union Medicale* in 1864 and it was made by Charrière and Mathieu with considerable mechanical skill (pl. 65).

Elevators and levers

> *One touch of that ecstatic stump*
> *Could jerk his limbs and make him jump,*

wrote Thomas Hood in 'A True Story'. The action of the pelican and other extracting instruments frequently left behind the stump of the tooth or a stubborn root, which required a different type of tool to remove. The elevator – there were many types, including the lever, punch and repoussoir – prised the tooth from its socket. The tapering blade was inserted between the root and the adjacent tooth and a turning movement elevated stump or root from the cavity of the gum. The elevator could, in addition, be used for extracting canine teeth and incisors. Its design changed little over the years.

A lead instrument for extraction, the odontagogon, was deposited in the Temple of Apollo – whom else? – at Delphi *c.* 1,000 B.C. This was presumably a symbolic model as the actual instrument – apparently a combination of forceps and elevator –

was made of iron. Some 2,000 years later the first known elevator, as such, was illustrated by Albucasis showing a simple, straight shaft with a small, crude finial. These early drawings are so coarse it is difficult to tell how close they might have been to their subject, especially as they varied considerably in different copies of the same book. John of Gaddesden showed an elevator with a sharpened end in preference to other extractors, presumably finding the same facility as the tooth-drawers recorded by the Dutch naval surgeon Cornelius Solingen (1641–87) who, despite the number of instruments he designed, lifted teeth with the point of a dagger. Walter Ryff illustrated several types, each having a different shaft: some straight, some curved and some bent at an angle, with varying heads, notched and grooved. Among them was the design that was to prove the most enduring, resembling the thumb held out straight, with the forefinger arched in a semicircle over it. John Scultetus of Ulm (1595–1645) described it as a tooth-pincer that might be employed where neither pelican nor forceps were suitable. Johann Jacob Heinrich Bucking (1749–1838), in his treatise of 1782, showed a similar piece, and the design was adapted by Gorz for his *geissfuss*, in which the curved section was attached by an adjustable screw. Scultetus showed elevators with heavy foliate handles or curved trifid ends and another lasting variant, the goat's foot elevator. Among others to show this latter type were Garengeot in 1725, the encyclopaedist Diderot in 1762, the instrument maker Savigny in 1798 and Serre in 1803. It was distinguished by a deeply cleft head, which afterwards became slightly hollowed between the two points. In *Rudiments of the Art of Surgery* by the surgeon August Gottlieb Richter of *c.* 1798 we find a goat's foot elevator with a hook to prevent slipping – another variation.

The particular type known as a punch had a branched head and, although it might be effective on its own, was used to loosen the teeth prior to extraction by other means. The tooth was tapped on both sides, the gum having been detached with a raspatory or scarificator. If necessary, a pound of lead was struck against the punch – common practice in the eighteenth century, even for Fauchard, but Etienne Bourdet rejected the idea as he found cerebral concussion could result. Woodall recommended a punch for the incisors and eye-teeth, instructing that the instrument should be well placed as low as possible at the root of the tooth and made from the hardest steel obtainable. Fauchard described two types of punch. One was for pressure 'from without inwards' and was a type of goat's foot; the other, for pressure 'from within outwards', had a forward angled head with cleft tip. Another Fauchard type entailed a straight shaft with a curved branch ending in a hook and operated by a rising screw, the height being therefore adjustable. 'I know M. Dionis praises it greatly,' he said, '. . . as for me, I use it seldom.' The handles of his elevators were smoothly pear-shaped, with a

20 *Repoussoir, as Garengeot, c.1725, 12 cm. (Musée d'Histoire de la Médecine de Paris; Cliché Assistance Publique)*

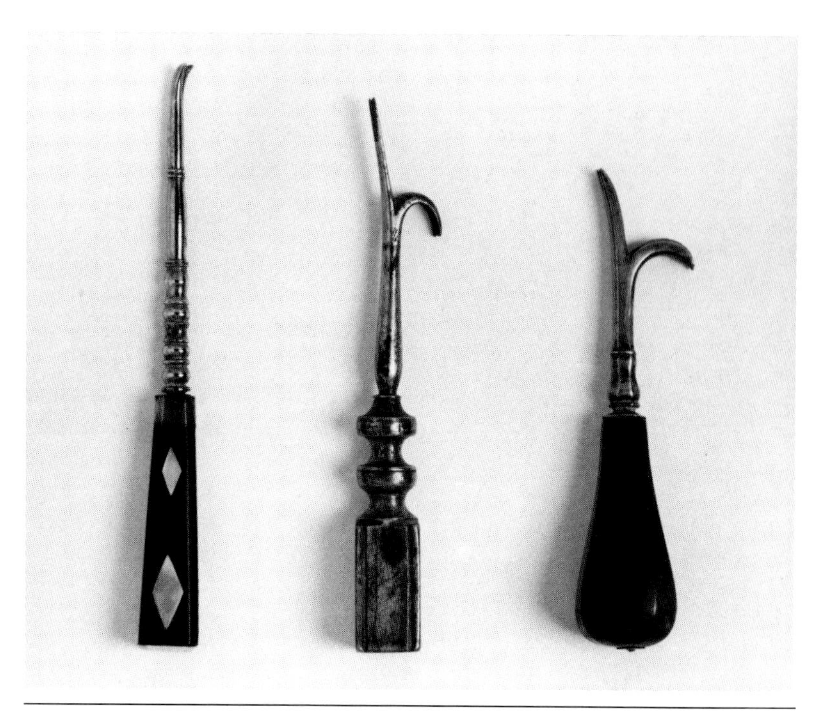

21 *Elevators, left to right: punch elevator, ebony and mother-of-pearl handle, c.1790; 'pied-de-biche' with mallet handle, possibly for striking a punch, c.1770; 'pied-de-biche', c.1800. (Musée Fauchard, Paris)*

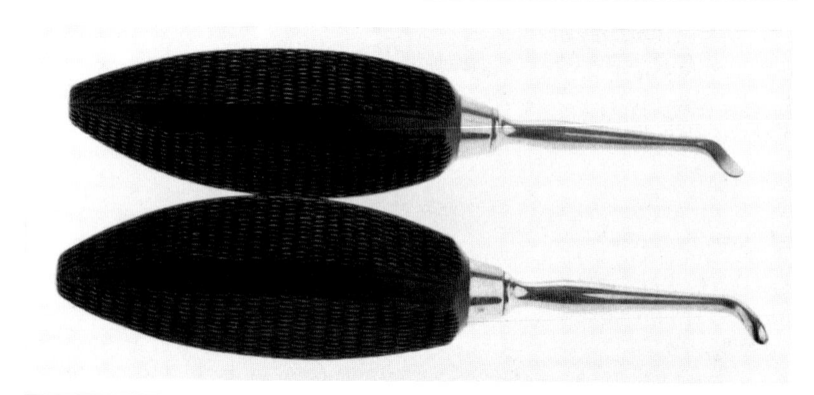

22 *Elevators with cross-hatched ebony handles, c.1840, 13 cm. (University of Alberta Dental Museum, Edmonton)*

23 *Elevator with ivory handle, as Thomas Bell, 1829, 15 cm. (Macaulay Museum of Dental History, Medical University of South Carolina)*

24 *Split-shaft punch elevator, c.1795, as introduced by Benjamin Bell in 1789. 12 cm. (Science Museum, Wellcome Collection, London)*

decorative ferrule. Garengeot showed similar handles but introduced an alternative, octagonal shape in ivory or ebony, which was to remain popular into the nineteenth century. A split-shaft punch was described by Benjamin Bell in 1780 (pl. 24). Here, two parallel shafts, each with its own head, were separated by a sliding-ring which increased the area over which force might be applied.

The elevator known variously as a repoussoir, a hind's foot or – confusingly – a goat's foot with claw had a two-branched head, each branch curving slightly away from the other. The upper branch was intended to displace roots, the lower to raise the roots to the outside. It was illustrated by Ryff and Martinez and through to Gariot in the nineteenth century.

The simplest form of elevator was a straight rod with the end cut at an angle. It was shown by Pierre Dionis (1643–1718) in 1708 and Fauchard in 1728. Over the years it was modified by flattening the end, grooving it, hollowing it out or giving it the appearance of an arrow-head. In the second half of the eighteenth century the handle was sometimes placed at right angles to the shaft. Adam Anton von Brunner of Vienna (1737–1810) improved this by adding a slight curve to the shaft in order not to damage the cheek. His new design was illustrated by Serre in 1803.

Another variant, introduced by Gariot in 1805, was the heart-shaped head, sometimes on a curved shaft, which became known as the carp's tongue elevator. By 1800, elevators were occasionally made with a ring for the forefinger, increasing the possible leverage.

John Tomes (1815–95) felt that the introduction of the elevator into general practice was chiefly due to Thomas Bell (1792–1880). Bell's elevator, of 1829, had a long, usually ivory handle and the head of the shaft was tapered with a curved point. He used it for many purposes, including the obviating of overcrowded incisors; it was said to be successful for the extraction of lower third molars. Samuel James Augustus Salter (1825–97) used a similar piece but with serrated edges to prevent slipping – an idea previously mentioned by Savigny as a raspatory tooth-punch. John Tomes adapted Bell's sturdy, short shaft to take his own particular type of head, flat on one side, rounded on the other and frequently sharpened. The long handle was coarse and heavy in design, with a metal plate between two cross-hatched pieces of ebony. This elevator is a typical Tomes instrument: high in efficacy, low in aesthetic appeal.

Louis Lecluse (1711–92) introduced his own variation in *Nouveaux Elemens d'Odontologie* of 1754. His elevator had a T-shaped handle with the actual elevating section at right angles to the shaft. This position was modified by the makers Evans & Wormall, who introduced an instrument with the upper shaft flattened to take the extra pressure of the finger; the whole instrument gave the impression of a hooded cobra. Justus

Christian Loder (1753–1832), author of *Anatomical Tables* (1794), distrusted all elevators as they used adjacent teeth or the jaw as their fulcrum, but if he had to use one he preferred a curved-shank elevator.

In 1828 C.F. Maury (?1786–1840), a dentist at the Ecole Polytechnique in Paris, introduced an elevator with a movable claw to act as a fulcrum. This principle was employed in the design of a piece at the Royal College of Surgeons in London, which has two ivory-handled parts. In 1861 William Fitkin took out a patent for 'Improvements in Apparatus or Instruments for Extracting Teeth', which must be said to have been of an excessive nature. One cross-hatched handle held the shaft of the fulcrum to be applied to one side of the gum and the other handle related to the cleft-headed elevator which attacked the other side, the two attached by a small bridge over the tooth in question.

Toothkeys

25 *Folding toothkey, the lower section hinged to store within the handle, c.1750, 15 cm. (Sotheby & Co., London)*

Toothkeys were first mentioned in Alexander Monro's *Medical Essays and Observations* of 1742 but they had probably been in use from *c.* 1730. The barber-surgeon's case of Newcastle, dated 1703, contains several extractors but no toothkey, and reports of a key 'in use in the reign of Queen Anne' appear unreliable. The original examples looked exactly like a doorkey of the period (col. pl. VI), with a straight shaft and large ring handle, which later became a transverse handle of wood – frequently ebony – or ivory. At the other end was a bolster together with a hinged claw; the bolster was placed against the root of the tooth and the claw engaged over the crown. The key was then turned as in a lock, the action dislocating the tooth – a very rapid method. The French and Germans referred to it as the English key and the English, variously, as the French or German key. The French maker Henry 'Coutelier de la Chambre des Pairs', in his book *Précis Descriptif sur les Instruments de Chirurgie* (1825), described the Garengeot key but says firmly that it is of English origin (pls. 27 and 29). Monro referred to it as Fothergill's Key but it is thought to have had no association with the surgeon Fothergill other than that he had sent it to Monro as an example of what was in use in London at the time. Monro was the first to replace the all-metal handle with wood or ivory, the first of an ovoid shape and then a straight bar with groups of fine reeding. By the end of the eighteenth century the accepted shape was a central cross-hatched section with the remaining part on either side being smoothly waisted.

Bourdet probably illustrated the first key to appear in France in 1757, a rather crude model with a slight curve to the shaft and a metal crossbar handle screwed through the end. He showed an example of a shaft with a double bend as well, a very early instance of this improvement. A far more fanciful conception

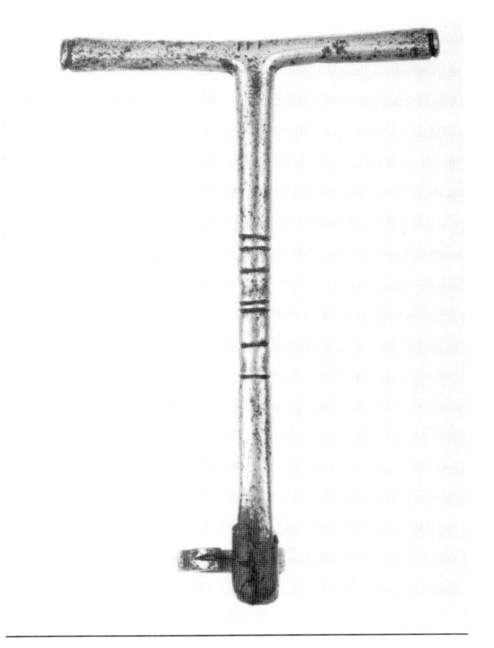

26 *Toothkey with leather bolster, c.1750, 13cm. (I. Freeman & Son, Simon Kaye Ltd, London)*

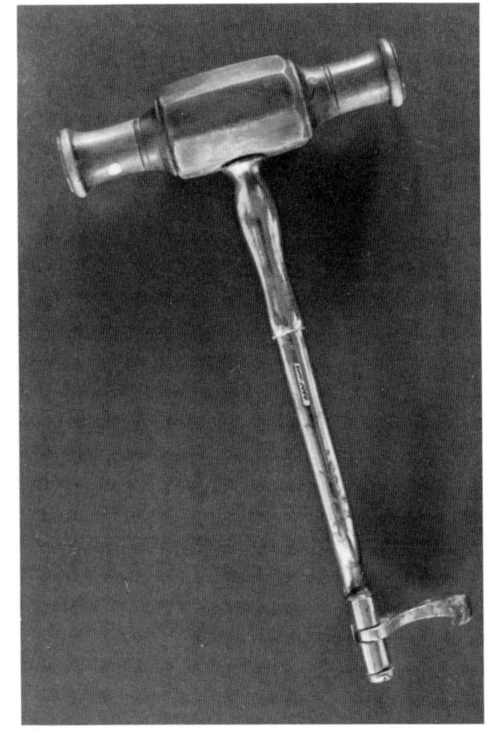

27 *Clef de Garengeot, c.1770, 15cm. (Musée du Val-de-Grâce, Paris)*

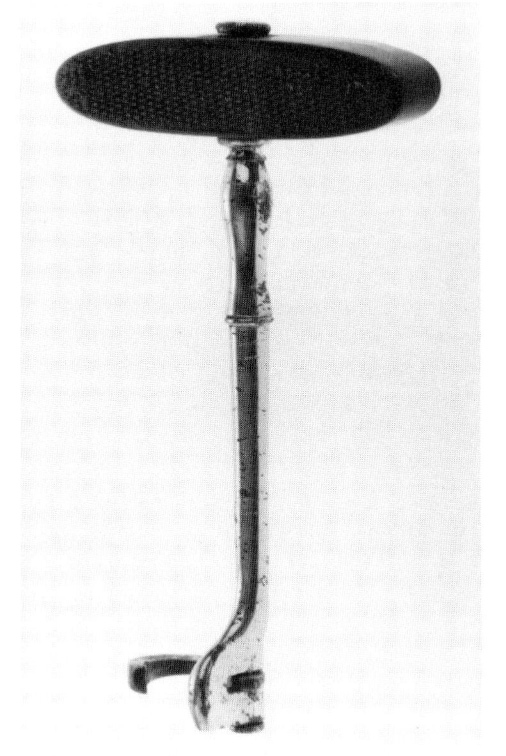

28 *Toothkey, c.1770, 13cm. (University of Alberta Dental Museum, Edmonton)*

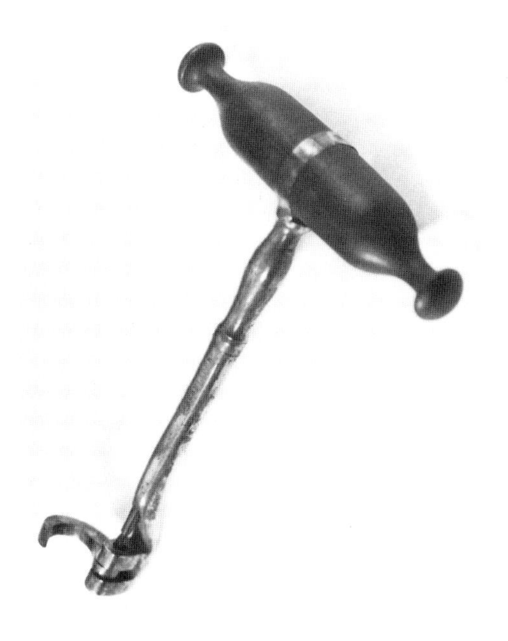

29 *Clef de Garengeot, c.1770, 13cm. (Musée d'Histoire des Sciences, Geneva)*

came from Mauro Soldo in 1766, a toothkey with a heart-shaped bolster and imaginative foliate handle. Louis Lecluse had mentioned, as early as *c.* 1747, 'a pelican fashioned from the English key'.

By the 1770s the toothkey was the favourite extracting instrument, and small-size versions for use on children were not uncommon (see pl. 33). It remained in use into this century and, indeed, the present writer found a full-size one being used in Marrakech in 1984, with no obvious concessions to the present day.

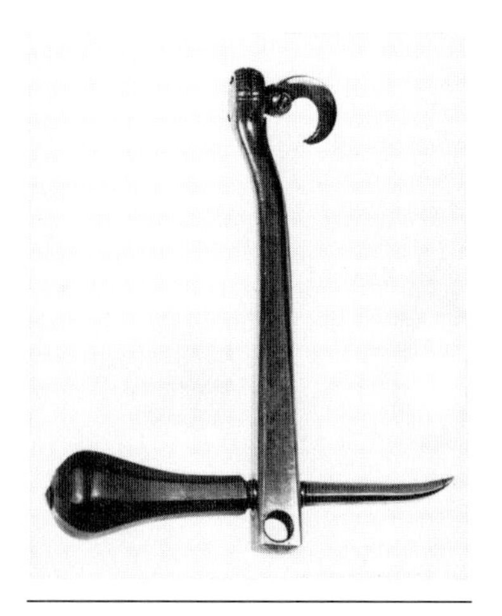

30 *Toothkey with handle which can be removed and used as an elevator, c.1765, 13cm. (Musée d'Histoire de la Médecine de Paris; Cliché Assistance Publique)*

A key illustrated in the *British Magazine* of 1762 shows a handle which can be removed and used as an elevator. The maker Perret, in 1772, described four keys, showing their development to that date: one was similar to Monro's design; one was an innovation of Garengeot which allowed rotation of the claw so that it could be used on either side of the mouth; one had its claw fixed by means of a sliding rod on the shaft; and one, known as Frère Côme's key, had a small screw to prevent the claw from rotating. This key sometimes had a handle which unscrewed to reveal the necessary screwdriver; it was a type later made by Charrière. All four keys had a single cleft in the claw and a serrated inner surface. A very rare, double-ended version of about this date is at the Royal College of Surgeons in London.

Benjamin Bell gives a detailed description of the toothkey, suggesting the bolster should be wrapped in linen before use, an idea echoed later by William Rae, who varied the suggestion with tow or chamois leather. By *c.* 1765 a slight curve was given to the hitherto straight shaft, which was developed into a distinct bend *c.* 1780 by Ferdinand Joseph Leber to prevent undue force against adjacent teeth. At the end of the century a second, right-angled bend was introduced by Robert Clarke (1767–98), which allowed the shaft to cross the mouth to the further jaw. Similarly, the claw was made more versatile and could be fixed into different positions by a spring catch, the second location introduced by James Spence (fl. 1760–80) and the third by Joseph Fox (1776–1816) in 1806. Fox added an auxiliary bolster for use against a tooth other than the one to be extracted; this was very useful where an abscess occurred.

The maker Savigny, in his catalogue of 1795, said the chief defect of the toothkey was the depth of bolster. He added that, with his new circular bolster, the tooth might be extracted in an almost perpendicular direction, always the desired aim. Charles Laforgue introduced a concave bolster and a deeply curved shaft, with a variety of interchangeable claws. Knaur, in 1796, had a removable bolster which enjoyed some popularity. Henry's key of 1825 looks fairly straightforward but is possessed of one of the grandest handles: octagonal with two bands of silver reeding and spherical, faceted ferrules. Many were the variations and all claimed that the adoption in practice of their version 'was universal'.

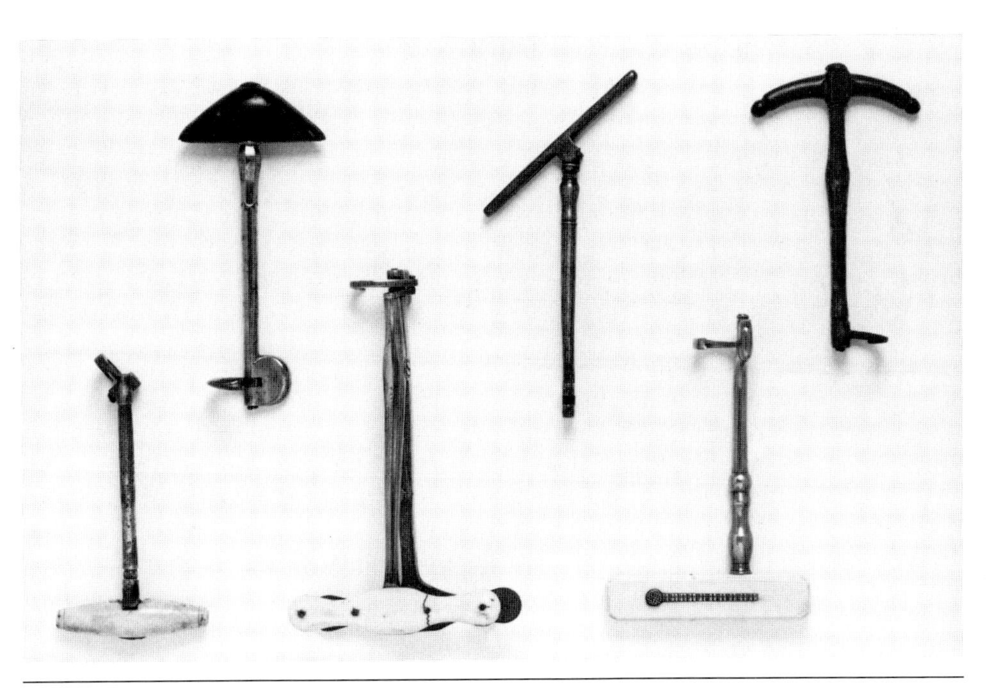

31 *Group of toothkeys, clockwise: solid bolster, c.1790; swivel handle, c.1770; bow handle, similar to Gariot, c.1805; 'la clef de Garengeot perfectionnée', as in Maury, c.1833; double ivory handle, split shaft, c.1825; swivel bolster, c.1795. Each approx. 12 cm. (Musée Fauchard, Paris)*

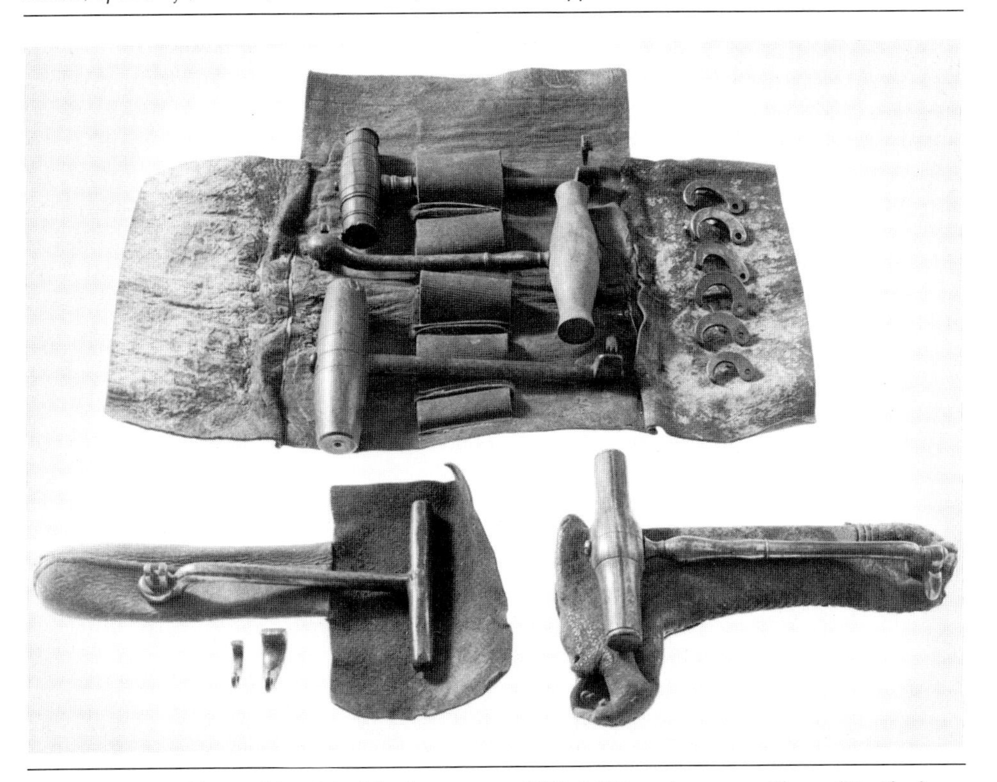

32 *Group of toothkeys with original leather cases, c.1750–1800, each approx. 12 cm. (Hartford Dental Society, Hartford, Conn.)*

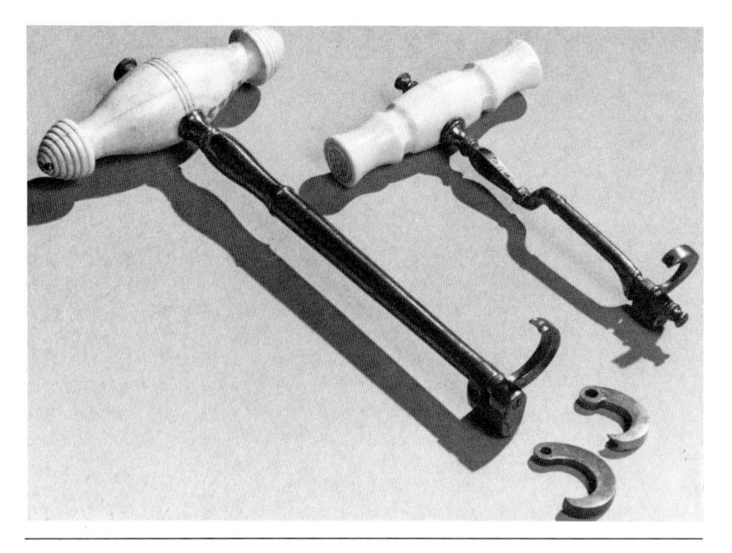

33 *Toothkey, c.1790, 12 cm and a child's version, c.1830, 9 cm. (Howard Dittrick Museum of Historical Medicine, Cleveland, Ohio)*

34 *Toothkeys, c.1810, 15 cm and 16 cm. (Macaulay Museum of Dental History, Medical University of South Carolina)*

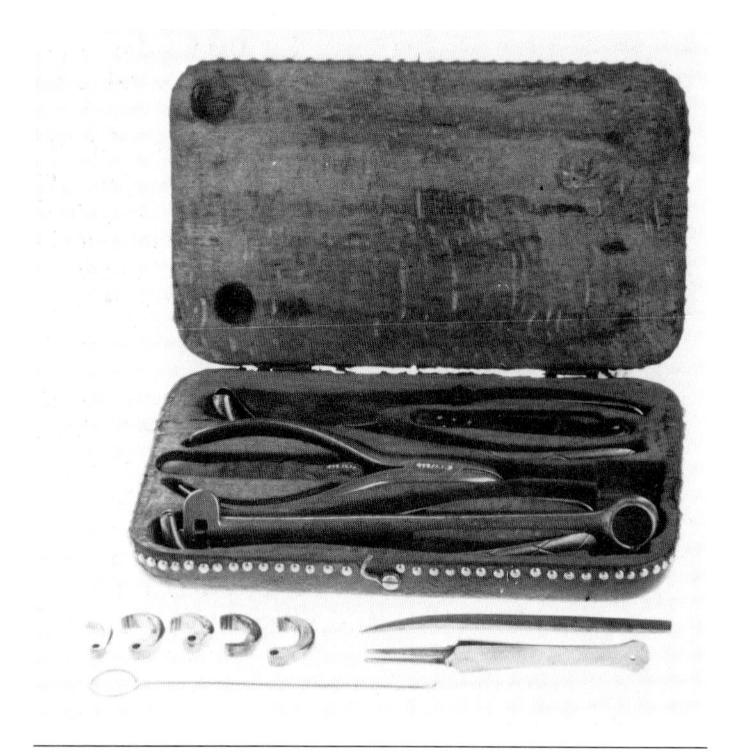

35 *Set of rustic extracting instruments: toothkey with five claws, forceps, gum-lancet, tweezers, elevator, c.1860. (University of Alberta Dental Museum, Edmonton)*

36 *Modified form of toothkey, c.1800. When the ivory bar on handle is depressed, the grip is operated. 14 cm. (Odontological Museum of the Royal College of Surgeons, London, J.28.1)*

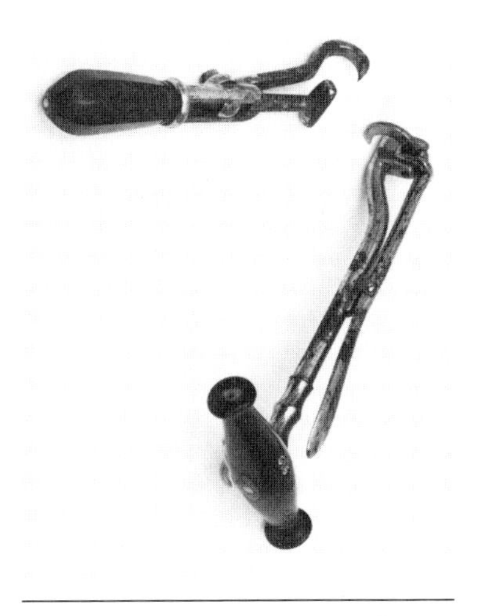

37 *Pelican, c.1840, 12 cm, and adjustable toothkey, c.1840, 14 cm. (Bichlie Collection, Museum of Swedish Dental Society, Stockholm)*

38 *Toothkey with movable bolster as designed by Duval in 1802, 14 cm. (Musée d'Histoire de la Médecine de Paris; Cliché Assistance Publique)*

In 1819 pieces of cork were fixed by silk thread to a concave bolster to reduce pressure on the tooth; in 1829 a spherical bolster appeared; in 1833 Maury illustrated a key with an ornate shaft fitting into one end of the handle by a spring catch, which allowed more force in the operation. Joseph Linderer (1809–79), a Berlin dentist, brought in a movable bolster in 1848, which could be pushed up and down on the shaft for cases where the fulcrum was not needed opposite the claw. Savigny showed some easily portable designs, a folding shaft and a shaft which fitted into a metal cylinder, removable by means of a thumb screw. James Snell (?1795–1850), author of *Practical Guide to Operations on the Teeth* (1831), insisted on the importance of the size of the claw being suited to the size of the tooth. Seldom has a dental instrument been the subject of so much ingenuity.

In 1811 the instrument maker Simpson described a key which obviated the need to adjust the claw with the finger while in the mouth by providing a small ancillary claw at the base of the bolster. Other methods of adjusting the claw were tried in the early part of the nineteenth century using spring appliances to the shaft to hold the claw in position. In 1843 F.S. Prideaux introduced a claw with a cutting edge. When the handle on his key was turned in the reverse direction the claw cut round and a little under the tooth.

In *Surgical Essays* of 1771 John Aitken (fl. 1770–90) said that the principal defects of the toothkey were the oblique direction in which it drew the teeth and the severe bruising of the gum it occasioned. He devised a very elegant and complex instrument to dispose of these problems. It had an octagonal shaft in a sleeve that allowed it to move back and forth but not in a circular direction; this was controlled by a handle on the shaft and an involved arrangement of the bolster and claw.

Many extended forms of the toothkey were devised which, though on the general pattern of the key, were applied with a force similar to that of the forceps, and these transitional pieces show a very important stage of development. As the proverbs said, 'Music helps not the toothache' and 'The tongue is ever turning to the aching tooth': the pressure to alleviate the pain was ever present. In 1799 Robert Simpson patented an instrument with a sprung claw which was attached to the tooth by means of forceps. When the forceps was removed, a key-like mechanism was applied which could be turned in any desired direction to remove the tooth. Another device was a shaft composed of four pieces of steel containing a bar fixed to a cross-piece inside the handle; when pressed, this latter piece operated the claw (pl. 36). A key in two parts was introduced in 1834. This had a flat-notched bolster with projections on either side to grip the tooth to be extracted, and a claw which fitted into whichever notch was most convenient. Of similar complexity is an early nineteenth-century key with a barrel-shaped shaft containing a screw operated by a transverse handle which operated the width between two claws. There were many other mechanical flights of fancy, each of undoubtedly well-meant ingenuity but of such involved application it is unlikely many reached more than the prototype stage.

Meanwhile, use of the simple toothkey flourished. It was said of a Cairo dentist that he extracted teeth by means of a common doorkey and a piece of twine 'with great dexterity and rapidity'. While this was possible, who needed the difficult procedures described above?

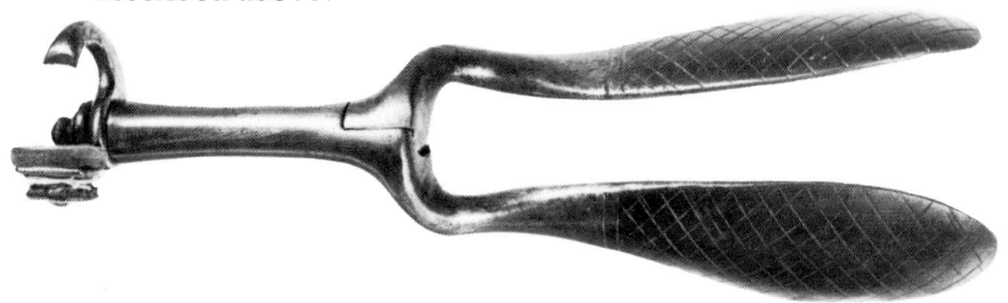

39 *Modified form of toothkey, Ash, c.1835, 19cm. (Odontological Museum of the Royal College of Surgeons, London, J.27.1)*

Screws

Dental screws were used for the removal of the stumps of incisors and canine teeth where no part remained which could be easily grasped. It is likely that those shown by Serre and Laforgue, both in 1803, were the first. Serre claimed that his screw, a series of three conical heads graduated in size and fitting into a plain straight shaft with a curved handle (pl. 42), would remove roots 'like a cork out of a bottle'. The French maker Henry illustrated some ornate examples of Serre's design in 1825, the important foliate handles having let-in shields to take a monogram. Laforgue's version was more basic: a fixed head on a short shaft with a transverse metal handle. Later innovations were necessarily more complicated, such as a screw inserted into the tooth with pliers and removed, together with stump, with a key-like instrument. Another combination was a screw with forceps (pl. 56). The *American Journal of Dental Science* in Baltimore published S.P. Hullihen's (1810–57) description of his 'Compound Screw Forceps', an instrument nine inches long. Between the jaws of the forceps is a metal tube containing a spring which ends in the screw. This, being engaged in the tooth, is withdrawn by the forceps. The device is thought to have been in fairly common use in America. It was followed by similar variations on another type of screw specifically for splitting roots, which took the form of a screw on one shaft and a claw on another, the two jointed together. In 1851 H.N. Wadsworth devised a screw to be inserted into the pulp cavity and then extracted with a lever. 'No root,' he said, 'can withstand it.' His method required a piece of hickory wood to be laid on the adjacent teeth to act as a fulcrum, and one is forced to wonder if they could withstand it either.

40 *Heavy iron dental screw, as illustrated by S.S. White, 1867. (Macaulay Museum of Dental History, Medical University of South Carolina)*

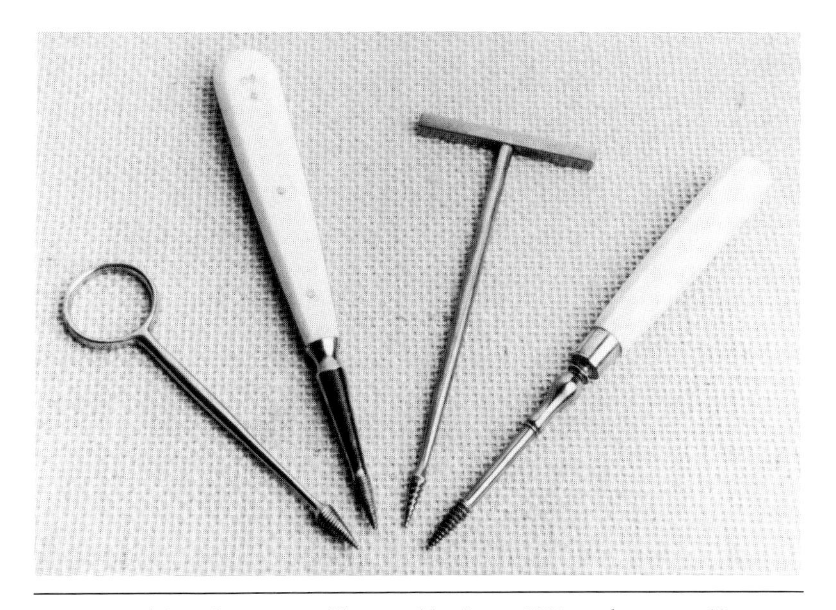

41 *Group of dental screws, as illustrated by Serre, 1803, each approx. 13 cm. (Museum of British Dental Association, London)*

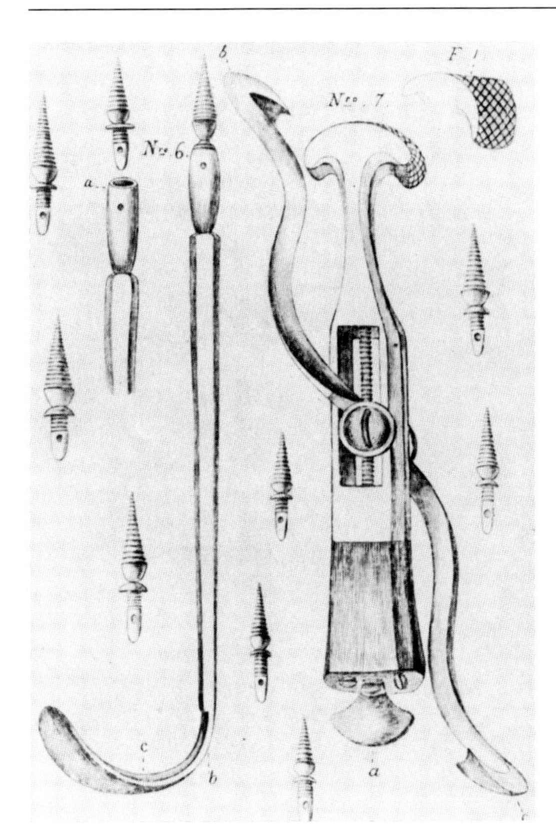

42 *Illustration from the work of Johann Jacob Josef Serre, 1803, showing screws, pelican, and a cheek-retractor.*

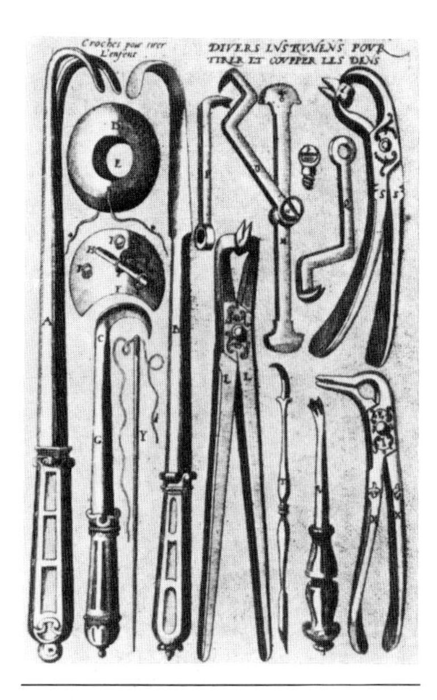

43 *Forceps illustrated by Walter Ryff in* Chirurgia Magna *(1545).*

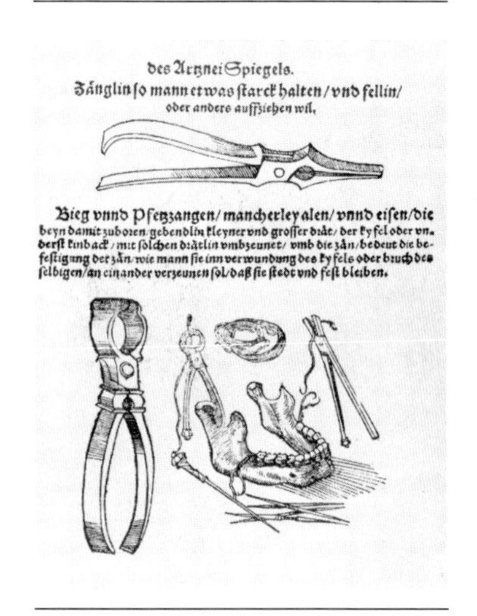

44 *Illustration from* Oeuvres de Chirurgie *by Jacques Guillemeau, (1598), showing on right of plate, three forceps, a pelican and two elevators.*

Forceps

The forceps is probably the oldest of all dental instruments after the fingers and preferred to them by Aristotle. Both Greek and Roman examples are known, and all the medieval writers show them. They were used apparently as much for shaking the teeth to loosen them as for extraction. Several different types developed, each designated by its resemblance to the beak of a particular bird or the jaws of a dog.

Albucasis illustrated six types, all made of damascened iron: four for whole teeth and two for roots. All show one jaw longer than the other and curving over it, the root forceps having pointed jaws striated on the inner surface for a firm grip. Ryff, in 1545, showed early forms of both the parrot's beak and the crow's bill and a root forceps with the lower handle reversed round the fingers, while Martinez, in 1557, described three forceps, all very plain and angular by comparison: one is the Ryff parrot's beak, one has the jaws aligned to the blades, and the third has the jaws straight and pointed, at an angle to the blades. Paré showed a variation on the parrot's beak, with the upper jaw cleft in two places. He advised that the patient be seated on a low seat with the head between the operator's knees, the gums scarified, the tooth shaken and forced with an elevator, the forceps used as a last resort, first one forceps and then another, according to size and position. 'I would have the Tooth-drawer expert and diligent . . . for unless one know readily and cunningly how to use them, he can scarce so carry himself that he will force out three teeth at once . . .' Andreas della Croce was another to feel that the forceps was a last resort, but he illustrated two versions. Jacques Guillemeau (1550–1613) used a parrot's beak and a crow's bill and a third type with parallel jaws turned at a right angle to the blade.

Scultetus showed the instruments advocated by Girolamus Fabrizzi (1537–1619), a professor at Padua. The ubiquitous parrot's bill 'is a pair of common pincers for the teeth', he said, but he updated it with a screw through the handle to regulate the pressure. His crow's bill was for roots; he observed that when a tooth was extracted, the roots were usually left behind. In addition, he mentions a stork's bill for use with incisors and a forceps 'with the bite of a dog'.

John Woodall, in 1617, wrote, '. . . if it bee any other of the great grinders, and that there bee reasonable hold on the inner side . . . it is best done with the pacis [forceps] . . . two sorts of pacis at least are needful in a chest.' Woodall listed the first authorized Army Dental Outfit on 10 July 1626 as requiring: Pacis (forceps), Pelicans, Forcers, Punches, Crowe's bills, Flegmes (possibly elevators but probably fleams), Gravers (scalers), Small Files.

Anton Nuck differentiates the teeth by size and attempts to fit a suitable instrument to each. He is sufficiently practical to suggest a rinsing basin as a necessity. Dionis showed the two

45 *Two forceps, c.1600. (Science Museum, Wellcome Collection, London)*

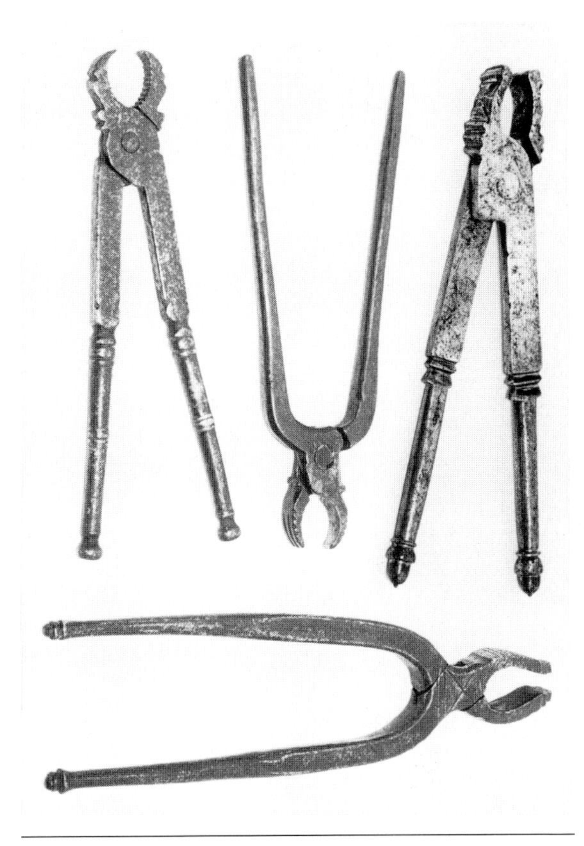

48 *Forceps, c.1700, each approx. 13 cm. (Museum of the History of Science, Oxford)*

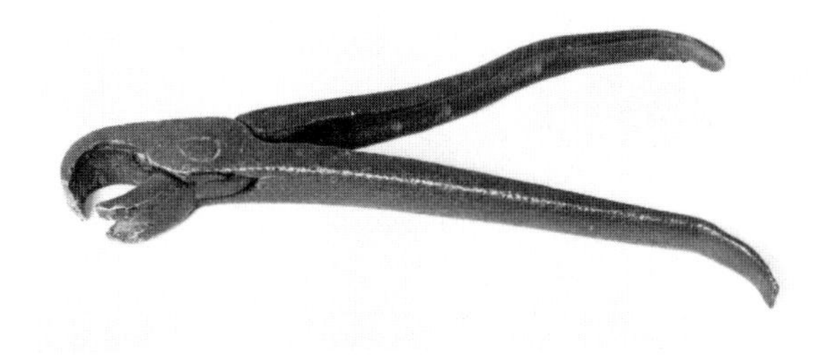

46 *Hungarian forceps, c.1650. (Semmelweis Museum, Budapest)*

47 *Forceps, c.1690; forceps with screw, c.1760. Each approx. 12 cm. (Museum of Swedish Dental Society, Stockholm)*

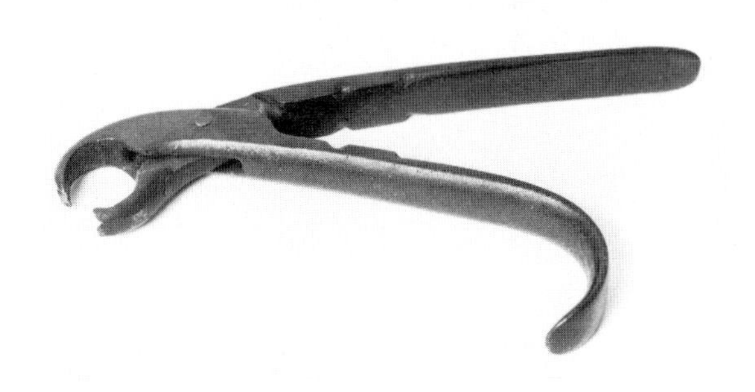

49 *Hungarian forceps, c.1790. (Semmelweis Museum, Budapest)*

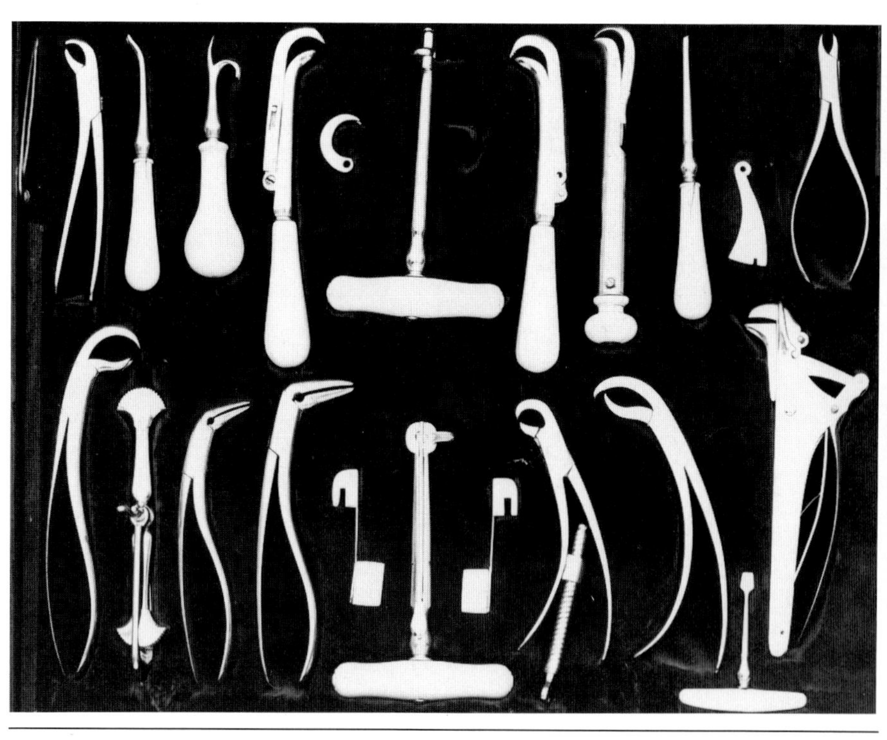

50 *Case of dental instruments of Juan Alexand Brambilla, c.1780. (Museum of the History of Science, Florence)*

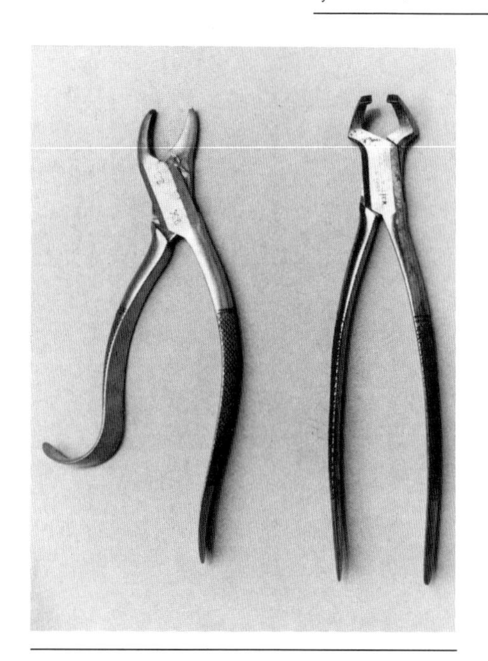

51 *Forceps: left, S.S. White, c.1870, showing the SSW trademark, and right, Chevalier as Cyrus Fay, 1835, 15cm. (Howard Dittrick Museum of Historical Medicine, Cleveland, Ohio)*

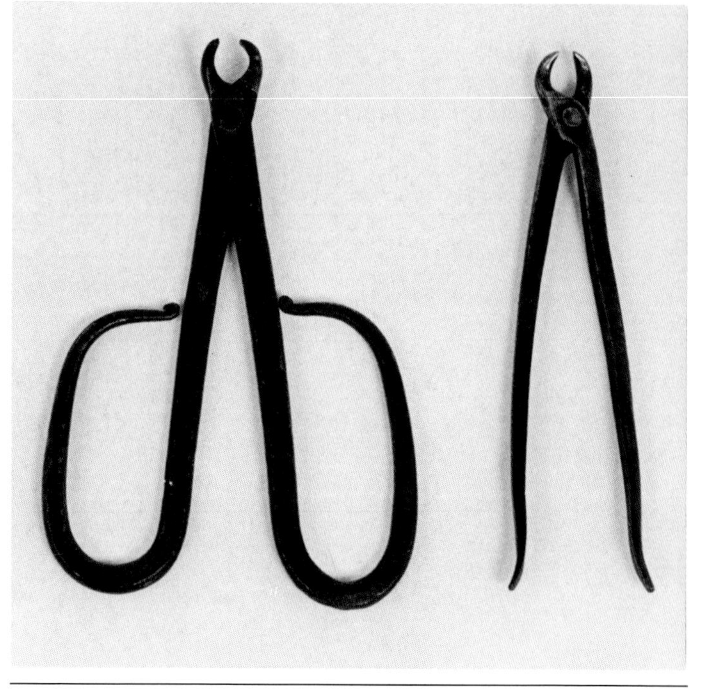

52 *Forceps, c.1840, probably made by local blacksmith. (Hartford Dental Society, Hartford, Conn.)*

VII *Part of a magnificent case of instruments, gilt and mother-of-pearl handles, Charrière, c.1825, showing elevators, scalers, a mirror and lancet. (Private Collection, Paris)*

VIII *A case of early 19th-century dental hygiene instruments, mother-of-pearl and silver-gilt. Dutch (Musem of the British Dental Association)*

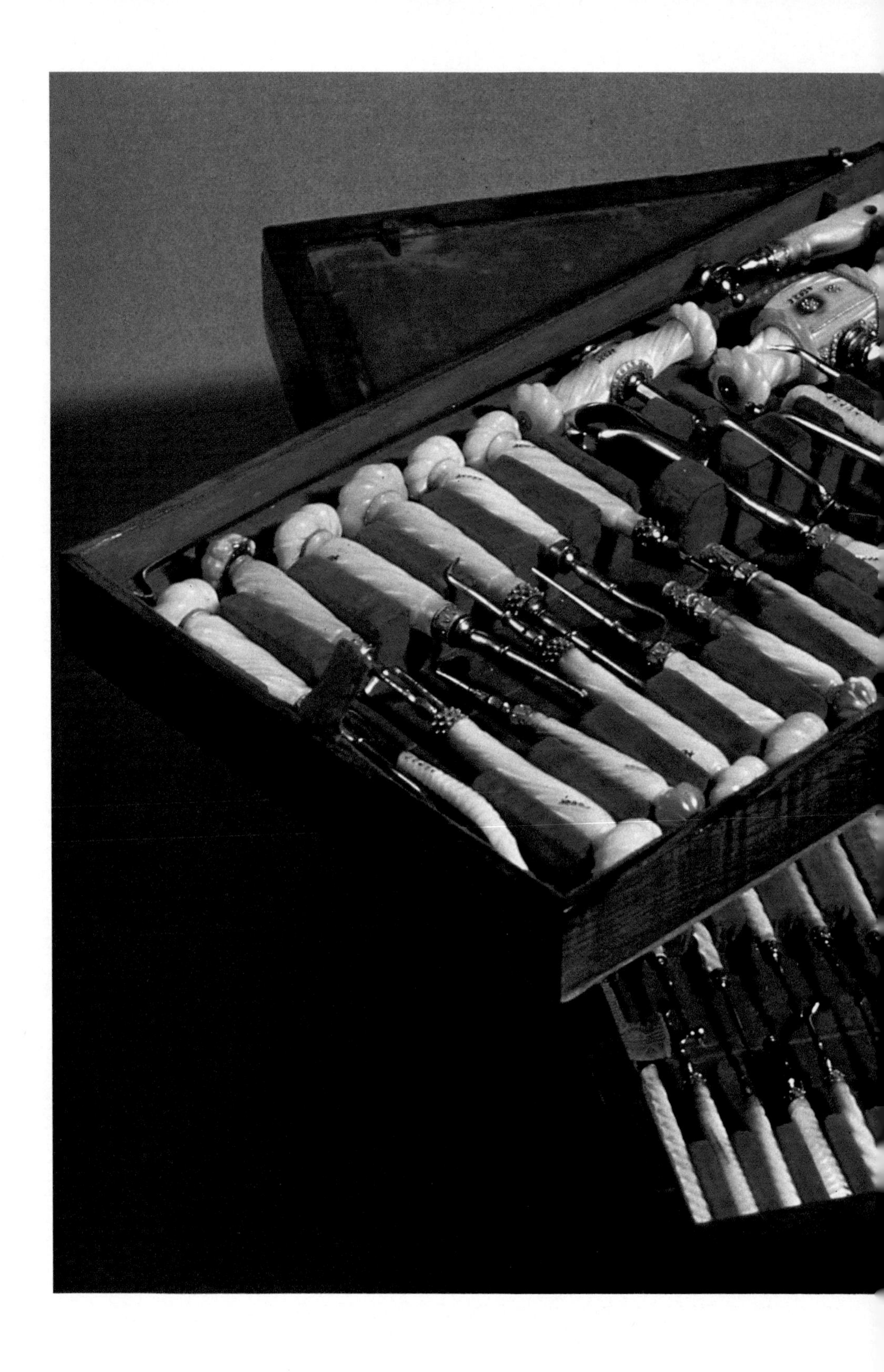

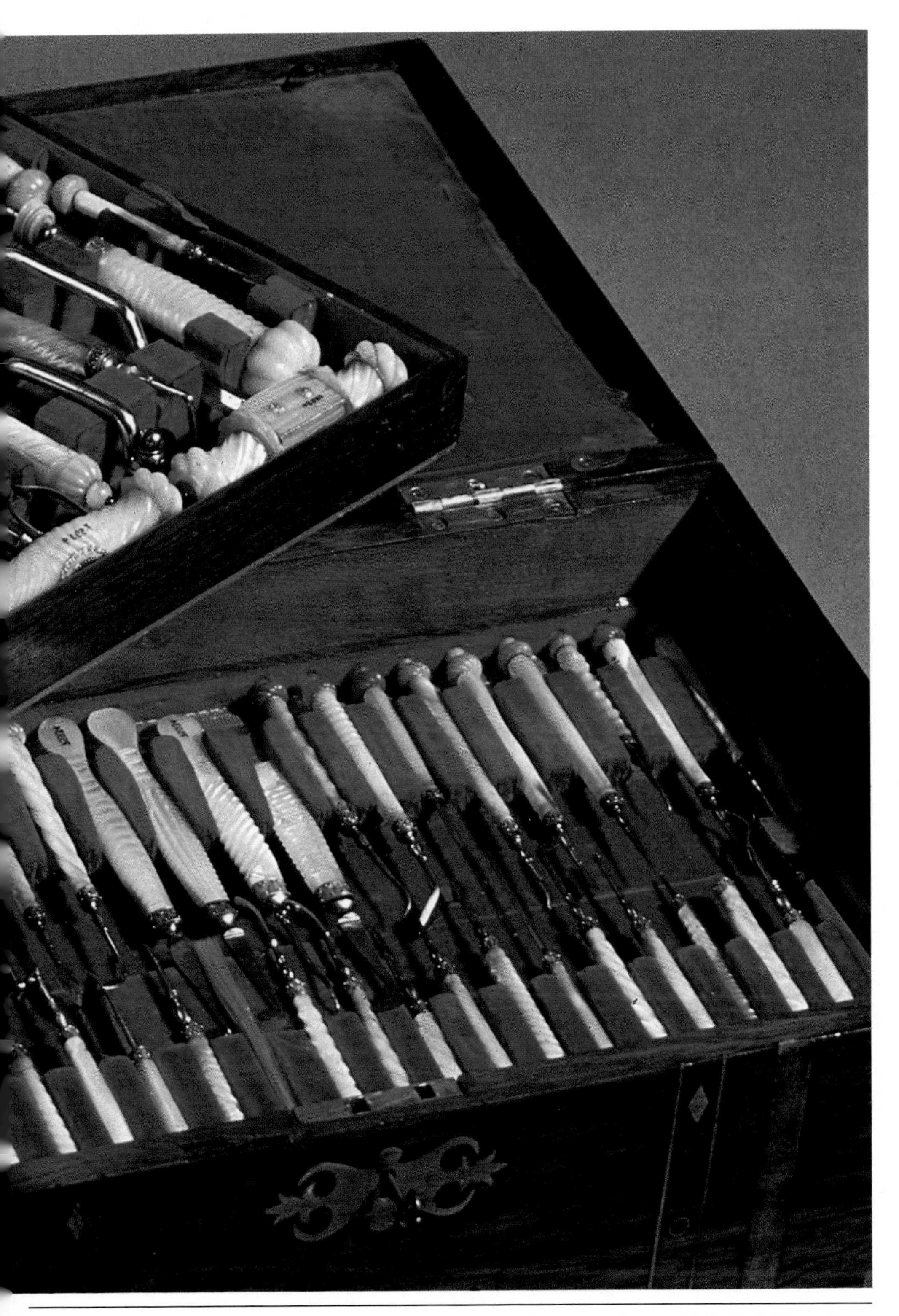

IX *Large brass-bound, rosewood case of instruments with six trays. American, c.1840. Probably made as an exhibition piece. (Science Museum, Wellcome Collection, London)*

X *19th-century dental workshop showing the conditions in which artificial teeth were made. (Rijksuniversiteit, Utrecht)*

main types of forceps but, in addition, a third version which he called a crow's bill but which actually had very sharp jaws which would 'cut off the extremities where they are too sharp'.

By the early eighteenth century more force was obviously required as a spring between the handles first appeared, and many new versions were seen. Garengeot showed a parrot's bill with handles that might be demonstrating a balletic position and he, again, has an example with jaws at right angles to the blades.

Fauchard illustrated four varieties in 1728: a parrot's bill, a crow's bill (which by now, with longer jaws, was becoming the crane's bill), and two pincer-like forceps with hollowed out jaws to take the shape of the tooth. All, he said, should have a box-joint, the blades joined by a bolt riveted on both sides in a sunken groove. He utterly rejected the spring between the handles, which he felt was often in the way and diminished the force of the hand.

A forceps with a screw to regulate the pressure was reintroduced by Leber in 1770 and by many others over the next 60 years. Perret invented a forceps in 1772 which had a hooded upper jaw, as in the parrot's bill, but with a heavily ridged inner surface, the lower jaw being T-shaped with slightly raised arms. This he specially recommended for the extraction of incisors, canine teeth and the pre-molars, front teeth evidently being thought to suggest difficulties. Bucking, in 1782, showed a ferocious forceps with long, curving handles and flat, short, curved jaws unlike any before, and Campani broke new ground as well, with a forceps in which the jaws had a serpentine bend. A very ingenious forceps was described by Serre in 1803, in which one blade ended in a loop which fitted over the tooth. Serre himself, however, referred to it as both a 'ripper' and a 'tooth-breaker'.

53 *Smaller forceps for vertical extraction, c.1800. Larger ditto, signed H.J. Batchelor, patented 1.7.1856. (Rijksuniversiteit, Utrecht)*

By the nineteenth century the many varieties of forceps were much more heavily constructed, with cross-hatched handles or, in the Maury versions of 1828, with a distinctive herringbone pattern. Serre, in 1803, showed no less than 13 types which were full of graceful curves but difficult to fit to the neck of the tooth. The first big breakthrough came in 1826 when Cyrus Fay (1778–1839), the first person to study the mechanics of extraction, was awarded a Silver Medal by the Society of Arts for his 'Improved Forceps for the use of dentists'. This forceps, he said, 'may be accurately applied to the necks of several classes of teeth . . . without any danger of breaking a carious tooth in the attempt to extract it'. It would not slip, and no cutting of the gum was necessary first; the beaked form of the jaws would grasp a stump even below gum level.

By now, dental practitioners were demanding forceps of rational design with handles curved to the shape of the hand, and jaws made to fit exactly the crown and neck of the tooth. Therefore a whole set was becoming necessary rather than just one or two. Josiah Foster Flagg of Boston (1763–1816) was said to

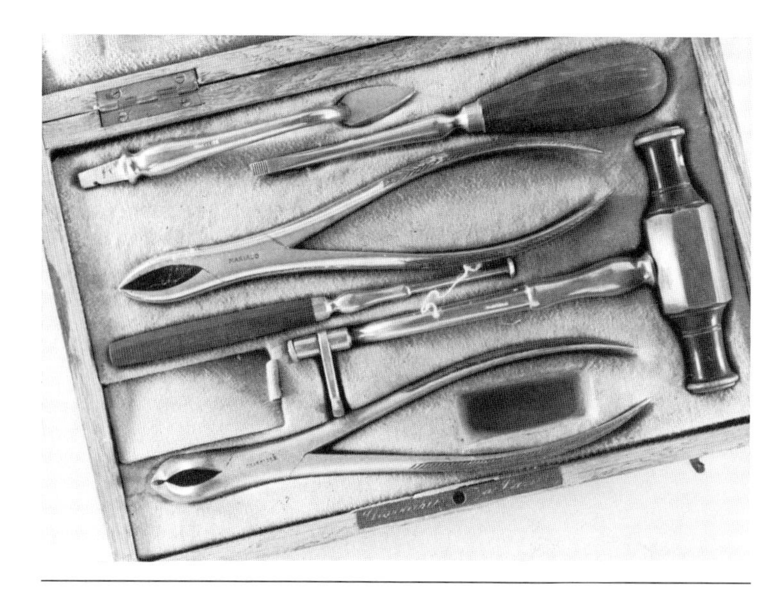

54 *Case of extracting instruments, c.1810, including (top) a carp's tongue elevator. (Musée du Val-de-Grâce, Paris)*

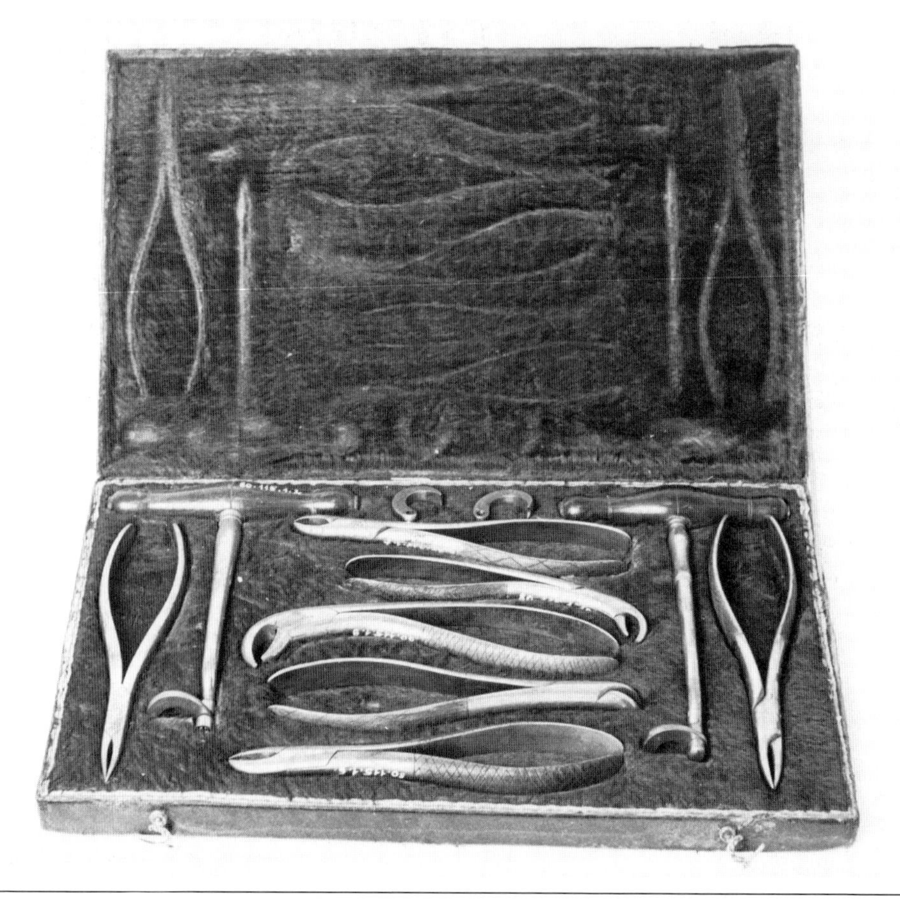

55 *Cased set of dental instruments, c.1800, Neuhold, Vienna. (Semmelweis Museum, Budapest)*

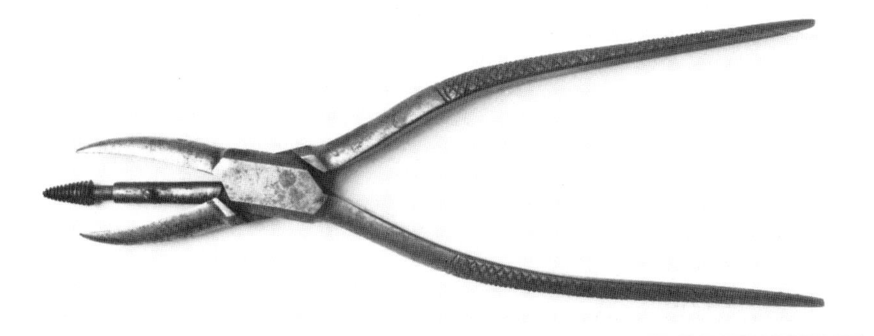

56 *Forceps as C.H. Dubs, 1848, 14cm. (Macaulay Museum of Dental History, Medical University of South Carolina)*

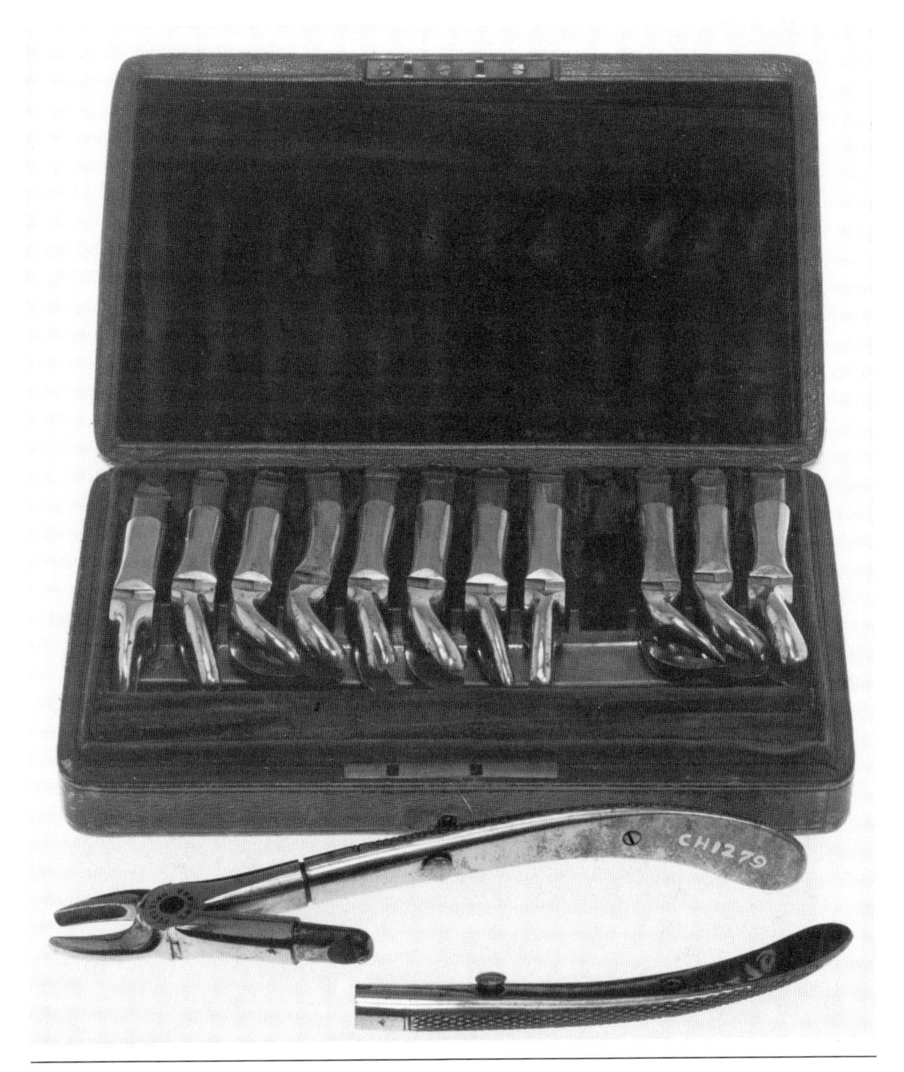

57 *Case of extracting forceps with interchangeable heads, Ferguson, 1865; formerly belonging to Dr Dentz, first lecturer in dentistry in Holland. (Rijksuniversiteit, Utrecht)*

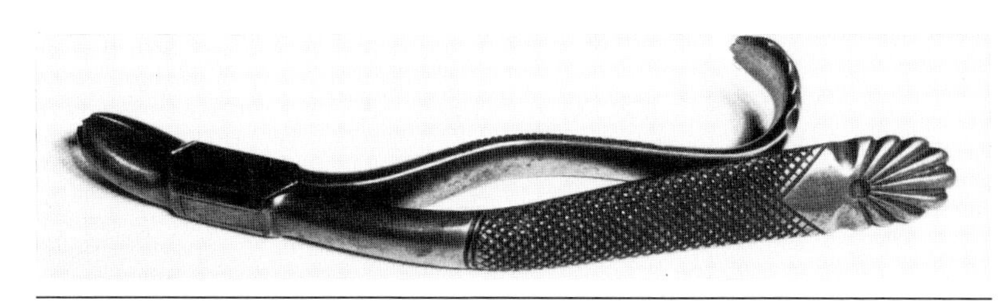

58 *Forceps, Arnold, c.1850, 14 cm. (Private Collection, Dr Gary Lemen, Sacramento, Cal.)*

have a set of eleven, each anatomically suited to individual teeth. James Snell designed a forceps with one handle recurved to grasp the little finger, thus avoiding slipping in warm weather. J. Glasford Shepherd, who introduced a whole series of forceps made by Weiss and shown in their catalogue of 1843, designed a stump-forceps with a cutting edge which made the use of a gum-lancet unnecessary. Another of his innovations was a safety forceps with jaws of an equal curve, which would take however bulbous a tooth. His confidence in it, however, was less than complete. '. . . the grasp by these forceps is so equal that it is scarcely possible to break it [the tooth], at least it is improbable.' Nevertheless, Thomas Bell thought highly of it. He himself, in *Anatomy, Physiology and Diseases of the Teeth* of 1829, had introduced a spring-ratchet between the handles of the forceps, a mechanism which allowed the tooth to be firmly grasped by mechanical force alone, thus freeing the hand to concentrate its force on moving the instrument.

It was Sir John Tomes who, building on the work of Cyrus Fay, designed the forceps of the type used today, which eventually supplanted the toothkey. In 1841 he published *On the Construction and Application of Forceps for Extracting Teeth*, which developed out of his dissatisfaction with the available keys and forceps of the day. He formed a working partnership with the maker Evrard (1808–82), who worked near the Middlesex Hospital to which Tomes was appointed dental surgeon. Evrard made the forceps to Tomes's specification, one for each kind of tooth; nothing like them had been seen before (pl. 154). In 1843 J. Chitty Clendon published a work showing similar forceps, again made by Evrard, and there understandably ensued an unseemly and long-lasting wrangle between the two men. Subsequent catalogues showed the forceps variously accredited to one or the other. History would appear to be on the side of Tomes, who was one of the many to be called the father of the British dental profession and was generally the more respected, having shown in his career that it was possible to bring original observation to his subject.

Towards the middle of the nineteenth century forceps appeared with interchangeable jaws, each screwing onto the blade near the handle. As they were not designed for individual teeth it is unlikely they found much favour by this time.

Compound instruments and those for perpendicular extraction

During the latter half of the eighteenth century a great deal of interest was shown in attempts to devise an instrument which would raise teeth in a perpendicular direction. The results were very ingenious but of little practical use. Designers employed the same principle as a one-armed corkscrew, trying hard to improve on the old method of rocking and loosening first. Philip Pfaff (1716–80), whose book *Abhandlung von den Zahnen* (1756) did so much to advance the course of dentistry in Germany, designed several on the ratchet method but force still had to be applied to direct the tooth upwards or downwards. Another version, of 1762, had a separate fulcrum. Benjamin Bell improved on this by devising a forceps with jaws at right angles to the handles and a cylindrical fulcrum, under the chin, so to speak, of the jaws. John Gray, in *Dental Practice* of 1837, described an instrument with a claw and fulcrum at each end, operated by placing the fingers between the lozenge-shaped shanks, which could be adjusted by screws (pl. 59).

There were several objections to this class of instrument, as the operator took a long time, adjacent teeth might be injured despite the careful leather covering of the fulcra, and often there were no adjacent teeth on which counter-pressure might be put. As examples of mechanical complexity and brilliance they are of no small wonder; they are unlikely to have been produced in any number. One in the Royal College of Surgeons in London consists of a square section outer case containing a screw which operates a claw at the end; an upper handle, when depressed, provides the upward force (pl. 60). A very heavy, clumsy instrument in the same collection, intended for the incisors, has two claws which close over the tooth with a thumbscrew, the tooth then being drawn down by a screw within the shaft. This is again very like a corkscrew.

59 *Instrument for perpendicular extraction designed by John Gray, 1837. The claws are opened by placing the finger between the shanks; the ivory fulcra are adjustable. 19 cm. (Odontological Museum of the Royal College of Surgeons, London, J.41.1)*

60 *Instrument for perpendicular extraction, c.1780. The claw is closed by the screw within the case and upward force applied by depressing the handle. 20 cm. (Odontological Museum of the Royal College of Surgeons, London, J.35.1)*

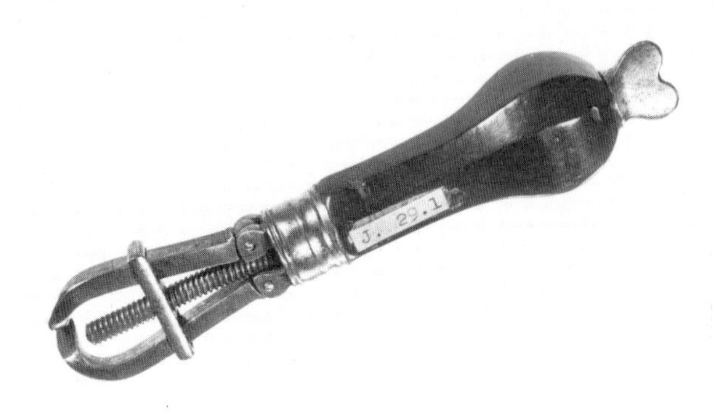

61 *Instrument for perpendicular extraction, c.1780. By operating the screw, the metal bar is raised and the beaks closed. 13 cm. (Odontological Museum of the Royal College of Surgeons, London, J.29.1)*

62 *Instrument for perpendicular extraction of incisors, c.1790. The action is very similar to that of a double corkscrew. 9 cm. (Odontological Museum of the Royal College of Surgeons, London, J.38.1)*

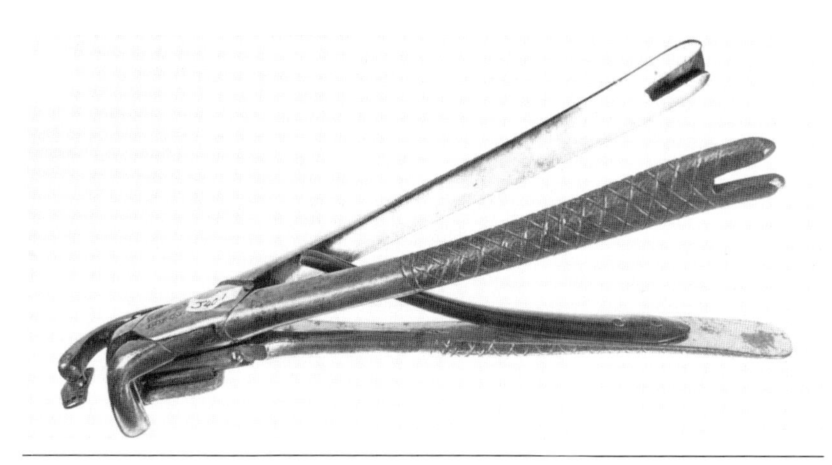

63 *Instrument for perpendicular extraction, c.1810. The fulcrum is placed on adjacent teeth and the beaks round the one to be removed. 18 cm. (Odontological Museum of the Royal College of Surgeons, London, J.40.1)*

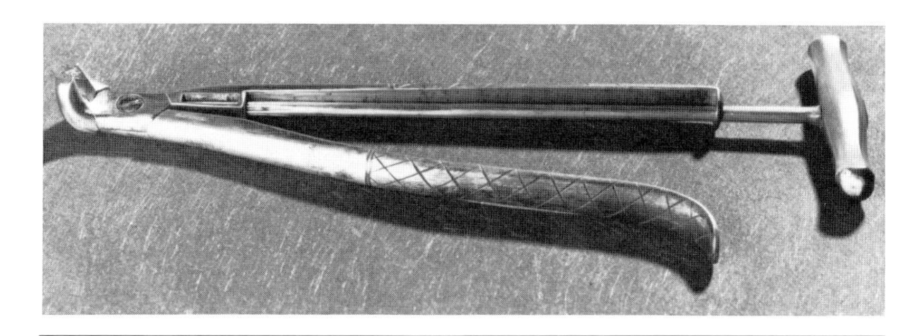

64 *Instrument for perpendicular extraction designed by Ludwig Puppi, 1841. (Museum of History of Medicine, Vienna)*

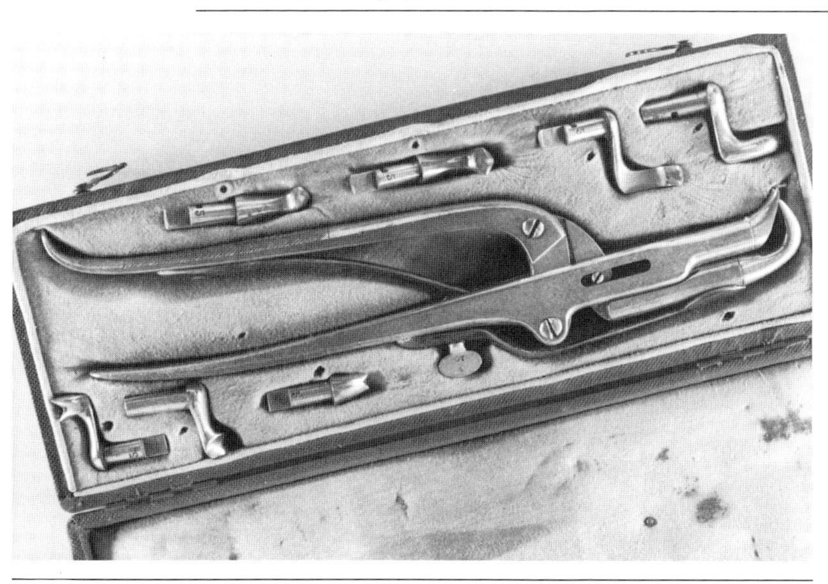

65 *'L'attractif de d'Estanque', 1861, with interchangeable heads. 22 cm. (Musée du Val-de-Grâce, Paris)*

A curious tool, apparently for home dentistry, was that known as Pfaff's lever-forceps, though not mentioned by him; Perret said it had been invented by the surgeon Charpentier. It was said it 'causes less tearing and therefore less pain than ordinary instruments' and was suitable for 'those who have the courage to operate on themselves'. Its method was the use of a broad flat blade attached to an upper hinged handle, which, when depressed, raised the tooth upwards between the claws. J.R. Duval (1758–1854), author of *Le Dentiste de la Jeunesse* (1817), found it difficult to accept the existence of this and similar instruments if not proved and said the inventors must have been ignorant of the anatomy of the teeth. Nevertheless, they continued to be produced, each one apparently cleverer than the last; each heavy, elaborate and tedious to operate but clearly giving great satisfaction to those of an inventive turn of mind.

John Palmer took out a patent for his invention in 1825, a multipurpose item combining the principle of a forceps with a key and several additions along the way.

One of the most interesting methods of extraction was patented by Henry Gilbert in 1848, which incorporated a chair for the purpose. He illustrates a straight, high-backed upholstered elbow-chair with, attached to the back at head height, a fixed rod with adjustable sliding socket on a steel bar. This bar swings round to the patient's mouth and becomes the fulcrum on which the extractor can rest, obviating any possible damage to other teeth or gums. Ordinary forceps were used and levered against the bar, either above it or below according to whether an upper or lower tooth were to be removed.

Simpler combinations included an example which is now in the Wellcome Collection at the Science Museum in London. This has a key at one end and a lever at the other. Another version, described by Heister in 1719, could be a pelican or an elevator. More interesting is the piece at the Royal College of Surgeons in London, which can be either a forceps, pelican or elevator. It comes from Virginia and is identified with a similar instrument owned by the surgeon of the Mayflower (pl. 66).

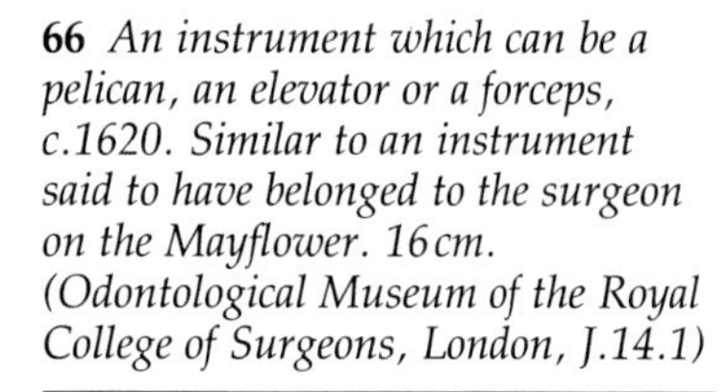

66 *An instrument which can be a pelican, an elevator or a forceps, c.1620. Similar to an instrument said to have belonged to the surgeon on the Mayflower. 16 cm. (Odontological Museum of the Royal College of Surgeons, London, J.14.1)*

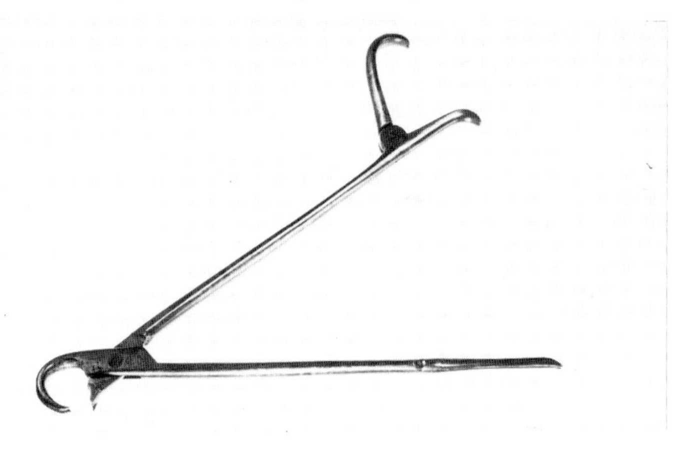

3 Excavating instruments, cauteries, filling materials

There is no question of dental caries being a modern disease; there is evidence of Pleistocene cave bears suffering carious teeth one million years ago. Undoubtedly early man was similarly afflicted, and methods of treatment were sought. These were largely based on the theory of the toothworm, a belief which died hard, as has been seen. As late as the eighteenth century, while René-Jacques Garengeot (1688–1759) examined the cavity of the tooth and did not see the worm, Nicholas Andry (1660–1745) just as positively did. During the same period, John Hunter (1728–93) carried out considerable work on the carious processes and concluded they started on the surface of the tooth and worked inwards and that the condition is especially liable to be found where food particles tend to lodge. Levi Spear Parmly (1790–1859), an American dentist working in London in 1820, examined thousands of teeth taken from the bodies of those fallen in battle and he showed that the initial aperture was so minute as to escape attention unless looked for deliberately. Not until 1830 was it possible to list 'odontalgia' as a cause of admission to a military hospital. After 1855 and the controversy following the Crimean War, the Medical Staffs Corps was formed and took over from the Regimental Surgeons. This body requested its officers to conserve rather than extract teeth, and sets of filling instruments were issued. However, these were totally inadequate and not used. Few practitioners, civil or military, were interested in preservation, much less preventive care.

Drills

It is hardly possible to say with accuracy when drills were introduced. Galen (A.D. 130–200), reported that the Roman physician Archigenes opened teeth with a small trephine. Giovanni d'Arcoli (1412–84) was one of the earliest of the modern world to mention the drilling of teeth, no doubt by a similar trephine, though he suggested it as a means by which the cautery might enter more accurately the exact source of trouble. Giovanni da Vigo (1460–1520), in his *Practica* of 1516, mentions excavation of the putrified part of the tooth with the use of a drill, file or scalpel. 'We may remove the said Corrosion with trepans, files or other convenient instruments.' Andreas della Croce (1500–75) illustrated, in 1573, both a bow-drill and a string-drill; Michael Blum, writing in Leipzig in 1530 in *Artzney Buchlein*, discussed a 'fine small chisel, or a little knife, or a file or . . . another suitable instrument'; Fabricius ab Aquapendente (1537–1619), in his *Pentateuchos Chirurgicum* of 1604, writes of using a drill followed by the instillation of a strong acid and the cautery. Cornelius Solingen (1641–87) devised an early form of hand-drill, filing cavities by constantly turning a polygonal stem with a burred head between his fingers. Some 60 years later, Garengeot had a 'serpent's tongue' for removing decay, a lozenge-shaped head with raised spine.

Charles Allen wrote, in 1687, that some diseased teeth 'not so far gone as may not still do good service' might be scraped out with 'proper instruments'. The rotten matter removed, the teeth could be filled with ingredients neither corrosive nor ill-tasting. His lack of precision one may suppose to have been as frustrating to his readers then as it is today.

Pierre Fauchard (1678–1761) was the first to describe excavation in constructive detail. He advised enlarging the carious spot with a half-round file, removing the decayed matter with a parrot's beak rasp and awl and piercing the cavity with a large sewing needle held in tweezers. This last was to pierce the interior membrane and drain any abscess which might have formed. The needle was to be threaded, and the thread held during the operation to prevent the risk of the patient swallowing it if it escaped the tweezers. Should a particular tooth make this method unsuitable, then a drill was to be used 'mounted on a trestle held in the left hand, the bow in the right'. The cavity must then be filled with a ball of cotton dipped in oil of cinnamon or cloves. Many weeks must then elapse before attempting to do more with the tooth, or possibly before the patient's permission could be obtained. Incisors and canine teeth, he said, might need to be trepanned. The bow-drill he illustrates, driven by a violin bow and used with the same ordinary sewing needle, he only describes in detail as being used in the manufacture of artificial teeth, but it would appear to be the same as the one mentioned here for excavation work. It was a type much favoured by jewellers and ivory-turners. Fauchard described two excavators to scrape out caries in addition to the parrot's beak and awl, one with four facets ending in a sharp point and the other with three facets on a curved shaft. As an alternative, he suggested that scaling instruments could be used.

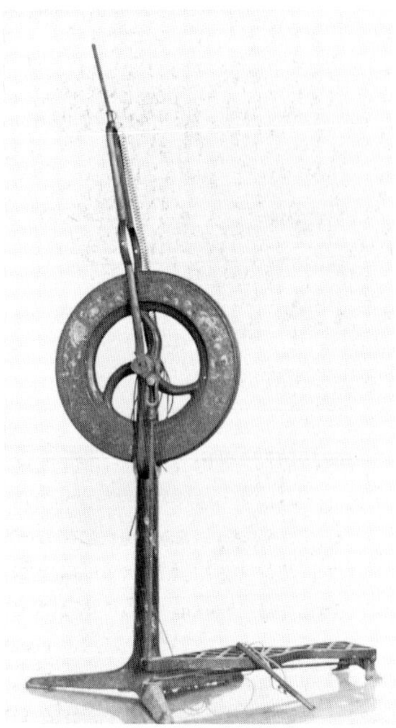

The drill of Johann Jacob Joseph Serre (1759–1830) was a needle-like instrument twisted between the thumb and index finger. This form of drill originally had a fixed handle but was later adapted to take several interchangeable heads in the one socket (pl. 69).

67 *Dental drill made from a spinning wheel by John Greenwood, c.1790. (New York Academy of Medicine)*

In 1790 John Greenwood (1760–1819) of New York constructed a rotary dental drill using a foot-operated spinning wheel as the driving mechanism (pl. 67). The half-educated son of an ivory-turner and mathematical instrument maker, Greenwood entered the army as a fifer at the start of the War of Independence. It is

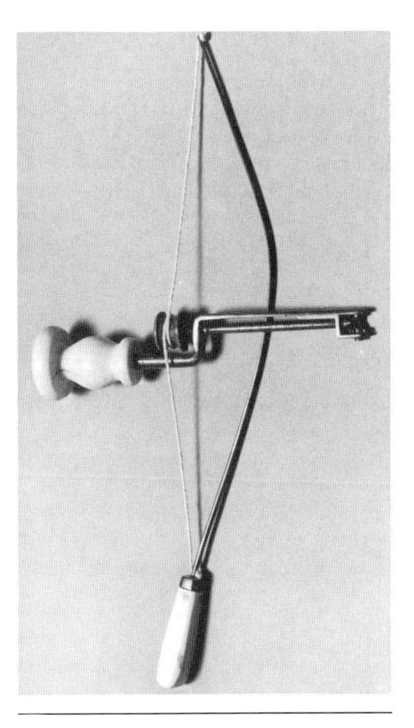

68 *Bowstring drill, c.1800. (Howard Dittrick Museum of Historical Medicine, Cleveland, Ohio)*

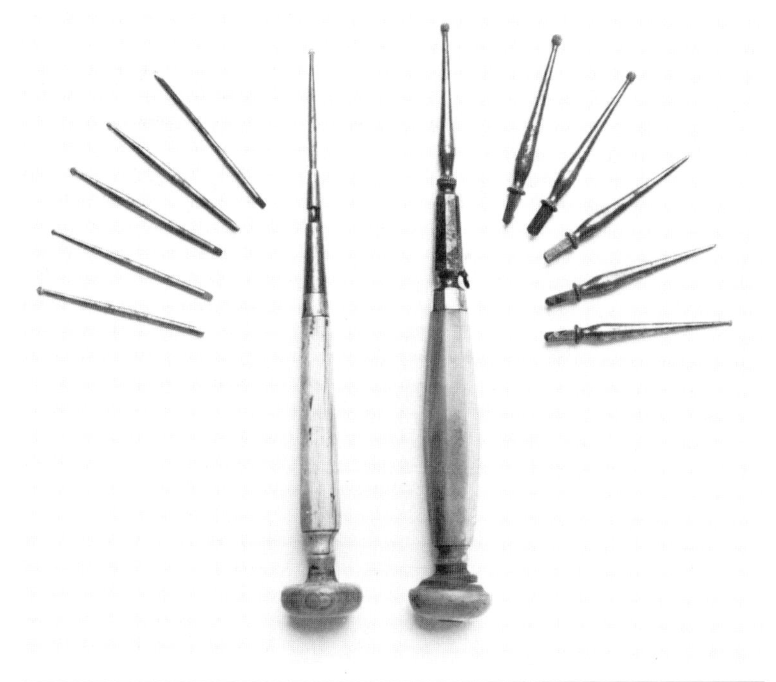

69 *Interchangeable rose-head drills to fit into a common handle, one ivory, one mother-of-pearl, as Serre, c.1820, assembled approx. 15 cm. (Macaulay Museum of Dental History, Medical University of South Carolina)*

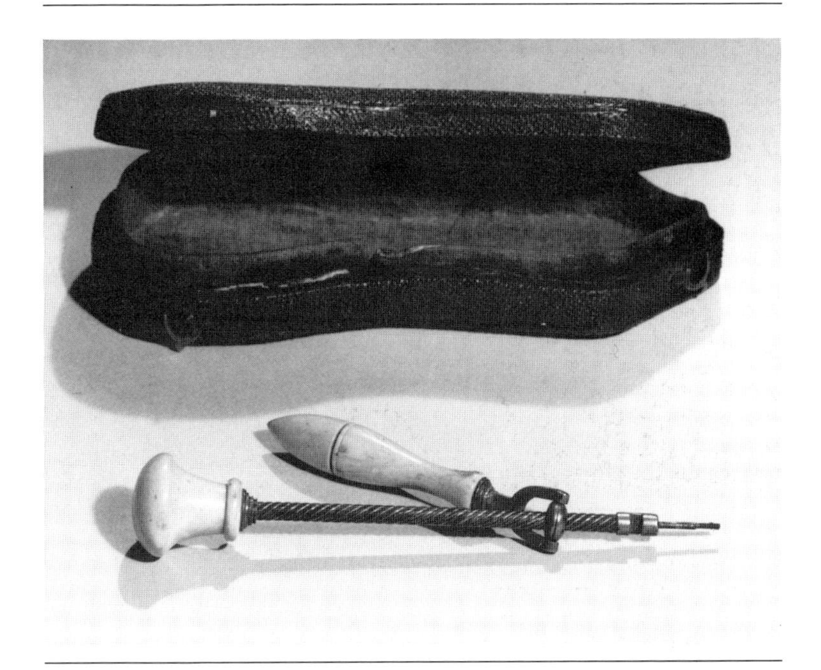

70 *Archimedes drill, ivory handle, fishskin case, c.1800, 15 cm. (Private Collection, the late Raymond Babtkis, New York)*

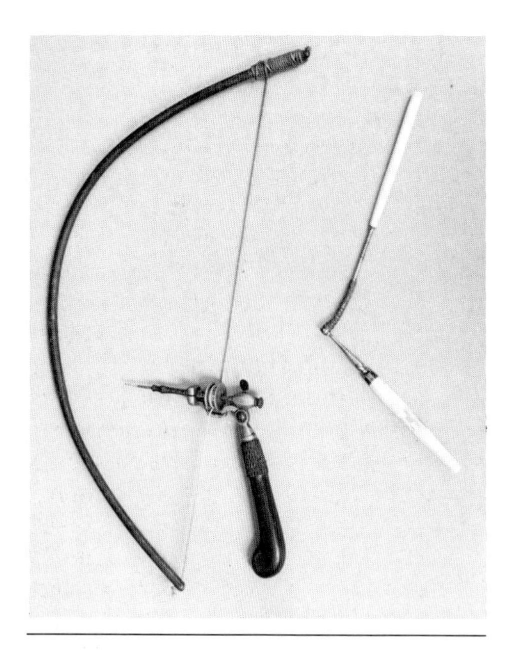

71 *Bowstring drill, c.1840; hand-drill, as Nasmyth, c.1830. (Museum of the History of Dentistry, Cologne)*

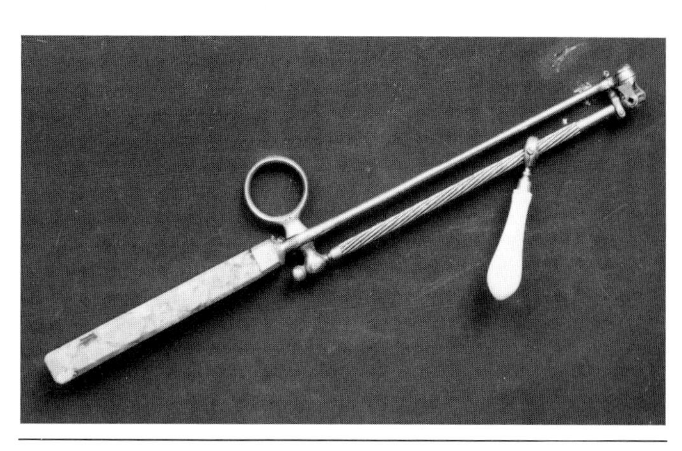

72 *Archimedes drill as developed by McDowell, c.1850, 17 cm. (Museum of the History of Dentistry, Cologne)*

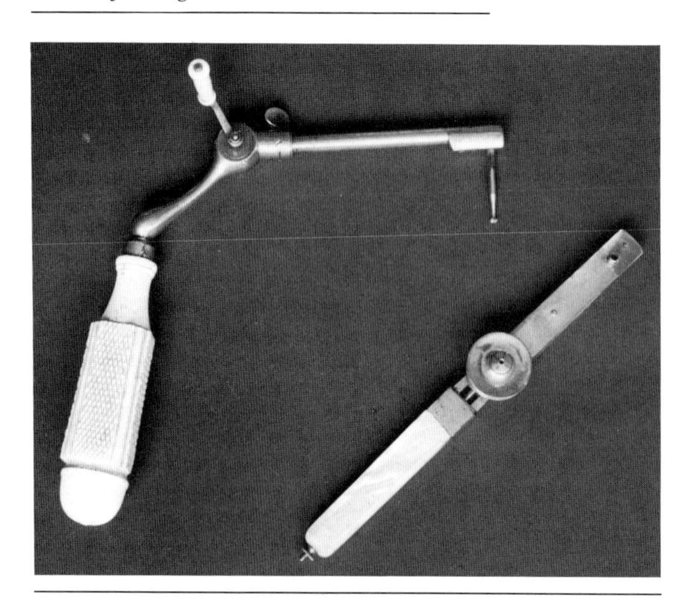

73 *Variation of Chevalier drill, c.1855; Maury's porte-forêt, c.1830. (Museum of the History of Dentistry, Cologne)*

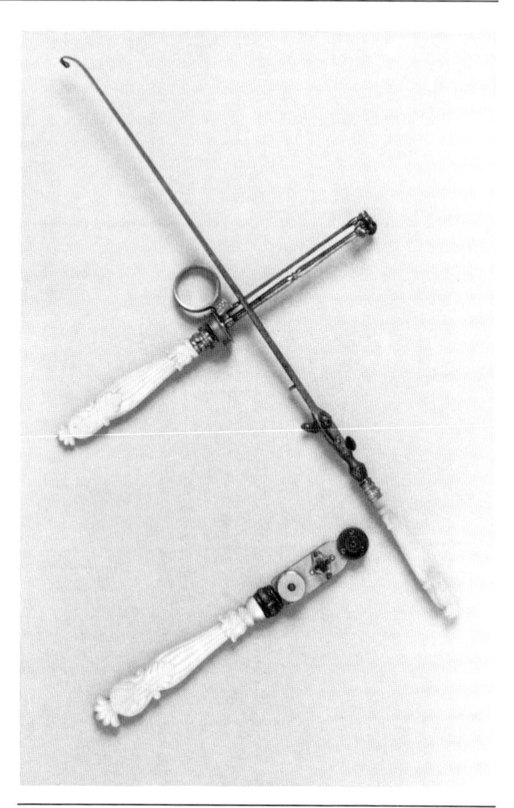

74 *Bowstring drill, c.1840, Blanc; Hand-drill of the porte-forêt type, c.1840. Both carved mother-of-pearl handles. (Musée Fauchard, Paris)*

possible he accumulated the necessary money from privateering to establish himself in dental practice in New York *c*. 1784. His drill was used to make holes in bone and ivory for pivots and posts, not to excavate caries, but his invention was important as it provided the necessary impetus for other methods.

The drill of Calmann Jacob Linderer (1771–1840) in 1797 was a longish wooden box with an extended wheel on which violin string was wound; the geared mechanism within revolved the drill. By the turn of the century the jeweller's bow-drill was still in common use (pl. 71), together with the joiner's type of Archimedes drill (pl. 72). The latter was so called because Archimedes discovered the spiral, which is its fundamental principle but, again, it is likely that it was seldom used for excavation of caries.

Little real progress was made until 1829 when James Nasmyth (1808–90), the Scottish engineer who invented the steam hammer, made a flexible shaft of close-coiled spring for driving small drills. Maury, in 1830, showed a *porte-forêt*, an ivory handle supporting two metal plates between which are wheels wound with gut and connected to five rose-heads (pls. 73 and 76(a)). The hand drill with adjustable head came in 1830, patented by John Lewis in America. A baluster wooden handle supported a revolving disc at its end; this was turned by a small second handle, and the head of the drill was at an angle to the cogs (pl. 76(a)). In the same year the London firm of Ash produced a drill with a ball joint. In 1841 Pierre Joachim Lefoulon (b. 1800) spoke of removing caries with a spoon-shaped excavator, having first used a hand-drill to shape the cavity. He dried the cavity with alcohol, filling it with metal foil by means of probe and tamper. The hand-drill he illustrated was a simple rose-head on a straight shaft with no mechanism.

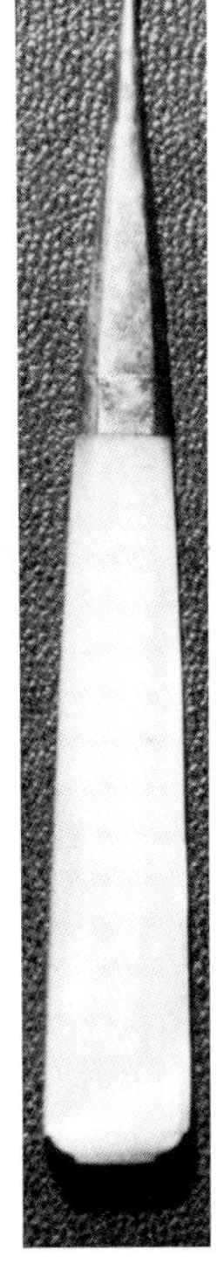

75 *Excavator, mother-of-pearl handle, c.1800. Made by Paul Revere for his student Josiah Flagg. 13 cm. (Macaulay Museum of Dental History, Medical University of South Carolina)*

By 1846 the American Josiah Foster Flagg (1763–1816) had already produced the first drill to receive the serious attention of dentists across the Atlantic, the forerunner of a drill which incorporated a ring which slipped over the index finger. The lower end had a bulbous-shaped handle which fitted into the palm of the hand, and the drill rotated by the action of the thumb and forefinger. This type of drill was developed by many dentists, among whom was another American, Amos Westcott (1815–73). Several hand-drills came into use in the mid-century, with many variations including examples by Spencer in America and S.L. Finzi, both in 1848.

Between 1850 and 1858 the crutch-handled holder, to take drills and burrs, became very popular. An elongated melon-shaped handle, usually of ivory, contained several interchangeable heads of different sizes (pl. 77). McDowell's Archimedes drill was still in use but a new invention of 1850 was Chevalier's drillstock in which a handle in mid-shaft could rotate the head in both directions, an added convenience. The best idea to that date came in 1858 when Charles Merry of St Louis introduced his dental drill, which he had adapted from the Nasmyth invention.

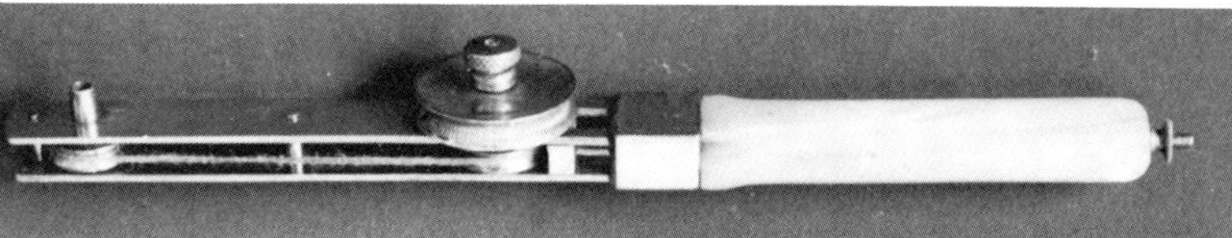

76(a) *Part of a hand-drill of the John Lewis type, c.1830, 14 cm; and the porte-forêt Maury drill, c.1840, 17 cm. (Museum of the History of Dentistry, Cologne)*

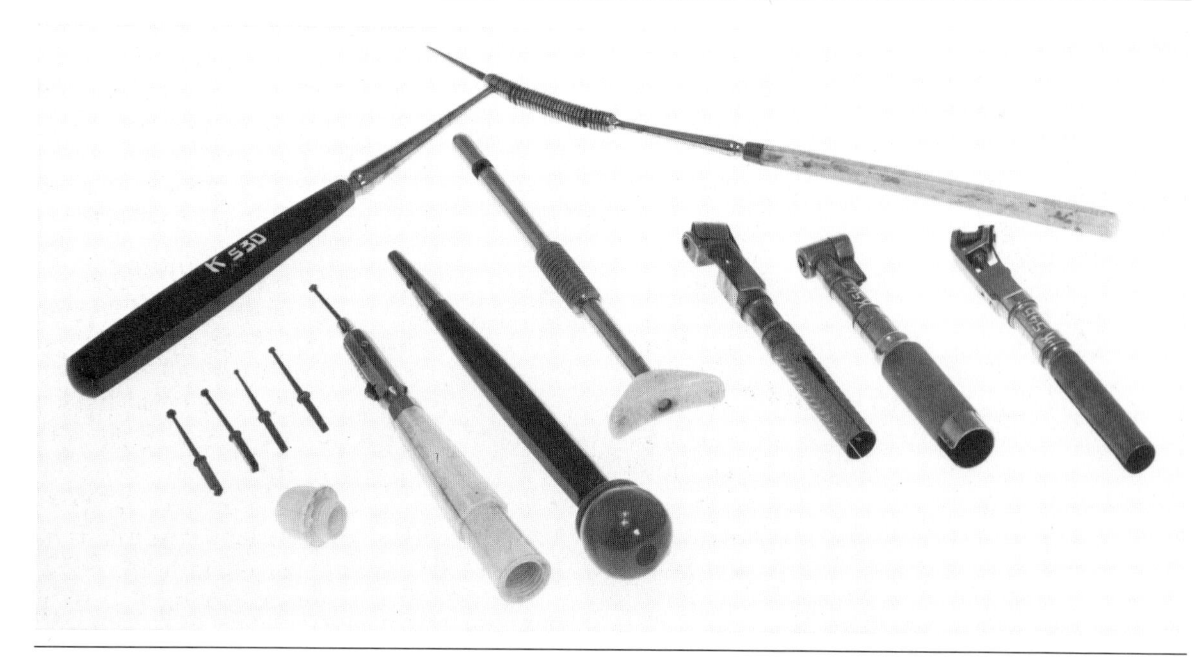

76(b) *Top, Merry's drill, c.1868. Bottom, left to right: drill with metal lever mechanism, Capron, c.1840; ebony, horn knop, Ash, c.1860; Tomes' drill, c.1859; drill with 90° angle, patented 1874; drill with 90° angle, patented by Hodge, 1884; 135° handle, S.S. White, patented 1874. (Rijksuniversiteit, Utrecht)*

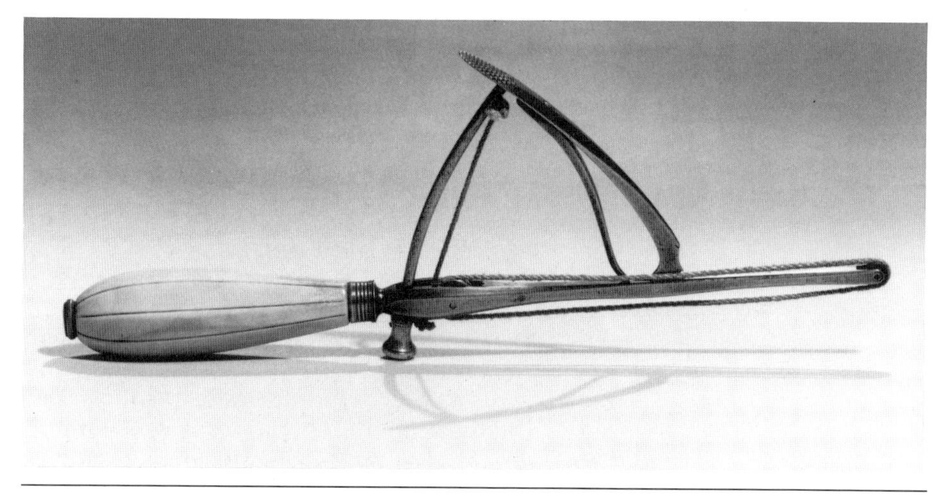

77 *Crutch-handled drill, the ivory handle containing a variety of heads, c.1850, 21 cm. (Private Collection, the late Raymond Babtkis, New York)*

78 *Harrington's clockwork drill, 1864. (Museum of the History of Dentistry, Cologne)*

There were two handles – one for holding and the other, incorporating a flexible cable, for propelling – enabling it to be directed with precision. In 1862 Merry added the first angled head. Jonathan Taft (1820–1903), in his textbook of 1859, described a simple, straight-shafted drill with rose-heads, driven once again by a supporting finger-ring. Perkin's drillstock appeared in 1862 followed by the spring motor drill of Philo Soper in America, a heavy, ugly cylinder from which a short shaft for the head protruded. George Fellows Harrington (1812–95) introduced his improved clockwork drill in 1864; interchangeable heads and contra-angles were added the following year. Made of brass and richly smothered in engraving, this hand-held drill resembled a musical box in appearance and was excessively noisy in application. The spring-wound mechanism and its popularity were limited, the dentist having an awkward control of the instrument.

The innovative firm of S.S. White of Philadelphia produced a most ingenious machine in 1868 to a design of the inventor George F. Green. This was a pneumatically-driven apparatus with a foot-operated bellows opening into a rubber hose, which in turn moved blades as in the action of a windmill. Water-powered drills were attempted, and Green designed the first electrical drill in 1874. This was found very difficult to control.

The great breakthrough came in 1872 when James Beall Morrison (1829–1917) introduced his patent dental engine. This foot-operated machine, on the same principle as the treadle sewing machine, achieved 2,000 rpm, thus making grinding simpler and better and making practical new possibilities in the dental field. Morrison wrote of,

> *. . . some quite nervous ladies, for whom I have removed caries previously by manual excavation. Their judgement was unanimous that this type of operation, that is with the aid of this machine, is completely painless and relatively more pleasant than any other method of resection.*

Following Morrison's Dental Engine, variants were introduced in profusion. In 1874 an engine came with the driving belt direct to the spindle of the handpiece and another with the first flexible shaft engine. Almost every year thereafter S.S. White produced an improvement on their previous model, once more engaging the services of the versatile George F. Green. In 1885 there came a motor-driven hand-drill, a particularly noisy affair. In the early 1870s the first electric engine had been introduced, followed by several improved versions in the next decade. Few of these engines achieved the success which was hoped for them but they provided a springboard for invention which has resulted in the relative calm with which we can today contemplate this particularly unpopular piece of dental equipment.

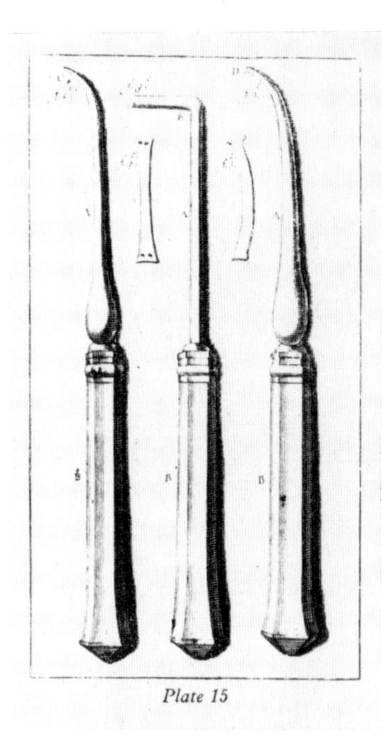

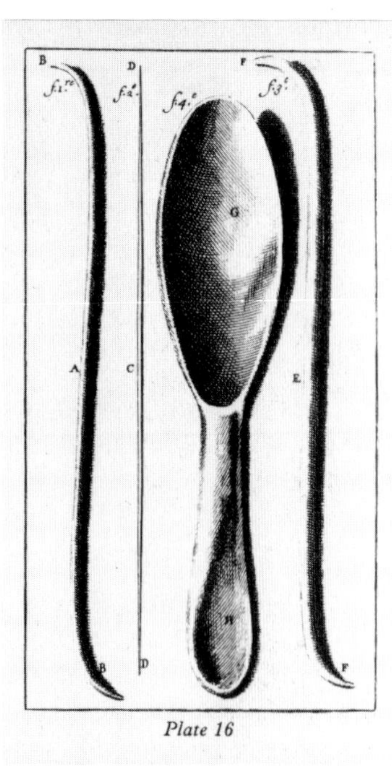

79 *Illustration from Pierre Fauchard's* Le Chirurgien Dentiste *(1746 edition) showing, on Plate 15, instruments for filing and regulating the teeth and, on Plate 16, three dental cauteries and a cheek-retractor.*

A further advance in the preparation of the cavity was the recognition of the fact that before the filling was introduced the cavity must be entirely dry. A sheet of rubber, shaped to surround the tooth and keeping away the saliva, was the first step in this direction and introduced in 1864 by Sanford Christie Barnam (1838–85). It was said in 1859, several years before antisepsis was understood, that instruments should be kept clean and bright as 'nothing was more calculated to disgust even the least sensitive patient than the employment of rusty or bloody instruments in their mouths', giving a balanced picture of dental practice at the time, despite the mechanical advances we have seen.

Cauteries

An early alternative to excavation in the treatment of caries was the cautery. Cauterization in dentistry was, in any case, used for many purposes: for application when haemorrhage persisted after extraction, for early root canal treatment, for gumboils, and as a palliative or counter-irritant for toothache. In the eleventh century Albucasis (936–1013) cauterized the gums as a treatment for pyorrhoea. The use of the cautery for toothache was frequently effected for Louis XIV, who suffered considerably from the complaint. The affliction caused his dentist, Dubois, to apply the actual cautery 14 times on one particular day – 10 January 1685. It was said his torments influenced his signing of the Revocation of the Edict of Nantes later that year.

During the Middle Ages the cautery was one of the most frequently used dental instruments (pl. 6). Jan Yperman (d. *c.* 1329), who studied under Lanfranc of Milan and wrote the first medical treatise in Flemish *c.* 1305, speaks of cauterization of the tooth with a protective cannula, which would seem to be very advanced. More often the cautery was just a copper rod, as at the medical school in Salerno founded in the ninth century. Dental cauteries were naturally long and slender and seldom had a wooden handle before the seventeenth century. One must suppose, therefore, that they were held in a pair of tweezers, which must have added to the difficulty of application. John Scultetus of Ulm (1595–1645) speaks of 'breaking off' the teeth, as opposed to extraction, in order to drop medication or the cautery into the tooth. Peter Lowe (?1550–?1612), in *A Discourse of the Whole Art of Surgery* (1612), mentions a gold cautery he reserved for use on the nobility.

Pierre Fauchard claimed to cure toothache with a cautery. He mentions cauterization of caries and speaks of receiving many patients where this method has failed, so presumably it was not one he used himself. The cauteries he illustrates in 1728 (pl. 79) are either flat and slender with reverse curves at each end, or sharp and needle-like; all are without handles. With them,

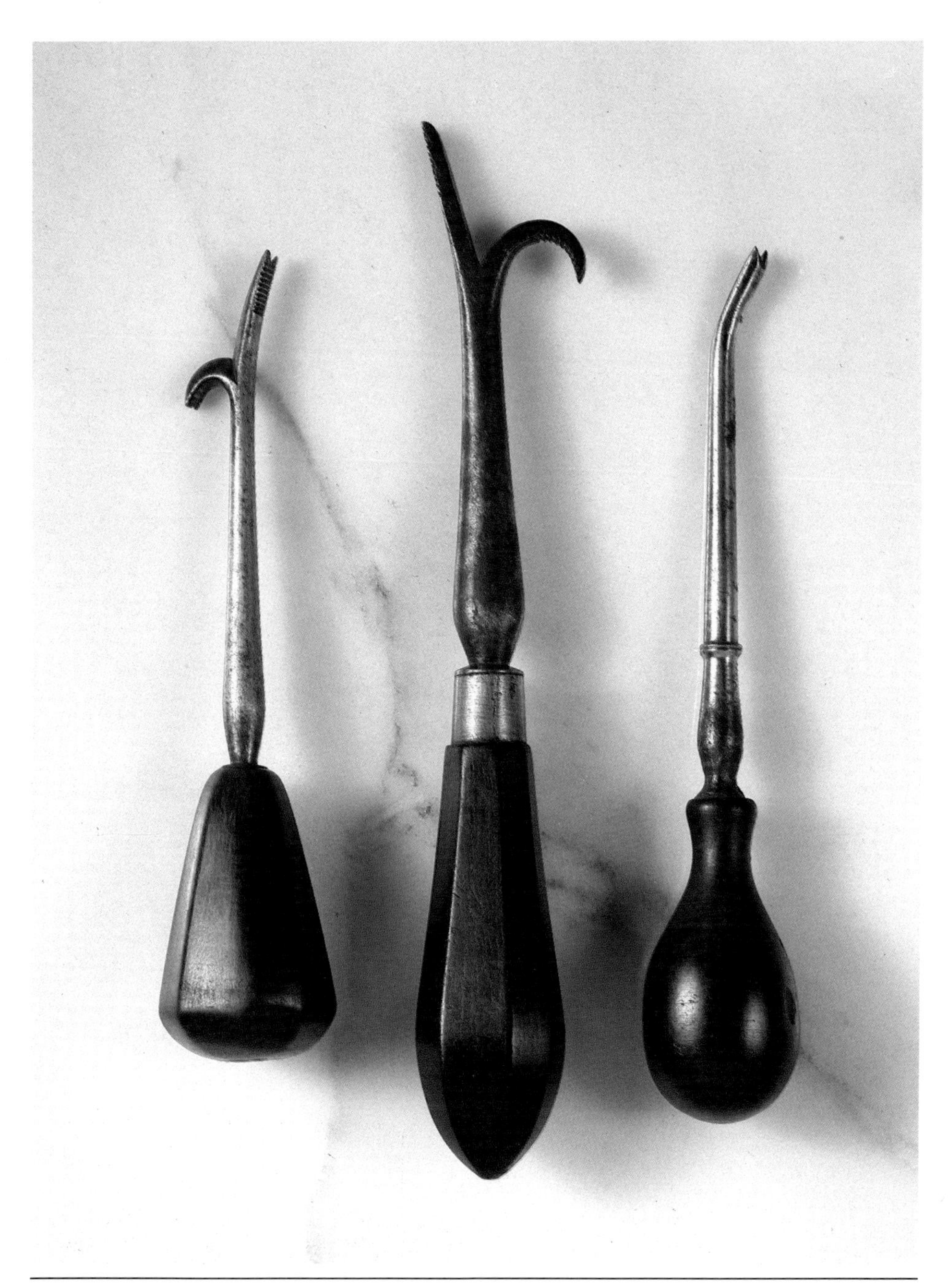

XI *Left to right: 'pied-de-biche' elevator, horn handle, c.1780, 11.5cm; 'pied-de-biche' elevator, c.1780, 16cm; goat's foot elevator, c.1820, 13cm; (I. Freeman & Son, Simon Kaye Ltd, London)*

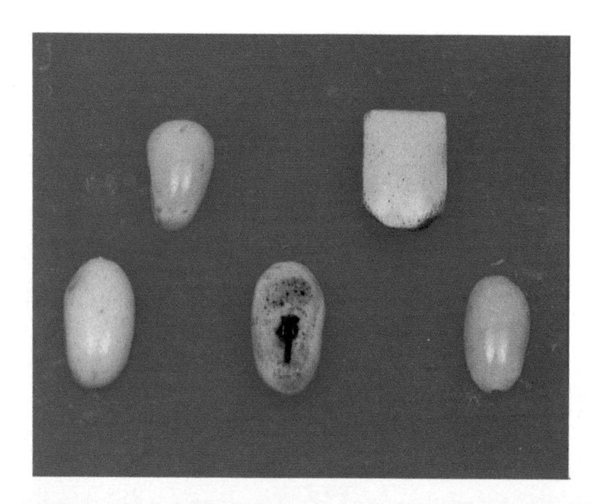

XII *Fonzi teeth, 1808–20 (above) and 1820–30. (Museum of Swedish Dental Society, Stockholm)*

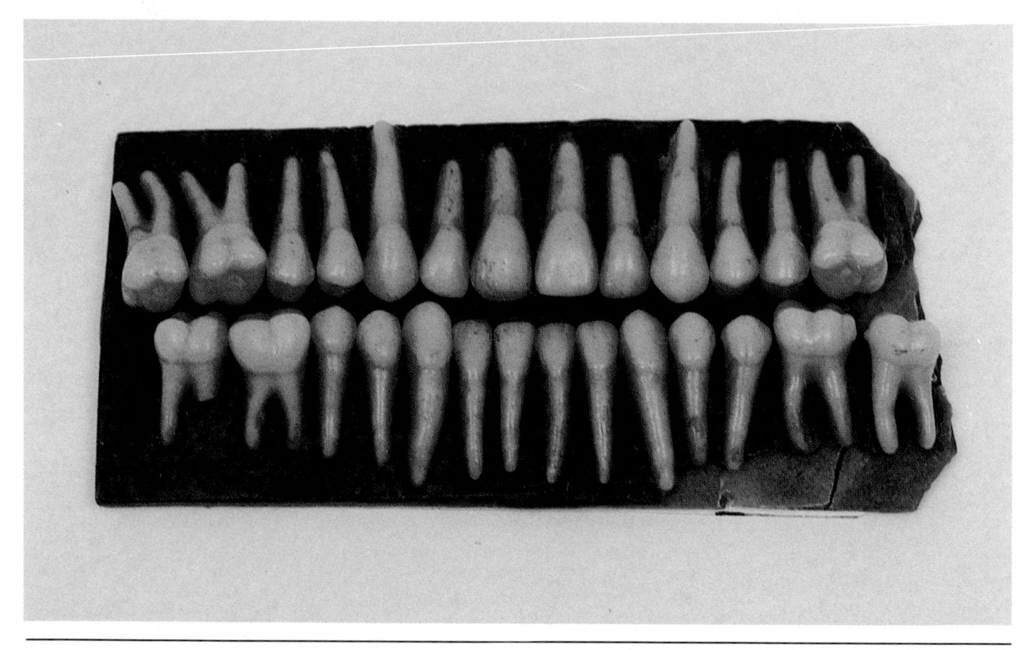

XIII *Set of artificial teeth for 'continuous gum' on the original wax plate, S.S. White, 1861. (Museum of Swedish Dental Society, Stockholm)*

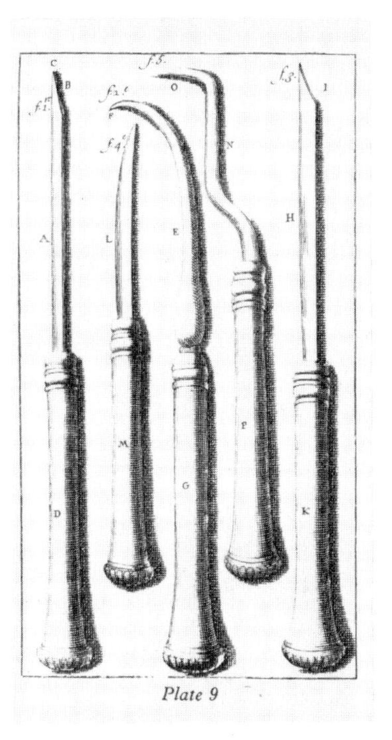

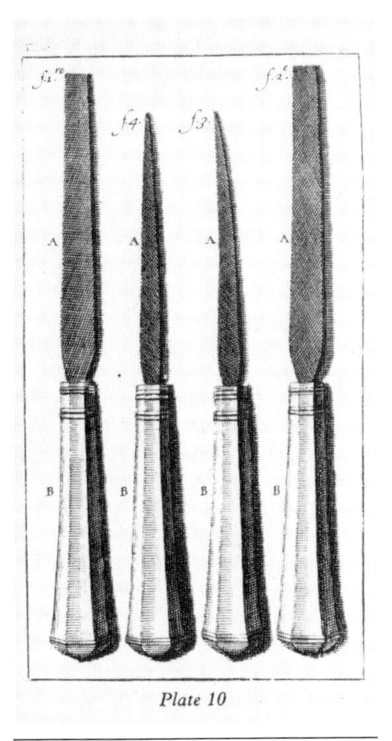

80 *Illustration from Pierre Fauchard's* Le Chirurgien Dentiste *(1746 edition) showing, on Plate 9, five dental scalers and, on Plate 10, four dental files.*

Fauchard shows a silver spoon-shaped cheek retractor, obviously a necessity with dental cauteries as he pointed out. If suitable cauteries are not available, he says, then brass wire knitting needles are most convenient and come in all sizes. Very similar cauteries and retractors to Fauchard's are shown by Philip Pfaff (1716–80), dentist to Frederick the Great of Prussia, in 1756. Etienne Bourdet (1722–89) was fond of scarifying the gums and then inserting a flat cautery between the gums and the root of the tooth, undoubtedly to aid extraction.

In 1824 Delmond of Paris described an invention of his own which he thought was much less painful than the current use of the cautery. It was a steel nerve extractor for removing dental pulp, with a hook at the extremity; he said its manipulation was swift and prompt. James Snell (?1795–1850) devised an ingenious new cautery in 1832, a steel instrument with a bulb on the end from which protruded a platinum wire; heat was retained in the bulb long enough to allow the wire to penetrate the root canal. An electric cautery by George Derby Waite (1804–80) was exhibited at the Great Exhibition of 1851 (pl. 110) and similar versions were made by Ash between the years 1858 and 1873. Other, simpler, cauteries continued to appear throughout the nineteenth century: slender steel shafts ending either in a sharp point or a minute cone-shaped head, the handle set as far away as the necessary dexterity would allow.

Types of filling material

Having excavated the cavity by whatever means, it then required filling. Fauchard illustrates a little syringe with a curved nozzle for washing out the cavity, and the swab-holder next to it was presumably to dry it. C.F. Maury (1786–1840) illustrated a similar syringe in 1828 and says he dried the cavity with alcohol. The introduction of the rubber dam has already been mentioned.

Early medieval fillings for dental cavities included wax from the Paschal candle, gum and resin, raven's dung in rural Germany, and stale bread and mastic. Lead was an early favourite, but gold became important too. One of the first people to use gold may have been Giovanni d'Arcoli, who recommended in his *Practica* that it should be pressed in very gradually, though it is possible it had been in use for some time before this. Giovanni da Vigo, describing the filling of teeth with gold foil in 1516, says, 'He, therefore, who desires to perform this manual operation in the best manner will derive great advantage by frequenting men who are expert in performing it and by seeing and impressing well in his memory their manner of operating.' One of these experts was undoubtedly Michael Blum of Leipzig (see above). Johannes Stocker (*c.* 1657), a physician of Ulm, describes an early amalgam, but it was Jacques Guillemeau (1550–1613), in *Oeuvres de Chirurgie* of 1598, who was probably the first to produce a

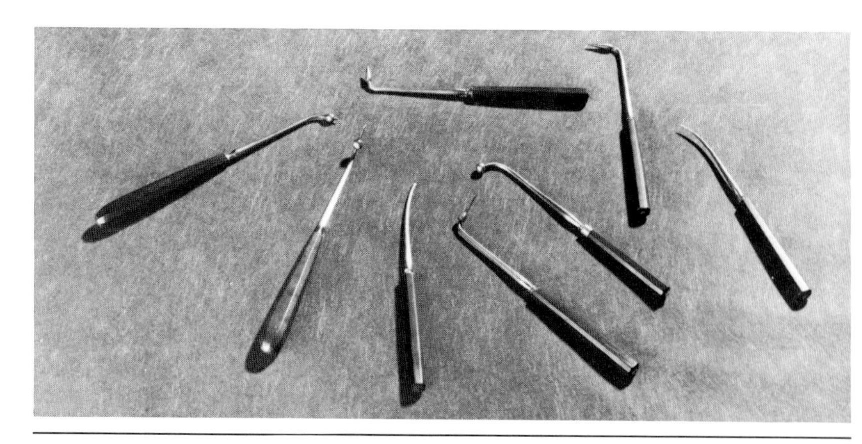

81 *A group of dental cauteries, c.1860. (Museum of the History of Medicine, Vienna)*

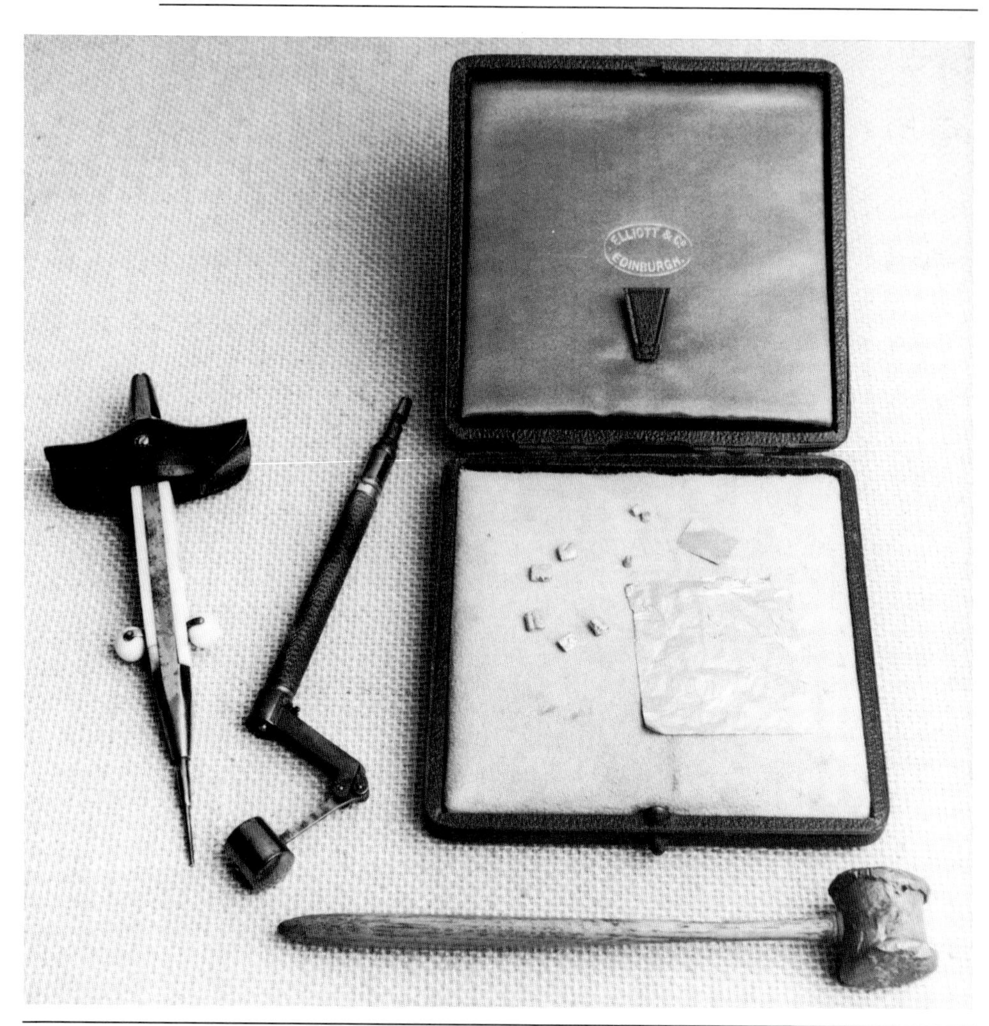

82 *Left, Tomes' spring-mallet, Evrard, 1860; centre, Kirby's Automaton Mallet-Plugger invented by Amos Kirby of Bedford, Ash, 1871; right, gold pellets and sheet of gold foil; bottom, a hand gold-foil mallet. (Museum of the British Dental Association, London)*

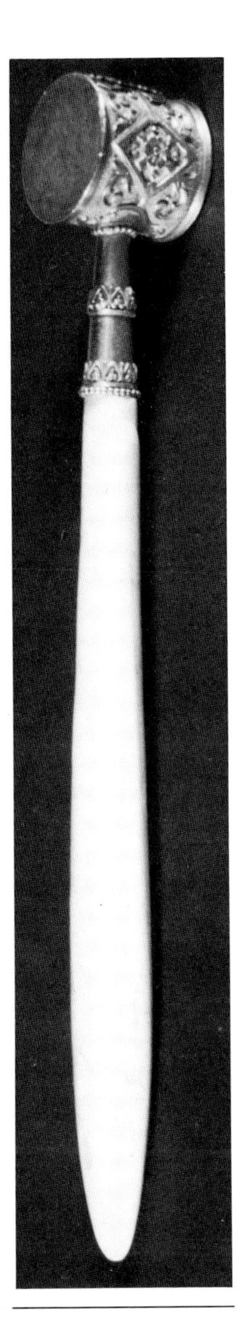

83 *Gold-foil mallet, ivory handle, c.1860, 16 cm. (Museum of the History of Dentistry, Cologne)*

satisfactory filling material. He advised white wax mixed with 'gumme elemni or a little masticke, white coralle and prepared pearles and thereof a paste being made'. René-Jacques Garengeot again refers to gold, tin and lead, the latter being in common use up to *c.* 1830. It was rolled between the fingers, forced into the cavity and polished. A small case of instruments at the Musée Fauchard in Paris has a compartment filled with the lead pellets.

There are many references to the less scrupulous practitioners colouring their filling to resemble gold. Lead or tin would be mixed with saffron, turmeric, amatto and gamboge and infused in brandy. Fauchard, however, had a poor opinion of gold as a filling and thought lead and tin, first beaten into foil, every bit as good, though tin was preferable as it did not blacken and lasted longer. Those who could bear the expense of gold could make their choice. John Hunter, who taught excavation of the carious tooth, recommended lead. Other eighteenth-century fillings included pitch and beeswax.

If gold foil was the chosen filling, it was rolled into cylinders and pushed as firmly as possible into the cavity. By the nineteenth century it was found possible to pass the cylinder over a spirit flame and push it into the required shape; one gold filling might take three hours. Nevertheless, proper shaping of the cavity was necessary first and this was not possible with the early hand-drills.

Auguste Onésime Taveau (d. 1843) introduced some amalgams in Paris between 1826 and 1835 which were previously known in China and Germany (see above). The 'silver paste' was an alloy of mercury and silver filings from coins, but as mercury and silver, when mixed, expand, a tooth often fractured when filled with it. There was some experimentation with an alloy of silver and tin, but this contracted and delicate proportions had to be judged. In 1848 an alloy of pure tin and a small amount of cadmium, to control the shrinkage, was tried. Good alloys did not necessarily produce good fillings, and altogether the amalgams were not popular and fell into desuetude.

Much more encouraging was the introduction of gutta-percha as a dental filling in 1848, although this was afterwards only found satisfactory as a temporary stopping.

Meanwhile, in America, from the early years of the nineteenth century dentists were using fillings of a solution of mastic and sunderac. Another compound, introduced in 1820, contained bismuth, lead, tin and mercury which was melted and poured into the cavity. Louis-Nicholas Requart (1780–1847) proposed the addition of mercury to lower the fusing point. In 1833 the Crawcour brothers arrived from France with their much-advertised 'royal mineral succadeneum' and rushed around filling cavities whether excavated or not; failing that, they filled the interstices of the teeth. In 1845 the American Society of Dental Surgeons adopted a pledge to expel members who used amalgam, which was not rescinded until 1850. Hill's Stopping, a

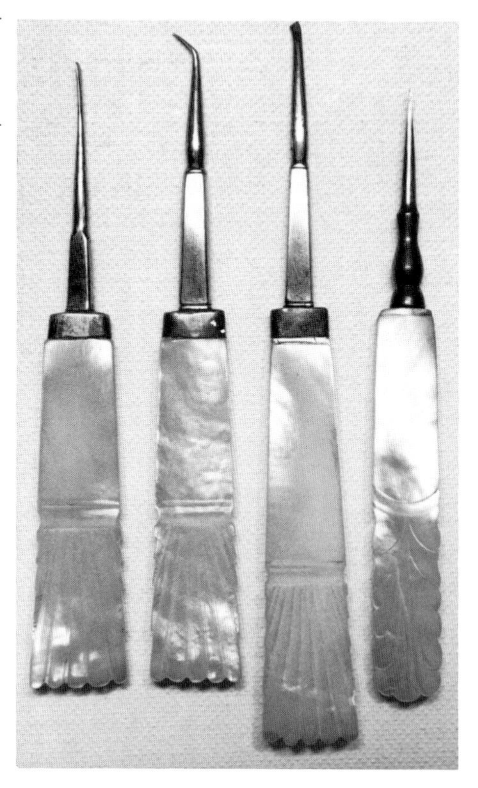

84 *Gold-foil pluggers, mother-of-pearl handles, American, c.1840–50, largest 19 cm. (Private Collection, Dr Gary Lemen, Sacramento, Cal.)*

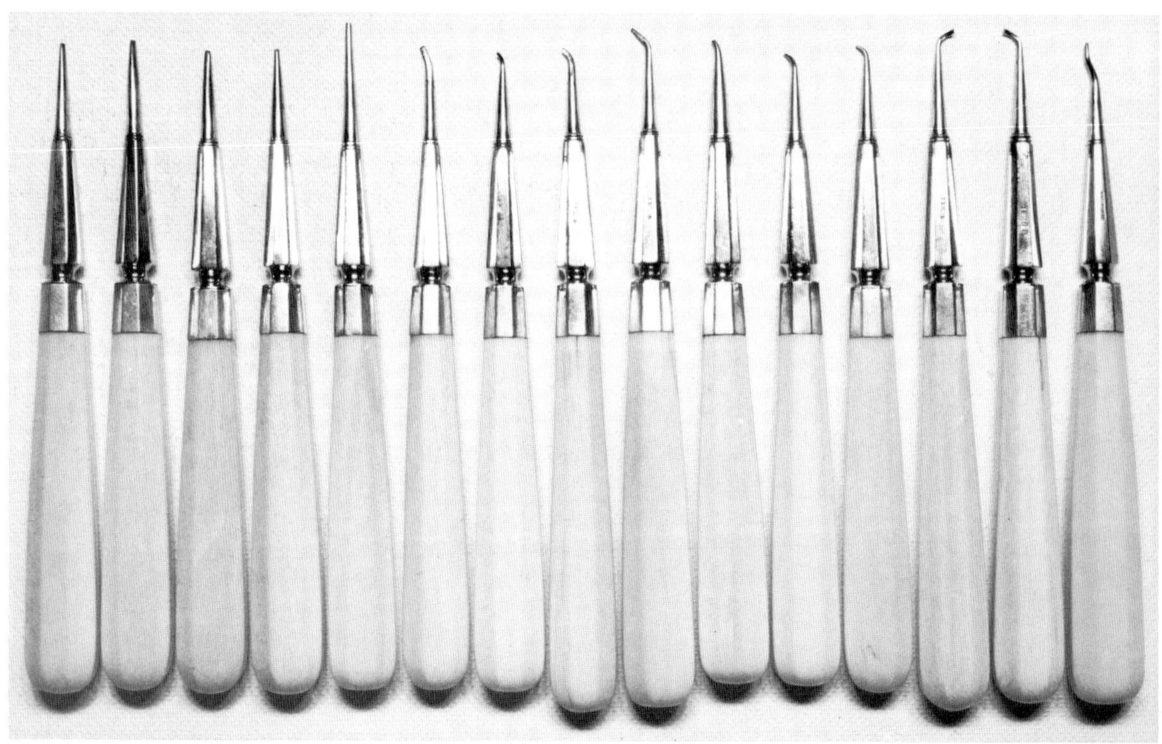

85 *Gold-foil pluggers, ivory handles, Leslie, c.1860, 15 cm. (Private Collection, Dr. Gary Lemen, Sacramento, Cal.)*

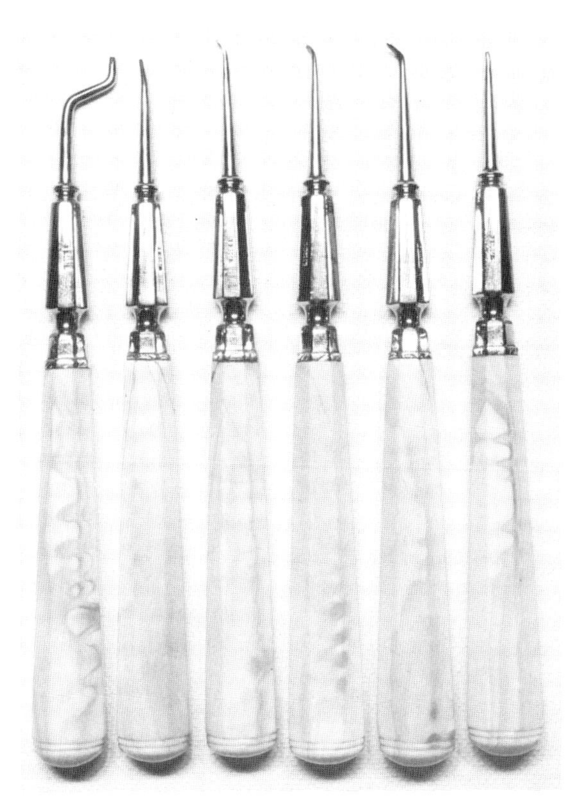

86 *Gold-foil pluggers, onyx handles, Leslie, c.1860, 16cm. (Private Collection, Dr Gary Lemen, Sacramento, Cal.)*

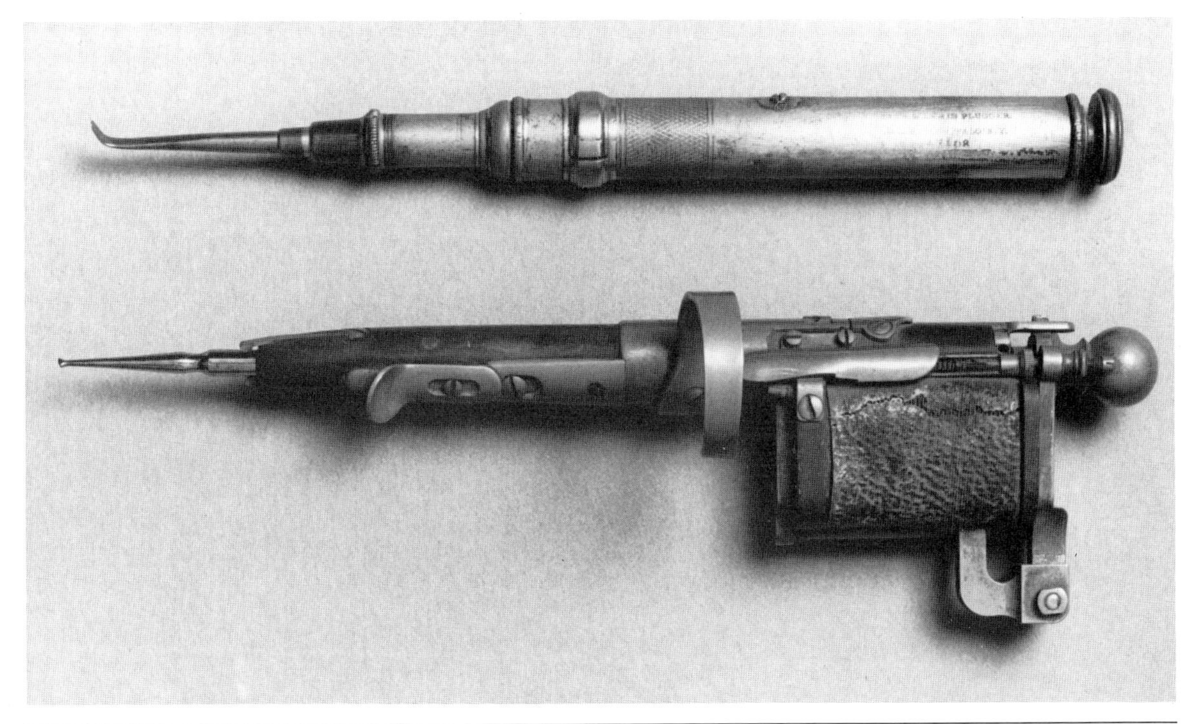

87 *Mechanical plugger and electromagnetic plugger, both mid 19th century, 18cm. (Howard Dittrick Museum of Historical Medicine, Cleveland, Ohio)*

mixture of gutta-percha, lime quartz and feldspar, came on the market in 1849 and became the origin of temporary filling material used today. In 1855 Dr Arthur Robert of Philadelphia described the cohesion of gold foil and its use in tooth filling, but the adequate excavating instruments were still not available. In 1876, at the Centennial Exhibition in Philadelphia, Eleazer Parmly Black invited inspection of his gold fillings in human teeth. Green Vardiman Black (1836–1915), who published several important papers, made considerable developments in filling materials to ensure the stability of the alloy.

Dental cement was introduced in France in the middle of the nineteenth century, but it was not satisfactory until the 1880s. It is interesting to observe that inlaying of teeth was hardly attempted with any success before the end of the nineteenth century, when one considers that the inlaying of wood, marble, tortoiseshell, etc. had been very skilled for at least 200 years. In the 1850s attempts were made to grind porcelain to fit the cavity but the difficulties were apparently insuperable. The appearance of the dental engine was paramount in importance, affecting fillings, crowns, teeth and filling materials.

As dental fillings became more sophisticated so the variety of pluggers and tampers increased. Fauchard was early in describing them in the list of necessary instruments. They were to be of three kinds, he said: one was to be cylindrical and pyramidical, with a curved sharp point; the second was to have the same shaft but the end more curved and blunt; and the other was to have a square shaft and the round end bent at right angles. They should all be of different sizes, have good ferrules and be well-fastened to the handle with mastic. These were sound principles which pertained with few variations for another two centuries.

4 Artificial teeth

The great drawback to the primitive, apparently healthy, diet enjoyed by our forebears was the quantity of grit and dust it contained which wore away the enamel of the teeth, causing cavities. This, inevitably, led to the loss of teeth and, as has been seen, this was associated with loss of virility and eventual death. Vanity and superstition were certain first steps to false teeth. The Talmudic references to prosthetic dentistry are mostly concerned with women; a new tooth might be of wood or metal, or a gold or silver shell to cover the mutilated natural stump might be fitted. Much argument was expended on the problem of whether the woman, who might be allowed out with a silver tooth, should venture out with a gold one. It is not clear if the doubt concerned the theft of the new tooth or the theft of her virtue due to added attraction. One story from the Talmud tells of Rabbi Haggai, who was rewarded, at the age of 80, with a complete set of new teeth in recognition of his involvement in the funeral of Rabbi Huna. In the classical Roman period Horace, in his Eighth Satire, describes two old witches running so fast that one of them, Canidia, loses her false teeth; and Martial wrote an epigram, 'Thäis has black, Laecania white teeth; What is the reason? Thäis has her own, Laecania bought ones.'

Queen Elizabeth I, in 1602, was seen to have padded out her cheeks with wads of cotton to disguise her lack of teeth. Blagrave, in his *Mathematical Jewel* of 1588, speaks of his nephew 'who caused his teeth to be all drawn out and after had a sett of ivory teeth in agayne'. *Love's Labour Lost* includes a reference to the artificial teeth of Boyet: 'This is the flower that smiles on everyone to show his teeth as white as whalesbone.' The seventeenth-century diarist Samuel Pepys, writing of his wife, said, 'She hath got her teeth new done by La Roche and are indeed now pretty handsome.' William Green, operator for the teeth of George III, inspired these lines by Charles Churchill in 'The Ghost':

> *Teeth, white as ever teeth were seen,*
> *Delivered from the hand of Green.*

In the eighteenth century the sensible Pierre Fauchard (1678–1761 wrote, 'If the teeth are very important for the preservation of health, they are absolutely necessary for speaking, the pronunciation and articulation of words and for the ornament of the face.' One can imagine the pride and admiration attached to the wearing of false teeth; they were unashamedly removed at the dinner table. Since only the better off would have been able to afford them, they may have been a rather adventurous status symbol. Embarrassment did not develop until the nineteenth century, when photographs of smiles behind tightly closed lips show the inhibitions which still survive.

Transplanting teeth from one mouth to another was the simplest form of tooth replacement attempted. At the end of the Middle Ages Guy de Chauliac (1300–68) mentions transplanted teeth lasting for years. The indigent poor were always available to sell a suitable tooth, or perhaps someone unable to refuse the extraction was used. Ambroise Paré (1510–90) speaks of removing a bad tooth from a princess and immediately replacing it with one from her lady-in-waiting; this took well and functioned satisfactorily. Charles Allen, in 1687, suggested animal teeth as surrogates. Pierre Fauchard describes the trimming of the replacement teeth with a file, preparatory to transplanting them. It was John Hunter (1728–93), however, who made the practice both popular and acceptable. The unwholesome condition of many of the artificial teeth he saw made him particularly enthusiastic about this method. 'The operation,' he said, 'is in itself a matter of no difficulty, yet upon the whole it is one of the nicest of all operations.' In some cases, where a carious tooth was too decayed to be excavated, he advised extraction and boiling the tooth to destroy its life, followed by replacement in the original socket. With transplants, he found some impediment in finding a donor with teeth of the necessary length of root, so suggested it was advisable to have two or three people at hand to supply new teeth. Then, if one were not suitable another might be. Indeed, several people were sometimes necessary in case the nerve of the first one or two should fail. The over-familiar cartoon by Thomas Rowlandson, showing a dental transplant operation, indicates this clearly. It was an expensive process as the denuded person expected handsome payment and the cost was not entirely financial. Occasionally, for instance, the new tooth came from an infected mouth, and at least one fatality was recorded. As late as 1833 it was pointed out that those wearing other people's teeth should not be surprised if they contracted tuberculosis.

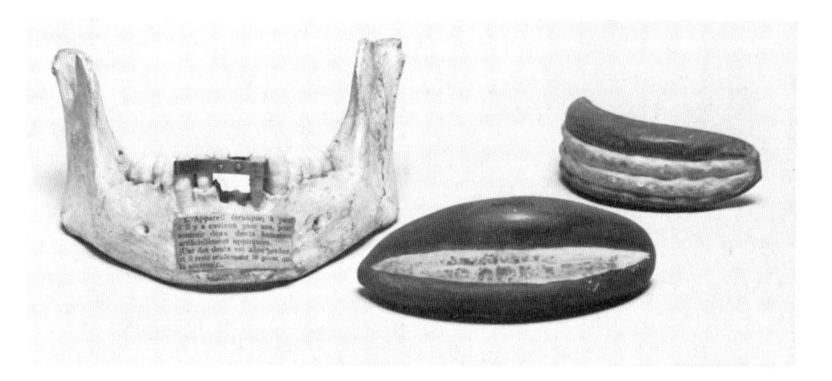

88 *Bottom jaw taken from an Etruscan tomb, showing wired prosthesis and two votive offerings, c.700 B.C. (Musée Fauchard, Paris)*

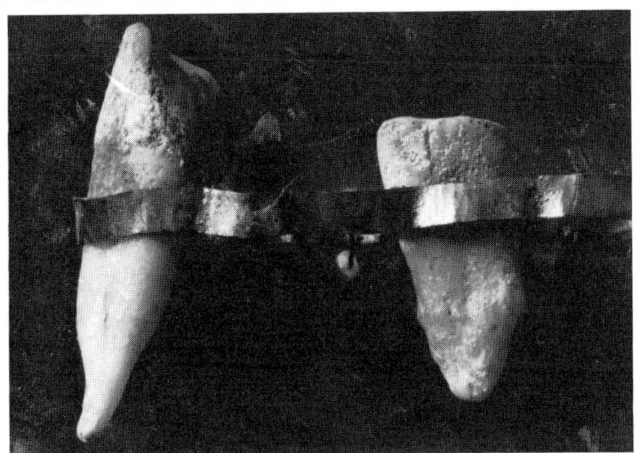

89 *Etruscan bridgework, c.700 B.C. (Archaeological Museum, Tarquinia)*

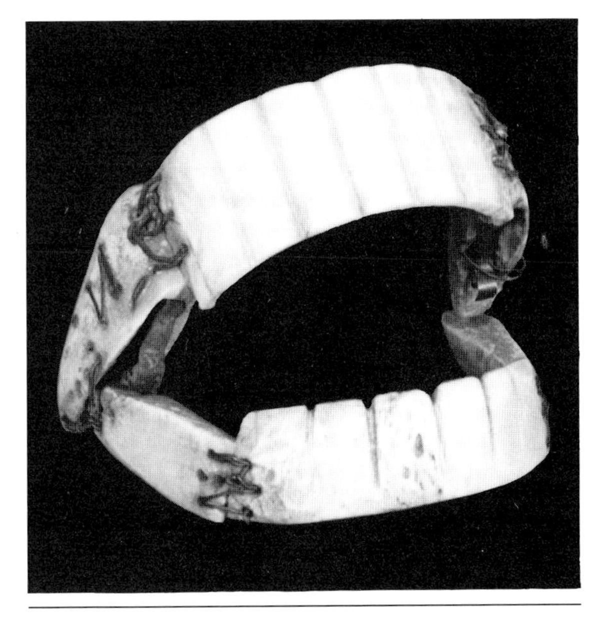

90 *Full-jointed dentures, carved oxbone, c.1500. (Museum of the History of Dentistry, Cologne)*

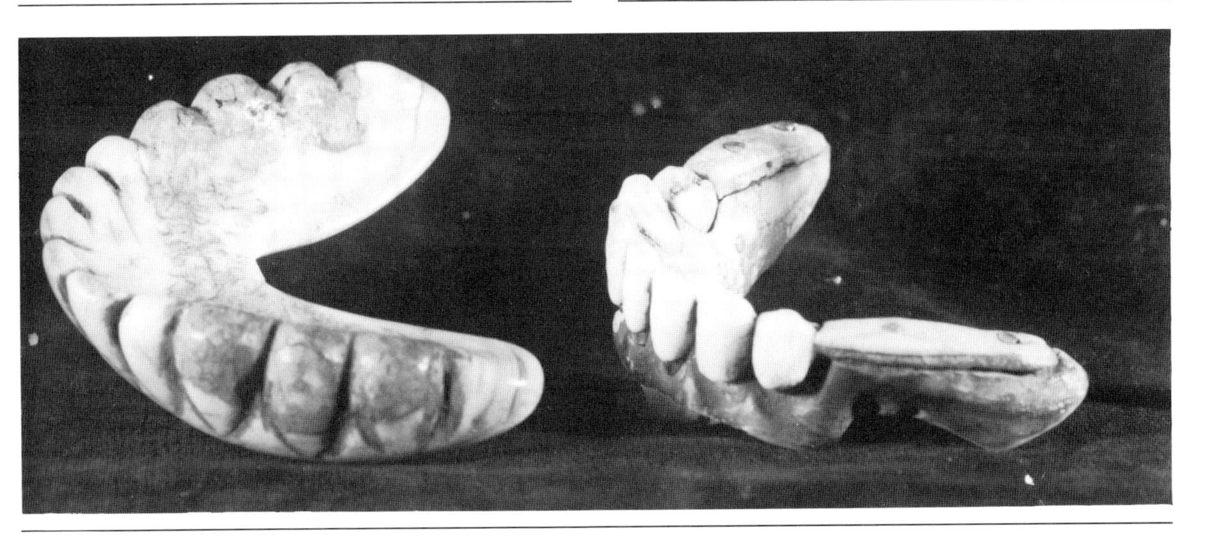

91 *Left, half-set of artificial teeth carved from one piece of ivory; right, half-set carved from one piece of bone with inset human incisors, c.1680. (Museum of London)*

Wholly artificial teeth were attempted from early times. A string of four teeth, fitted by gold wire to adjacent teeth and found in a Phoenician grave at Sidon (600–400 B.C.), is the earliest known denture. The Etruscans, the most enterprising dentists of the Ancient World, accomplished partial gold bridgework as early as 700 B.C. The teeth were either human teeth from another mouth or carved from ox teeth. Each substitute tooth was set, at its base, in a band of gold, soldered to the next one and to a similar band at the base of the adjacent natural teeth. This was a fairly sophisticated method, capable of mastication, and some were even removable. Nothing as proficient as this was made again until the nineteenth century. Martial refers to artificial teeth of bone, ivory and wood, and it is known that Roman dentists practised crownwork; after them, dental skills deteriorated.

Albucasis (936–1013) advised the wiring together of teeth when some were loose, using fine gold wire; and he mentioned the wiring in of false ones made of oxbone to fill the gaps, a process again described by Gerard of Cremona (1114–87) and Guy de Chauliac (1300–68). In 1557 Francisco Martinez (1518–88) published a book on dentistry (unusually for the time in Spanish not Latin) which contained a chapter on prostheses; a later book, by Mattheus Gottfried Purmann (1648–1711), recommended the construction of a wax model before making a denture. Jacques Guillemeau (1550–1613) was the first to suggest artificial teeth of inorganic materials, advocating white coral and pearls. These suggestions achieved little progress, and it is clear that none of the teeth was satisfactory. Curious accounts survive of the morning ritual of tying on the bone false teeth of Henry III of France in the late sixteenth century. As it was difficult for the wearer to tie in the teeth himself, dentures were often left *in situ* for considerable periods and became prone to tartar. In 1654 there are references to teeth made of ivory and whalebone. Charles Allen claims he made artificial teeth; he describes the substitution of teeth from animals – goats, baboons, sheep and dogs – but does not say he has done it. He was very fond of his own ingenuity, dismissing out of hand much that had gone before. At the end of the seventeenth century, Anton Nuck (1650–92), a Dutch surgeon, was recommending hippopotamus ivory for artificial teeth, as it maintained a better colour. Dupont, 'Operateur du Roi,' so full of himself with extravagant claims, averred in his book *L'Operateur Charitable* (1633) that his teeth could be used without stuttering – possibly a damning comment on the general run of seventeenth-century false teeth.

The beginning of the eighteenth century saw little improvement. Lorenz Heister (1683–1758) refers to false teeth as not having been tied in and, therefore, capable of removal for eating and sleeping; he describes them as made of ivory or hippopotamus tusk, and of obviously rudimentary fitting. The Duchess of Portland wrote, in 1735, of Lord Hervey, known to have no teeth of his own: 'Lord Hervey has the finest set of Egyptian pebble teeth you ever saw.' This was a contemporary description of agate, probably inserted in a wooden base and made in Italy, which Lord Hervey had just visited. Teeth of mother-of-pearl, silver or enamelled copper, attached to an ivory base, were other alternatives. Full lower sets were weighted to help keep them in place, and few full upper sets were attempted. Around 1733 Pézè Pilleau (fl. 1715–55), 'Goldsmith at the Golden Cup in Shanders [Chandos] Street', additionally advertised himself 'in ye Art of Making and Setting Artificial Teeth, No ways discernable from Natural ones'. He was the first to take a horseshoe impression of the jaw in beeswax, rather than measuring the mouth with compasses. This was a great step forward at a time when many false teeth were ordered by post. Some false teeth were even advertised to fit over stumps and roots, the painful extraction of these being sufficient to deter many people. The excessive use of the fan throughout the eighteenth century was certainly encouraged by the need to hide a defective mouth and deflect bad breath.

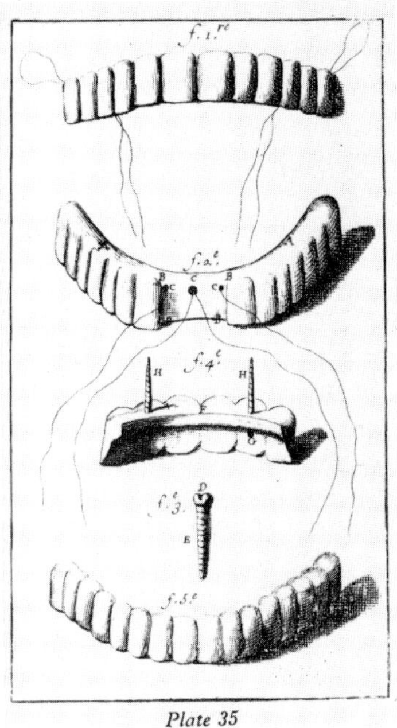

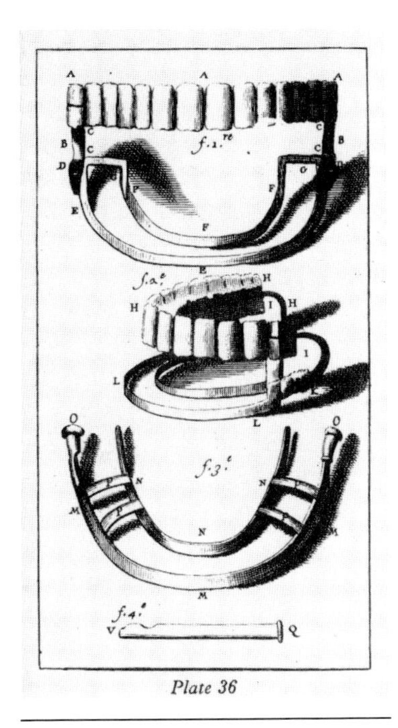

92 *Illustration from Pierre Fauchard's* Le Chirurgien Dentiste *(1746) showing various methods of prosthetic construction.*

With the publication in 1728 of Pierre Fauchard's remarkable book, *Le Chirurgien Dentiste*, matters improved considerably. In contrast to other dentists he did not keep his inventions a secret but published them for the benefit of the profession. Though his teaching was slow to reach this country (see Chapter 1), his is the point from which dentistry was able to make some rapid progress. His outstanding accomplishment was in improving the fitting of false teeth. 'When an artificial tooth is needed, it must be approximately of the length, thickness and width of the natural tooth the place of which it is to occupy.' Hippopotamus teeth, sea-horse (presumably walrus) tusk, ivory, and teeth and bones of oxen were all suitable but human teeth and sea-horse were best; he even experimented with enamelling the front of his teeth to improve their appearance, the enameller being given a pattern of the natural colour. Fauchard used the traditional method of wiring a group of teeth together and attaching them to the natural ones with ligatures of fine wire or silk; by a later method he assembled them together on the inside by a small gold plate. The outer teeth were drilled right through from side to side to take the thread; he preferred to use wire made of ducat gold but only if the adjacent teeth were hard enough. However, his inventiveness produced many other methods. A single damaged tooth would be filed to the root and covered with a carved crown. Having chosen his replacement tooth, he filed down the excess root with a saw and file or on a grindstone, and filled both its cavity and the cavity of the host root with lead, which was then drilled to take the post, made of either wood or gold. Few could have been very successful or lasting but it was a further stage forward.

Another part of Fauchard's practice was the construction of full lower dentures, turned on a lathe from one piece of bone. He bleached the leg-bones of oxen by boiling them in quicklime, rinsing and drying them and then exposing them to dew. They were better than ivory, he thought, as they did not discolour so easily, the less porous parts being more suitable. These simple dentures, intended merely to rest on the arch of the lower jaw, needed very careful fitting; Fauchard rashly claimed that it was possible to masticate with them in position. Eventually, his fertile mind contrived a better procedure, developing his post and crown method for the purpose. Having pierced canals in the remaining roots of the jaw to take the posts, he placed quills filled with writing ink in the holes. The denture was lowered on to them, thus marking the position of the hole to be made in the denture. The posts, often of wood, swelled on contact with the saliva and kept the teeth in position.

Fauchard's work on artificial teeth for the upper jaw was much more radical. Initially, he pierced the gums and suspended the teeth from the jaw, or made a full upper set attached to a framework which fitted over the lower gums. His best-known invention was the attachment of the upper set to the lower by steel springs. These were very strong and needed considerable force to close the mouth; springs of whalebone as an alternative were not of much use he found. Strips of gold or silver were placed round the base of the teeth, natural or not, both inside and outside the jaw and attached to the springs, the latter of a type still used into this century. However, inevitably, all false teeth of Fauchard's day slipped sideways as there was no covering of the palate. He admitted that a full set was 'only for ornament and pronunciation' but was more confident of his lower sets. 'Just recently I have renewed one which I made twenty-four years ago, which was worn continually with success.' He illustrated several instruments necessary for the manufacture of artificial teeth: a vice, a bow-drill, a rasp and file, a scraper and a sturdy bow-saw. In addition, there are two sculptors with large, octagonal, bulbous handles having a head at either end, each curving forward with a snake's head appearance, and three reamers for enlarging the roots to take the posts. Two of the reamers have circular turned handles, and one has a ring like a key for better purchase.

Philip Pfaff (1716–80) was the first to use plaster of Paris in making models of the jaw. He based his models on impressions taken in sealing wax softened in hot water – a process again described by William Rae in 1782. Pfaff, who had his false teeth made by 'an artist', was also the first to advise the placing of an artificial cap over an exposed nerve rather than using the cautery. In the same period Etienne Bourdet introduced dentures with a base made entirely of gold covered in flesh-coloured enamel, the teeth being either human or carved from hippopotamus tusk and fixed with gold pins and rivets. Gold, though strong and not subject to erosion, was not easily worked, and the fitting of individual teeth was tedious; for the wearer, it must have been heavy. Experimentation abounded, and in 1778 a Francis Gillanders took out a patent for 'A Method of Covering Artificial

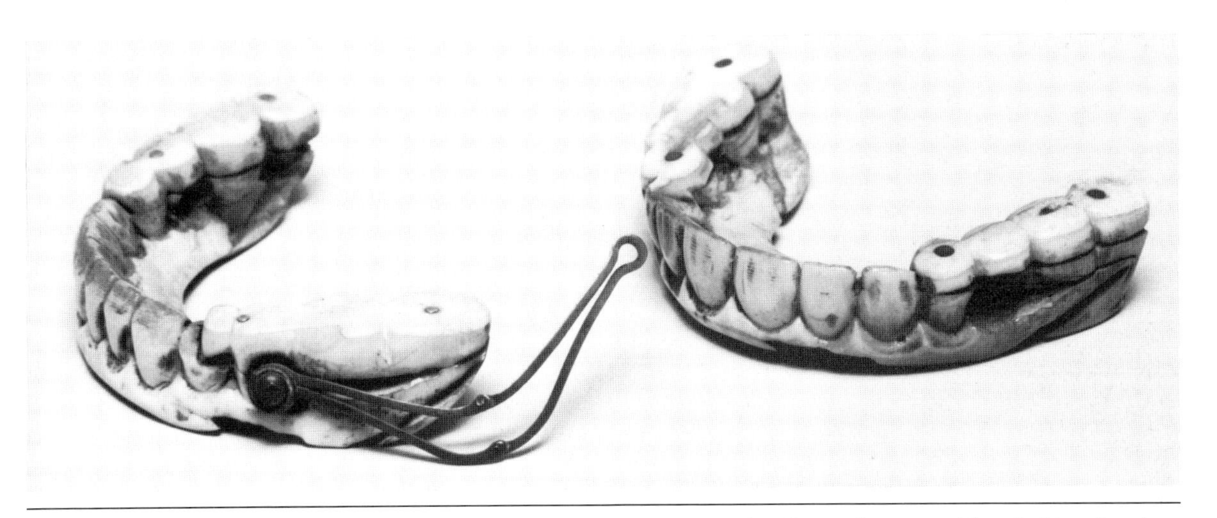

93 *Two half-sets of artificial teeth showing second layer applied after wear of earlier surface, one with early hinged spring, c.1730. (Musée Fauchard, Paris)*

95 *Group of early boxwood impression trays, c.1780. (Musée Fauchard, Paris)*

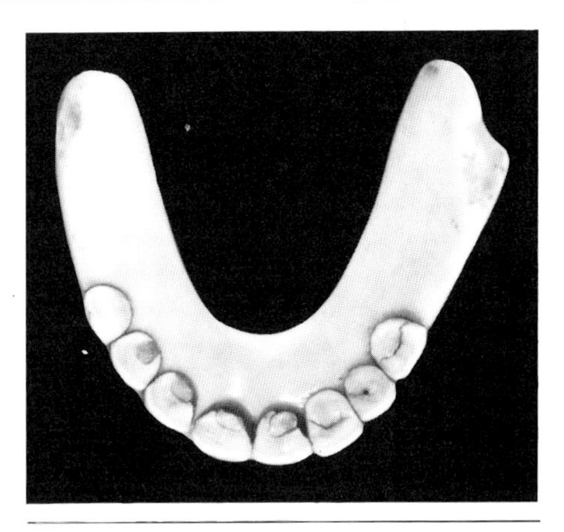

94 *Ivory denture with calves' teeth fastened on with gold wire; owned and worn by George Beckwith in England, c.1750. (New York Academy of Medicine)*

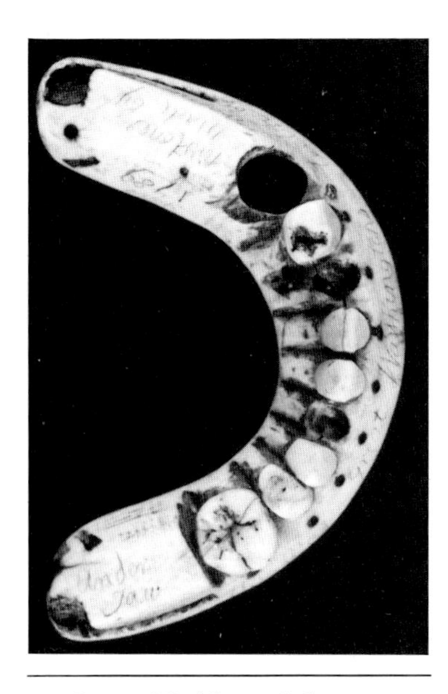

96 *George Washington's lower denture, showing space for his one remaining tooth, made by John Greenwood, c.1790. (New York Academy of Medicine)*

Teeth, and also Decayed Natural Teeth and Gums, and that will not corrode, or stain, or lose its Colour in the Mouth.' In the same year John Channing devoted an entire book to prostheses: *Artificial Teeth made of Calves' Bones*.

Meanwhile, in America, John Greenwood (1760–1819) was constantly searching for satisfactory materials, not least for the mouth of George Washington. Washington had had experience of a number of dentists and the confidence he placed in Greenwood is evidence of his skill. Greenwood, typical of the self-taught enthusiast fascinated by his work, pointed American dentistry in the right direction. Washington had perpetual trouble with his teeth and tried several sets of dentures, as is seen by his differing appearance in portraits and certainly by his twisted mouth on the dollar bill. He had them made from elephant ivory, lead, human teeth, cows, hippopotamus and walrus; one of his sets weighed three ounces. When he became President in 1789 he had only two of his own teeth, and one of those was mounted on a denture. Ivory dentures smelled and tasted foul in time, and Washington did not help by soaking his overnight in port. Greenwood had many original ideas and made teeth not to be removed at night, which he claimed fitted naturally; he introduced dental springs to America and was probably the first to use porcelain there. Even so, Washington had to have the contours of his mouth padded to resemble, even slightly, himself.

In 1788 the French apothecary Alexis Duchâteau (1714–92) and the Parisian dentist Nicholas Dubois de Chemant (1753–1824) collaborated in the production of the first porcelain dentures, baked in one piece. De Chemant published a pamphlet on his mineral teeth, explaining the use of the material as incorruptible and unalterable. Later he emigrated to London and obtained a patent for his method in 1791. In it he described the ingredients of different pastes, the taking of an impression, the enamelling, the final firing and the fitting of the springs. Porcelain dentures were not liked at first and were reported as sounding in use 'like cracked bells'. In 1808 Giuseppangelo Fonzi (1768–1840), a Neapolitan dentist, built on these advances by making single porcelain teeth, known in Britain as 'bean-teeth', which were mounted on a gold base. Each tooth had a platinum hook fixed in it to facilitate its attachment to the baseplate (col. pl. XII). These porcelain dentures were very difficult to make successfully as the clay contracted in the firing and they could crack in the mouth, so making a grinding noise in speaking and eating. However, some thought any material must be an improvement on ivory and its rapid putrefaction by the oral fluids. Norman William Kingsley (1829–1913) studied dentistry with an uncle who stipulated that his secret process of making porcelain teeth would not be included in the course, but Kingsley apparently mastered the process without help. The use of porcelain declined a little in the 1820s but isolated examples were still found in the middle of the century.

By now the manufacture of artificial teeth was partly in the hands of dentists and partly in those of craftsmen; most dentists were only taking impressions. It was found possible for the dental mechanic to produce acceptable dentures, thus saving the dentist time on their production.

In 1800 Jacques Gardette (1756–1831) of Philadelphia, but born in Bordeaux, made a springless top set of dentures and discovered the use of atmospheric pressure; in 1835, in the United Kingdom, suction pads were first introduced, though not very satisfactorily. In 1848 the makers S.S. White of Philadelphia announced Gilbert's suction cavity plate. The advent of spiral springs in Britain *c.* 1850 gave some confidence to wearers of false teeth who always feared their teeth might come adrift. Disraeli, referring rather unpleasantly to Lord Palmerston's false teeth, said that 'they would fall out of his mouth when speaking if he did not hesitate and halt so in his talk'.

The most common materials for artificial teeth in the nineteenth century were still ivory – the London firm of Ash was supplying blocks of ivory for carving teeth as late as the 1870s – and, increasingly, human teeth (such a rich source of infection) set in a solid base. These last became known as Waterloo teeth, so many of them having been pulled from the corpses on the battlefield (pls. 97 and 98). High prices were paid for teeth from plundered graves, and those from the dead during the American Civil War were shipped to England by the barrel. Claudius Ash (1815–92), who disliked handling dead men's teeth, introduced the tube tooth *c.* 1838 and, in a modified form, it is still in use. The original had a small tube of precious metal fused in its centre, which was fitted over a projecting pivot in a natural root or in an artificial base. It was made by several makers, among whom, apart from Ash, were Corbitt of Cork and Lemale.

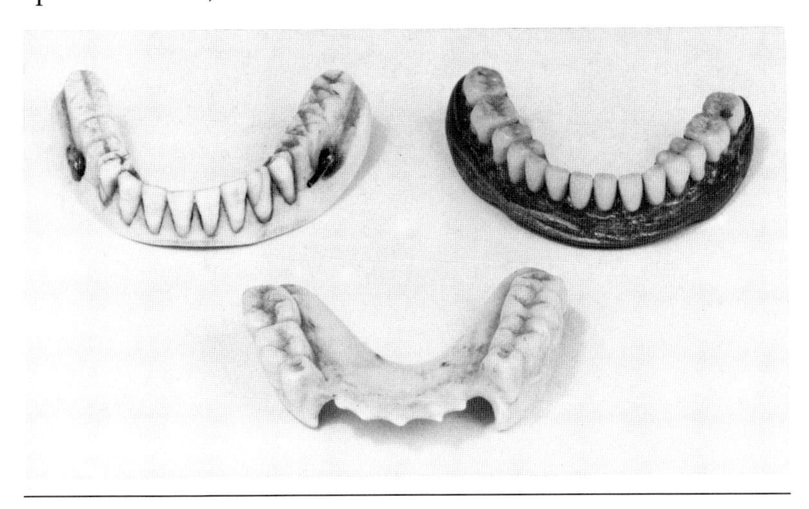

97 *Three half-sets of artificial teeth. Top left, Waterloo teeth set into a solid piece of carved ivory, c.1840; top right, Waterloo teeth set in lead, c.1810; bottom, solid piece of carved ivory, c.1800. (I. Freeman & Son, Simon Kaye Ltd, London)*

98 *Above: a half-set of Waterloo teeth set in carved ivory, c.1820, with fitted wooden case, the lid having a complicated mechanism that the teeth might be kept secret; case possibly later. Spaces for the missing incisors show the gold fixing posts. (Private Collection, London) Below: Masticator, Weiss, c.1860, 17cm. (I. Freeman & Son, Simon Kaye Ltd, London)*

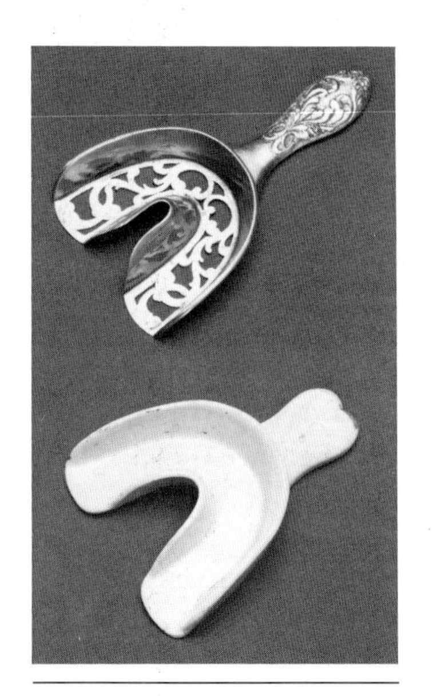

99 *Impression trays, English, c.1865. Top, ornamental metal handle and pierced tray; bottom, white pottery. (Science Museum, Wellcome Collection, London)*

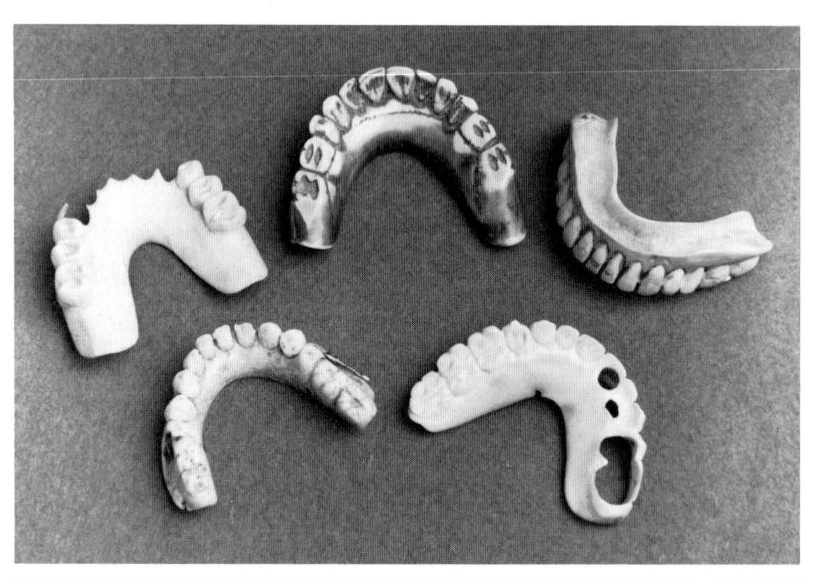

100 *Five half-sets of artificial teeth, early 19th century. All are carved from hippopotamus ivory, some with traces of cochineal colouring remaining on the simulated gum. Clockwise: the third and fifth have human incisors inset, the fifth has remains of connecting springs and the fourth shows the holes into which the hickory pegs would be placed. (Royal Army Dental Corps Historical Museum, Aldershot)*

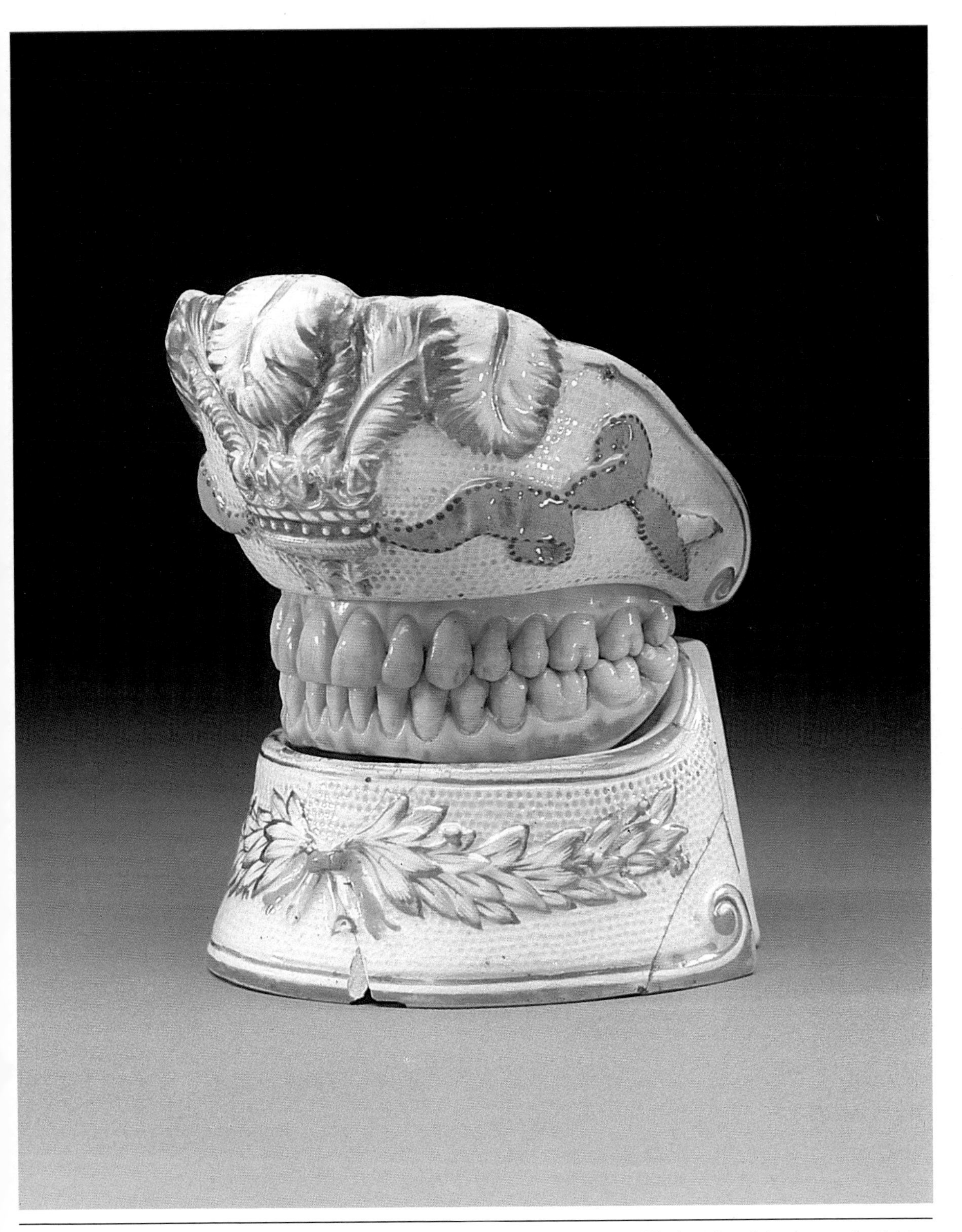

XIV *Porcelain denture stand decorated with Prince of Wales feathers, c.1810; possibly from Ruspini, who was dentist to the Prince of Wales. (Science Museum, Wellcome Collection, London)*

XV *Seven scalers in suede-lined leather case with mirror in drawer, ebony handle, c.1800; six scalers in green shagreen case, ivory handle, c.1800. (I. Freeman & Son, Simon Kaye Ltd, London)*

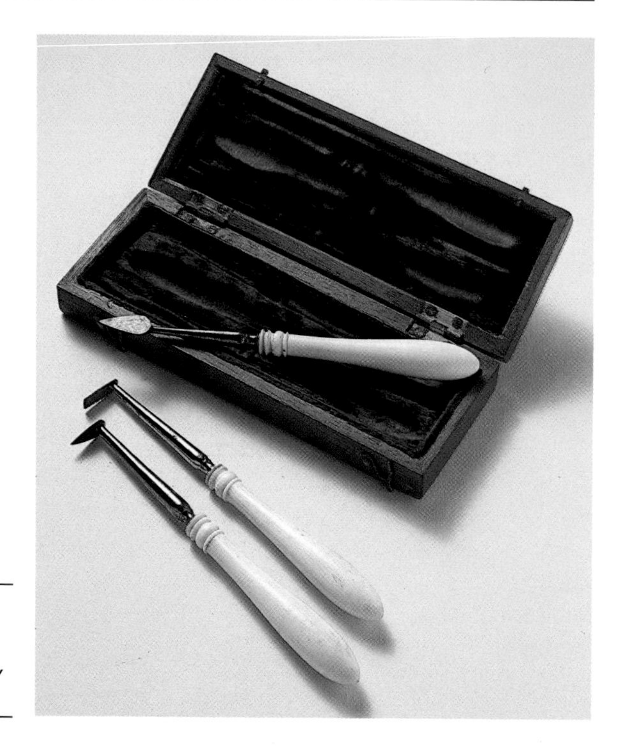

XVI *Cased set of three ivory-handled scalers, c.1840, 11.5 cm. (Private Collection, Peter Gordon, London)*

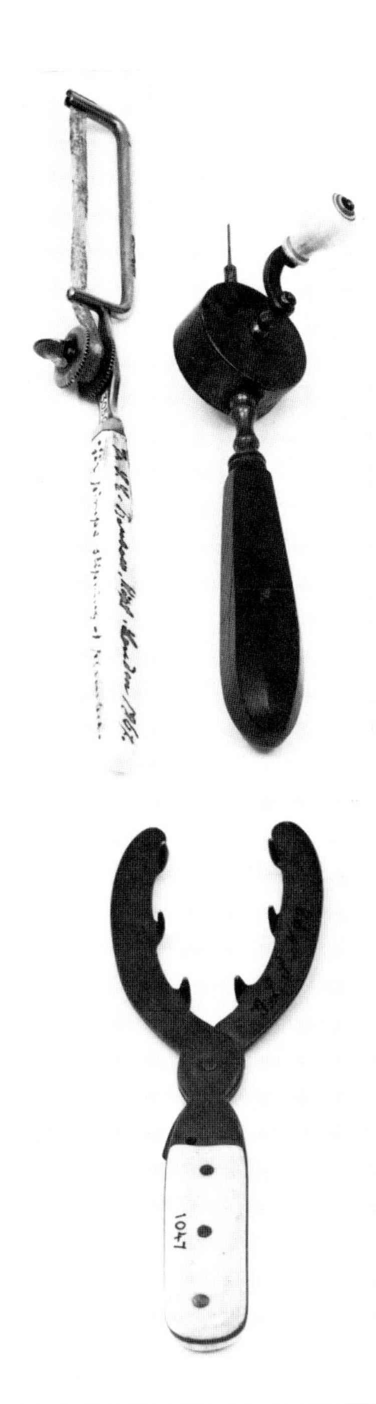

101 *Polisher to take linen strip, inscribed on handle 'Bought in London, 1867'; crank hand-drill, ebony handle, c.1840. Brass impression tray, ivory handle, c.1840; (Bichlie Collection, Museum of Swedish Dental Society, Stockholm)*

The search for a satisfactory base for dentures was tireless. Gold had, so far, proved the most satisfactory either as a mount or a base but was far beyond the reach of most patients. Silver was tried but found unsuccessful; moulded tin was introduced in America in 1820, then cast tin, but both corroded; even lead was used (pl. 97). Then vulcanite, a composition of sulphur-hardened rubber, was invented by Charles Goodyear (1800–60) and this remained a favourite for nearly 100 years, Thomas Wiltberger Evans (1823–97) being one of the first to experiment with the substance. The invention became a timely landmark as the possibilities of anaesthesia had made more people willing to undergo extraction and therefore more people wanted false teeth. Vulcanite marked the beginning of artificial teeth for the masses. A patent for the material was taken out in America in 1851, which made necessary the issue of licences to use it. Afterwards the head of the Goodyear Dental Vulcanite Company, which owned the patent, was killed by an outraged dentist whose practice had been destroyed. Other materials included gutta-percha, introduced in London by Edwin Truman (1809–1905) in 1847, and tortoiseshell in 1850. The latter was brought in by George Fellows Harrington (1812–95) of Portsmouth, who having heated it then pressed it into shape, its appearance being very like celluloid. Sets of dentures on a base of 'continuous gum', a synthetic resin, were patented in America by John Allen (1810–1902) in 1851 but these were very heavy, very expensive and difficult to repair if broken. Collodian was tried about this time and a compound called Rose-Pearl; porcelain was reintroduced in America by the experimental dentist Mahlon Loomis (1826–86) in 1854. In 1870, in London, celluloid was first used as a base and enjoyed considerable vogue until the end of the century, despite the occasional accident to smokers.

Beeswax in horseshoe-shaped trays was the favourite material for impressions at the start of the century. Gutta-percha was tried in 1848. The same year S.S. White of Philadelphia could advertise a new refined beeswax, 'pure, refined, absence of tobacco and other unpleasant odours'. Later paraffin wax was used, and a special impression compound was introduced by Charles Stent in London in 1857 and in the United States in 1874 (pls. 95, 99 and 101).

Methods of making the actual teeth improved throughout the nineteenth century. Machines for their special construction were patented by William Lukyn in 1839, by John Tomes (1815–95) who, in 1845, patented a 'dentificator' or dental carving machine on which copies of depressed or relieved surfaces could be exactly reproduced, and by Henry Valentine Bartlett of Sheffield in 1846. In America, James Cameron of Philadelphia patented his Dental Articulator in 1840, which improved the mutual adjustment of the upper and lower sets. George Fellows Harrington invented a complicated mechanism in 1849 for measuring, shaping and moulding the dentures. Altogether, artificial teeth had become

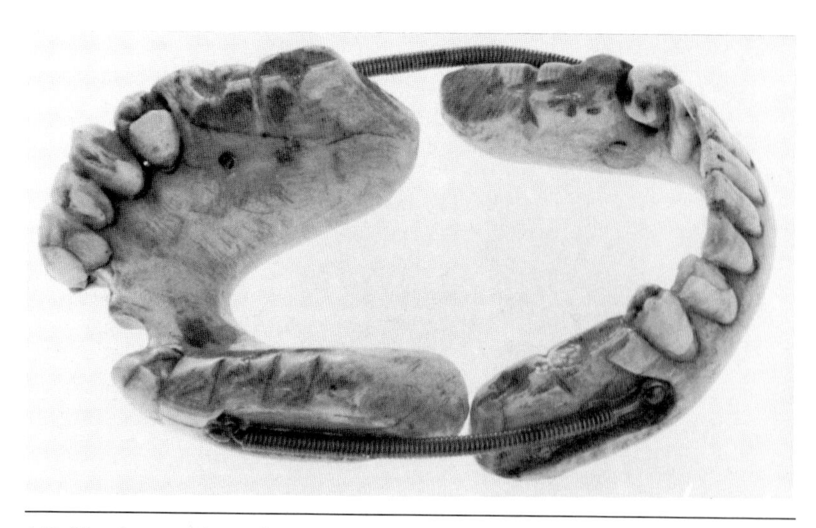

102 *Hand-carved ivory dentures, inset human teeth, c.1870. (University of Alberta Dental Museum, Edmonton)*

big business, not least in the ancillary tools required. Instrument makers' catalogues by now even included emery-wheels, grindstones and vices to hold the teeth while grinding them.

Without teeth, over-closing of the lower jaw could cause deafness, particularly affecting the very poor who could not afford false teeth or preventive dental treatment. Without teeth, imperfect food was imperfectly masticated and caused frequent and serious digestive problems, undermining general health. Without teeth, one was seen as unnecessarily old and useless. However, the nineteenth century, while making commonplace the wearing of artificial teeth, brought embarrassment in their use which would still seem to exist today, despite modern perfections. Anxiety can still be encountered about eating and sneezing and difficulties in clear speech; there is more unwillingness to be discovered without teeth than without clothes and extreme diffidence in admitting to a loved one that one's teeth are false. Whatever personal insecurities are experienced, they are aggravated by the thought of the anticipated social response to false teeth. A factor probably unthought of in the nineteenth century is the modern fear that, by wearing dentures, one is indicating previous dental neglect and that that, in turn, is a reflection of low social class.

5 Anaesthesia equipment

Mandragora, opium and other drugs were used by surgeons in the Ancient World and through the Middle Ages onwards as soporific pain-killers. Where they were not actually successful as the latter, they would probably have been effective in calming the patient sufficiently to undergo surgery. The ancient Assyrians used opium, and the Greek use of soporific sponges is frequently mentioned even in mythology, as in the story of Demeter and Persephone. Galen (A.D. 130–200) developed the use of opium and, as adviser to Marcus Aurelius, passed his knowledge on to the Romans. Pedanios Dioscorides (fl. A.D. 50), army surgeon at the time of Nero, wrote a compendium of drugs, listing opium as a sedative and pain-killer. It was then taken up by the Arabs, Avicenna (980–1037) becoming so obsessed by opium he eventually died of it. The Crusades stimulated interest in it in England; its use in surgery was advocated but seldom used, as the precise quantities necessary for pain-killing and not just killing were not adequately understood. There is no record of its use in dentistry except as a measure to prevent further decay, kill worms and sweeten breath. Mandragora, inducing twilight sleep, was sometimes used as a medieval pain-killer, as was laudanum, a mixture of opium and alcohol. Much later, in 1758, the Rev. Edward Stone experimented with willowbark, leading to a preparation for the reduction of body temperature and partial pain-killing; this eventually resulted in the introduction of aspirin in 1899. In about 1805 Friedrich Wilhelm Sertürner (1783–1841) developed a new drug he called morphium, after the God of Dreams, which he used successfully for toothache. Morphine was used so liberally during the American Civil War that the soldiers became addicted, and it was known as the Soldiers' Disease. Addiction was always a complication in the early pain-killers. The apothecary was the figure most concerned in relief of pain and sold preparations such as 'eyes of crabs', 'powdered sapphires', etc. for this purpose. Alcohol was another long-established pain-killer.

All of these are natural drugs, whereas anaesthetics are artificial. The term was suggested by Oliver Wendell Holmes (1809–94), who said the only natural anaesthetics were sleep, fainting and death – none suitable for dentistry. First, it had to be learned how to make these artificial agents before it was possible to learn how to use them. Some were used for therapy, some for exhilaration, some eventually for anaesthesia. David Howarth writes, 'Men in those days, one must suppose, were not less sensitive to pain than they are now. But pain was familiar in themselves and others. So they were less afraid of it than later generations brought up with anaesthetics.'

Ether

The invention of ether is credited to an Arab chemist, Yeber, in the twelfth century, but it remained laboratory property until William Thomas Green Morton (1819–68) gave its first demonstration at Boston, Massachusetts on 30 September 1846, using it, in fact, to extract a tooth. The rectified ether was merely poured onto a pocket handkerchief and inhaled by the patient. The next day, the *Boston Daily Journal* printed:

> *Last evening we were informed by gentlemen who witnessed the operation, an ulcerated tooth was extracted from the mouth of an individual, without giving the slightest pain. He was put into a kind of sleep by inhaling a preparation, the effects of which lasted for about three quarters of a minute, just long enough to extract the tooth.*

Practice of anaesthesia may be said to date from this incident and, quite understandably, patients flocked to Dr Morton. Dr Crawford W. Long (1815–78) is thought to have been the actual originator of anaesthesia for surgery in 1842, but as he came from the more remote town of Jefferson, Georgia, the news was not generally known until after Morton's success. Another experiment of 1842, receiving no real publicity at the time, was made by William Clark, a chemistry student in Rochester, New York, who painlessly extracted a tooth with the use of ether.

Morton gave a public demonstration of ether at the Massachusetts General Hospital a few weeks after his first successful attempt, on a patient with a vascular tumour of the jaw. He used a more sophisticated apparatus which he had designed himself.

Morton's history is interesting. He studied dentistry at Baltimore but had no medical degree, and he came to use ether through his work with artificial teeth. In order to further this work he needed to remove all remaining stumps and roots in his patients' jaws, but he found few patients prepared to endure the agony. He therefore experimented with various pain-killing methods to enable him to complete the extractions. Success came, and what some saw as the excessive praise heaped on Morton's head apparently turned it: having patented his apparatus – not realising this was ethically unacceptable – he later became so phrenetically upset over claims by Charles Thomas Jackson (1805–80) to the first use of anaesthesia in surgery that he took his own life in Central Park, New York. It has always been held against him that he sought personal benefit from his discovery; it is reasonable to suppose that Jackson advised Morton on the preparation of ether but Morton protested the obligation went no further than that. The inscription on Morton's tomb in Boston reads, 'Inventor and Revealer of anaesthetic inhalation, by whom pain in surgery was averted and annulled; before whom, in all times, surgery was agony; since whom, science has control of pain.' Undoubtedly he made a most important contribution in

103 *Morton's ether inhaler, 1846. (Massachusetts General Hospital, Boston, Mass.)*

making the public aware of the possibilities of anaesthesia, which were accepted far more eagerly, in America, by the dentists than by the physicians and surgeons. But there were some who feared it: a cleric wrote of ether as a 'decoy in the hands of Satan'; it was thought as likely to be employed by thieves and generally not an instrument of humanity and a joy forever; Morton's dental practice was broken up and he was even burned in effigy in a small town near Boston. Many dentists found their work easier without it: protracted anaesthesia with the mouth open was very difficult and the dentist had to operate with great speed were there any large number of extractions, therefore leaving broken roots and damaged gums.

Morton made several attempts to devise a successful ether apparatus, some with the instrument maker Joseph Wightman. From the crude handkerchief method he progressed to a glass funnel with a tube attached, through which the vapour could be inhaled from an ether-soaked sponge. Another version he described as 'composed of a quart tabulated globe receiver, having a cork fitted into it instead of a glass stopper, through which cork a pipette was inserted to supply the ether as it evaporated'. The apparatus used for the public demonstration was like that devised by the instrument maker N.B. Chamberlain, which was 'a small two-necked glass globe' containing the vapour, with sponges to enlarge the evaporating surface (pl. 103).

> *One aperture admits air to the interior of the globe, whence, charged with vapour, it is drawn into the lungs. The inspired air thus passes through the bottle but the expiration is diverted by a valve in the mouthpiece and, escaping into the apartment, is thus prevented from vitiating the medicated vapour.*

British doctors quickly adapted this model to variations of their own invention. Ether, always more popular in America, was often given in the original handkerchief method there, whereas in the United Kingdom an inhaler was found preferable. The first surgical operation using anaesthesia in the United Kingdom – amputation of a leg – employed an inhaler; this was the Nooth apparatus, which had its origins in the work of a London dentist, James Robinson (1816–62). Robinson used ether for a dental extraction in 1846; his apparatus can be seen in the British Dental Association. News of his experiment reached Robert Liston (1794–1847), who later performed the celebrated first surgical operation in December of that year. 'It is a very great matter,' Liston wrote, 'to be able, thus, to destroy sensibility to such an extent . . . It is a fine thing for operating surgeons.' On pl. 104 is shown a modified version of the apparatus Liston used, made to a design by Francis Boott (1792–1863), a physician, and the dentist James Robinson, and made by Hooper of Pall Mall. A sponge, in the upper part, soaked in ether, drips on to a sponge in the lower part; the vapour is then drawn off into the tube and the

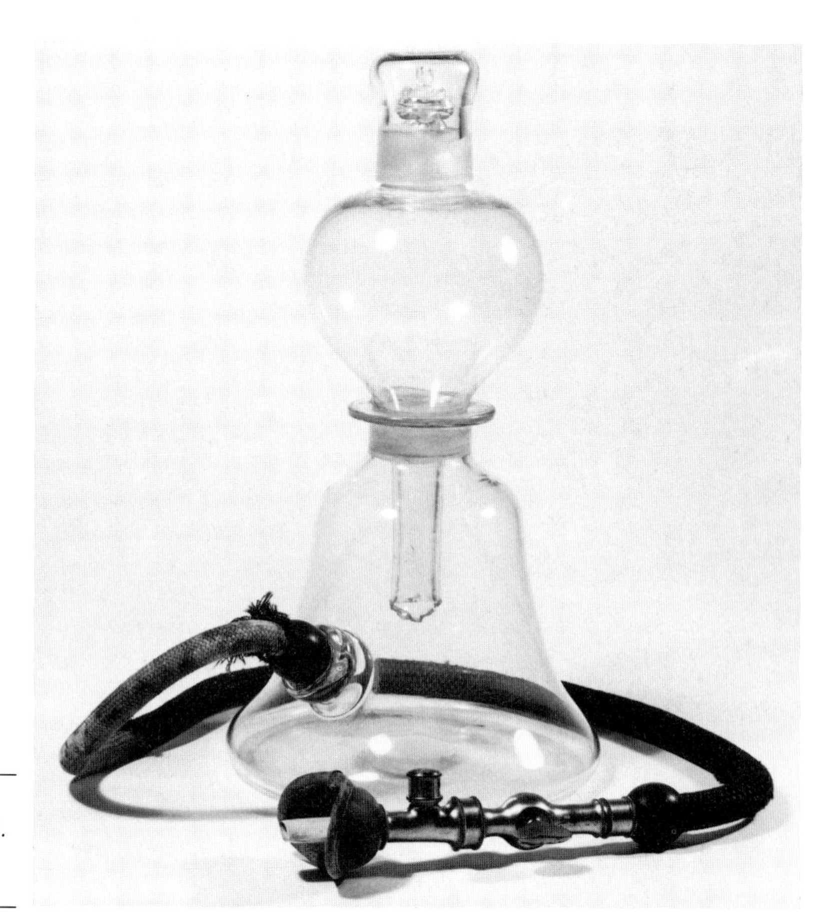

104 *Ether apparatus of the Hooper type, showing rare bitepiece, c.1850. (Museum of the History of Science, Oxford)*

105 *Engraved silver-plated ether inhaler with hinged nose-clip, c.1860, used by a dentist in Jersey City, N.J. Overall length 10cm. (Private Collection, Rosalind Berman, Cheltenham, Pa.)*

106 *Ether drip bottle, Mayer, c.1865. (Museum of the History of Science, Oxford)*

mouthpiece. The latter incorporates a bitepiece and is the only known example of this early type in the United Kingdom.

John Snow (1813–58), the first specialist anaesthetist, designed his own apparatus in 1847; it was later made by Ferguson, Coxeter and others (see Directory) – 'there is no restriction regarding the making of it'. It took the form of a flat, rectangular, wooden box from which came a three-foot tube ending in a valved face-piece made of sheet lead covered in silk or glove leather, the valves made of vulcanised rubber. Attached to the same side of the box as the inhalation tube was an upright metal inlet tube which screwed into position. Inside the case was a drum containing five spiral baffles, beneath which was a small gap between it and the bottom plate. Snow gave very precise details of the dimensions; they 'are not a matter of indifference', he wrote. The air, entering through the inlet tube, passed four times round the surface of the ether and became saturated by its vapour. The drum stood in a rectangular water-bath (in fact, the container for the whole), which 'will supply the calorific necessary to the conversion of 1–2 ounces of ether into vapour without being much reduced in temperature'.

Morton, meanwhile, had become dissatisfied with his various methods and had reverted to a mere sponge, of concave shape, held over the nose and mouth of the patient. He reported this to *The Lancet* in 1847, but the editor added a dry footnote to his letter, to the effect that the method 'had been recommended and practised for some time, in this country, by Dr. Smith of Cheltenham'.

By 1850 several forms of ether-inhaler were devised, including Hedley's Inhaler, a simple bottle-shaped container for the sponges of ether but made of wood and ivory, one of the drawbacks of a glass ether-inhaler being that it could not be kept warm. A metal inhaler with a chamber for hot water was an improvement, and one of this type, a cylinder with perforated mouthpiece, was made by Atlee *c.* 1847. Another version was the Letheon Inhaler, which was adapted from Morton's original: a flat-bottomed glass container with a tube to the mouthpiece. Friedrich Turnovsky (1818–77) of Budapest devised an ether-apparatus made from an ox bladder in 1856.

The relatively short length of anaesthesia required for dentistry compared to other forms of surgery presented rather more than less of a problem, and by 1850 the use of chloroform was becoming the preferred method for ease of use and action. Ether then fell out of fashion until the 1870s. At this time the *British Medical Journal* started advocating ether again on account of its greater safety, and gradually it began to oust chloroform for general use.

A sponge or towel was once again in frequent use, but John Clover (1825–82), in 1877, produced his Portable Regulating Ether Inhaler, which achieved universal fame and was copied and adapted by many, regaining popularity for ether. It was the

107 *Portable regulating ether inhaler by John Clover, c.1880. (The bag is not shown.) 26 cm. (Museum of the British Dental Association, London)*

first apparatus to regulate the amount of ether inhaled. It consisted of a spherical ether chamber attached to a tubular extension of the same diameter as the water container. This insulated the chamber which was, in any case, sometimes immersed in hot water before use to prevent evaporation. Within the chamber was a fenestrated tube on which it rotated. To the end of this was attached the mask, and at the other end, where it protruded, was the bag. No air was admitted, but when the pulse and respiration indicated it was required, the patient was allowed a gasp of fresh air. Later, Frederick William Hewitt (1857–1916) and others modified Clover's invention with the addition of a stopcock, but it remained a basic method for many years (pl. 107).

Still more popular was the Ormsby Ether Inhaler, again of 1877, introduced in Dublin by Lambert Hepenstal Ormsby (1850–1923). It consisted of a sponge in a bag, contained by a wire cage, and connected to a valved mouthpiece. Open ether masks were introduced about this time and are discussed below.

Chloroform

Chloroform was discovered in 1831 by Eugene Soubeiron (1797–1858) in France and, quite independently, by Samuel Guthrie (1780–1848) in New York. The great controversies over its introduction resulted less from the personalities involved than the properties of chloroform itself. Patients died under its use and there were endless commissions and committees of enquiry. Francis Sibson (1814–76) of Nottingham General Hospital, writing in the late 1840s said, 'In dental surgery (except in extreme cases) and in trivial operations, the use of chloroform is not justifiable.' John Snow insisted on the safety of low, and therefore measured, amounts to be administered, resulting in the development of apparatus in the United Kingdom and in France. He wrote,

> *It is the custom in the medical journals and medical societies to object occasionally to the use of chloroform in tooth-drawing, as if the operation were not sufficiently severe to require it . . . I have notes of 867 cases in which I have administered chloroform during the extraction of teeth . . . The number of the teeth extracted at one operation has been 1–19 but . . . better, as a general rule, to make more than one operation when the number of teeth to be drawn exceeds 10 . . . The patients have been seated in an easy chair in all these operations on the teeth.*

There was considerable discussion on the safety of giving chloroform to a patient in the sitting position; Snow felt no difficulty in the matter except in cases of extreme illness.

Chloroform was first used in the United Kingdom in 1847, principally in midwifery – the first child to be born with its use was christened Anaesthesia. It was pioneered by James Young Simpson (1811–70), who tried it upon himself and a friend one day. The next day he initiated its obstetric use, which was much attacked on religious grounds. He had already used ether but was quick to observe the advantages of chloroform, using only a bottle and a handkerchief. Later, when given a baronetcy, he chose as his motto 'Victo Dolore'. However, earlier in 1847, Jacob Bell (d. 1859) had already used the gas in dentistry at the Middlesex Hospital in London.

The open sponge or handkerchief gave way to mechanical inhalers in which the ratio of anaesthetic to air could be controlled. In 1850 Coxeter (for 6/6d. or, silver-plated, for 12/6d.) made the chloroform inhaler of Edward William Murphy (1802–77). It was probably mostly used in obstetrics as it was small and convenient. The main drum held the sponge and might be closed off by two rings when not in use, the rim of the face-mask being protected by cloth. It was particularly suitable for inducing analgesia. A simpler and more common inhaler, used for both chloroform and ether, about the same time, was an oval metal box holding a sponge, with a perforated mouthpiece presented to the patient; a plate behind the perforation prevented the liquid being drawn into the mouth.

Arthur Ernest Sampson (1838–1907) modified Snow's ideas *c.* 1865, with an inhaler which reduced the chloroform content. It had a perforated cap for the intake of air and a chamber filled with rolled blotting-paper or lint, with a side-tube connected to the face-mask; alternatively a smaller tube might be directly applied to the nostril. John Clover invented a chloroform inhaler in 1862, an apparatus with a bellows which forced chloroform into a vaporizing chamber. It is doubtful if this was used in dentistry. Another idea unlikely to have reached the dental surgery was that of William Friedrich Hahn (1796–1874) who introduced anaesthesia via the trachea with a cuffed tracheotomy tube and a tampon of chloroform. This was obviously very helpful for extensive operations on the mouth but probably excessive for dentistry.

In 1867 came the inhaler of Ferdinand Adalbert Juncker (1828–*c.* 1901), which comprised a graduated bottle of liquid attached on the one hand to a vulcanite face-mask and on the other to a bellows consisting of two rubber bulbs. It was very simple in use: the bottle hung from the anaesthetist's lapel; he held the mask in one hand and worked the bellows with the other. However, without valves this could be dangerous, and the makers, Krohne & Seseman, modified it and suggested the use of a Skinner's Mask.

Thomas Skinner (d. 1906) of Liverpool introduced his wire frame mask in 1862. It could be used for both ether and chloroform and remained popular well into the twentieth cen-

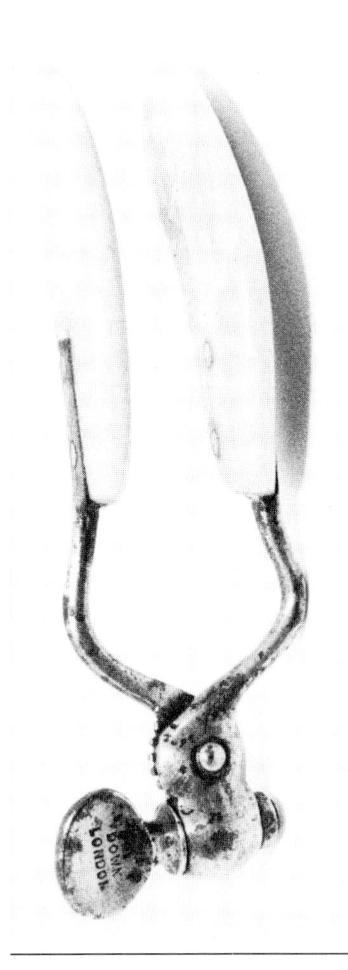

108 *Nasal clamp, Down, c.1880, 12 cm. (Museum of the History of Science, Oxford)*

tury, when it was more often called the Schimmelbusch Mask. It took the form of a folding wire frame with a second wire to hold the layer of lint away from the face. A handle was provided, and the whole object folded flat to be carried, inevitably, in the top hat; a drop-bottle was used for this very simple form of administration. For use with these masks and some of the other forms of inhaler it was necessary to employ a nose-clip, a double piece of metal with flaring ends which fitted over the nostrils. Pls. 108 and 109 show more sophisticated adjustable versions. The Skinner Mask was modified by John Murray (1844–73) in 1862, and by many others. The Murray Mask allowed the framework to enclose the nose as well as the mouth, obviating the need for a nose-clip. The version by the Swiss surgeon Gustave Julliard (1836–1911) had an impermeable outer cover and a rosette of flannel inside, onto which the ether was poured.

The bell-shaped sponge and the handkerchief were still employed. Joseph Lister (1827–1911) said in 1861, 'enough chloroform is poured on to it . . . the precise quantity being a matter of no consequence whatever'. Later, Simpson devised a simple method of a towel arranged in a cone, with a sponge in the apex.

Mouth gags were necessary in the administration of chloroform, particularly in dentistry, and these are dealt with in Chapter 6.

Nitrous oxide

The study of gases and the 'new airs' became very fashionable in the late eighteenth century. Discoveries were described by Joseph Priestley (1733–1804), who wrote of oxygen, 'who can tell that, in time, this pure air may become a fashionable article in luxury'. One very interested physician and chemist was the original and outspoken Thomas Beddoes (1760–1808), who founded the Pneumatic Medical Institution at Clifton in 1799 where the use of gas in medicine could be studied. The first superintendent to be appointed there was Humphrey Davy (1778–1829), with James Watt (1736–1819), the distinguished engineer, to make the equipment. Davy had been attracted by Priestley's description of nitrous oxide and had experimented with its use on animals; at Clifton he carried out a complete investigation of its properties and published his findings in 1800 in his book *Researches*. His friend the poet Robert Southey wrote to him, 'The Atmosphere of the highest of all possible heavens must be composed of this gas.' Despite his many experiments with the gas on himself and others, Davy went on to other subjects and the Institution came to an end a few years later.

During the next 40 years it became part of the student scene to hold parties at which nitrous oxide, or 'laughing-gas' as it became known, was sniffed. The antics of the intoxicated participants were hilarious; its use was thought 'better than drinking liquor', until one fell down in a dead faint amid considerable consternation. Then, since his recovery was complete, the serious possibilities suggested themselves. The soporific effects were noted, but this very factor reduced its popularity. 'It is necessary to use caution . . . a gentleman was thrown into a very lethargic state.' Michael Faraday (1791–1867), a pupil of Davy, discovered in 1823 that the gas could be converted, under great pressure, into a liquid. This was slow to attract the attention of the medical profession and, as late as 1824, it was suggested to Davy, by this time President of the Royal Society, that it had 'probable utility in surgical operations on the human subject'. Henry Hill Hickman (1800–30), in the same year, was performing painless surgery on animals with its use but received no publicity. When it was put forward to the Academy of Medicine in Paris only the far-sighted Dominique Larrey (1766–1842) saw its possibilities but he was outvoted in his support for its use.

In 1844 Dr Horace Wells (1815–48), a dentist of Hartford, Connecticut attended a laughing-gas party and was so impressed that he afterwards asked for it when he had a wisdom tooth extracted. 'It is the greatest discovery ever made,' he said. 'I did not feel it as much as the prick of a pin.' He then made a study of nitrous oxide and designed an apparatus to produce and administer it. With Morton and Charles Jackson he went to the Massachusetts General Hospital in 1845 and asked to give a public demonstration. Nervousness possibly induced a faulty application, and the patient screamed throughout, with resulting derision against the two dentists. It also retarded the use of nitrous oxide for many years, except as a music-hall gimmick. Wells, however, used the gas on many patients back in Hartford and later turned to experiments with chloroform. Under the influence of too much chloroform he threw acid over a group of prostitutes and was put in prison, where he committed suicide.

Following Faraday, M. Natterer of Vienna had liquefied nitrous oxide in 1845 by compressing it with a small iron pump in a wrought-iron tube. However, it was not until the 1860s that there was distribution on a commercial scale. In the United Kingdom this was done by Coxeter who, in 1869, made a case with iron cylinder, mouthpiece and bag.

By 1867 successful claims were made for its use in dentistry, at the New York Dental Institute, by Gardner Quincy Cotton (1814–98), who demonstrated at the International Exhibition in Paris in that year. This caught the attention of the American Thomas Wiltberger Evans (1823–97), a very colourful character. He immediately employed the gas in his own cases in France but, not attracting the attention he felt he justified, he went to England and gave a demonstration at the Langham Hotel and then for a group of London dentists. The 'single bottle of liquid gas' which Evans brought from Paris inspired Charles James Fox who wrote, 'I had the pleasure of operating with it at the Dental Hospital, Mr.

Clover administering the gas.' The latter was inveterate in persuading Coxeter to produce simple cylinders, in which he was eventually successful. 'I administered the gas with uniform success to several patients at the Dental Hospital of London,' Clover was able to say. Later, the firm of Barth, as well as Coxeter, started large-scale production of the gas; the charge for refilling empty cylinders was 3d. per gallon. By 1873 it was on the American market.

At the end of 1868 nitrous oxide rather than chloroform was firmly established for use in dentistry among London dentists, and nearly 2,000 successful administrations were reported from the provinces. On the Continent, too, it became very popular; and Cotton, who had set up dental associations in the principal cities of the United States, reported 40,000 operations with its use without a fatal result.

In 1868 Alfred Coleman (1828–1902) and other London dentists took up the use of nitrous oxide with enthusiasm, Coleman devising several types of apparatus. John Clover gave his name to an apparatus of his own invention which delivered anaesthesia in three stages. There were, however, two disadvantages to the latter: there was no way of air mixing with the laughing-gas and no exit for exhaled carbon dioxide. He soon saw that his chloroform bag was a suitable means of administration and made modifications for its use with nitrous oxide. The apparatus, which was made by Coxeter, had the addition of a stopcock to prevent the entry of air and a long supplemental bag to be carried over the shoulder of the anaesthetist. Storage cylinders came next and then a means by which gas could be inhaled direct. Clover experimented with many a complicated and cumbersome apparatus during this period.

When nitrous oxide was first used in dentistry it was found acceptable for short operations, such as a single extraction, but its effects were of short duration and not suitable for long, complicated operations. In 1876 Clover introduced his nitrous oxide-ether equipment, which was seen as bringing safer anaesthesia very much nearer, both prolonging the anaesthesia and being pleasanter for the patient. Clover's apparatus consisted of a cylinder of gas, an upright can of ether and a Cattlin bag (named after W.A.N. Cattlin, a Brighton dentist). Through the bag, which was 15 inches long, passed a rubber tube connecting it to the facepiece so that a mixture of gases might be inhaled.

During the 1860s it had been seen that the administration of nitrous oxide was improved by the addition of oxygen, but the idea gained little popularity. When, however, compressed oxygen became readily available in cylinders – principally from S.S. White in the United States and Coxeter in the United Kingdom – progress became possible. S.S. White of Philadelphia produced the White Nitrous Oxide Bag *c.* 1865 on the principle of the bag used by Cotton and Wells in 1844. A simple bag of oiled silk (the original had probably been an animal bladder) was attached to a wooden tube leading to the mouthpiece. The anaesthetist held the mouthpiece in the patient's mouth with one hand and closed the nostrils with the other. Later, a stopcock was added and a nose-clip provided. The bags were very small to achieve satisfactory anaesthesia, and it is possibly because Wells' bag was not small enough that his original demonstration failed.

Experiments in mixing other gases were made, and when the possible dangers of chloroform became accepted, a combination of one part chloroform to six to eight parts ether was tried in Vienna in 1859. Elsewhere, others were trying out different proportions and combinations. Difficulties occurred; as John Snow said, 'Ether is about six times as volatile as chloroform' and would therefore evaporate more quickly. In 1864 the society which was to become the Royal Society of Medicine investigated a chloroform committee which eventually promoted the use of mixed gases. Robert Leslie Ellis (1817–59) produced his Alcohol-Ether-Chloroform Apparatus in 1866 and a paper rhapsodizing about the virtues of mixed vapours. It was mostly used for surgery and obstetrics. An upright cylinder enclosed three chambers from which came three wicks conducting the vapours; a breathing tube, with air-hole, connected it to the mouthpiece.

Local anaesthesia

Anaesthesia by injection was tried by the Hon. Robert Boyle (1627–91) and Christopher Wren (1632–1723), using a quill with tubing attached since they had no hypodermic syringe; their results were neglected for a century and a half. The first investigation into nerve-blocking was undertaken by L. Lafargue at St Emilion in Paris in 1836, when he punctured his inferior dental nerve with a lancet dipped in morphine. The hypodermic syringe was invented in Edinburgh in 1844 and improved over the ensuing years. By 1853 Charles Gabriel Pravaz (1791–1853) of Lyons had made a subcutaneous syringe with a screw for measured injections, and the same year Alexander Wood (1817–84) of Edinburgh perfected his syringe, which was made by Ferguson. This he used successfully with morphine for the relief of pain, although dentists did not find it very suitable for their purposes. In 1864, during the American Civil War, the first injection for local anaesthesia was undertaken by a military surgeon on a patient whose condition was beyond that in which chloroform might have been administered.

Cocaine, an extract of the sacred plant of Peru, the coca plant, was discovered by a visiting Austrian botanist in 1860; Albert Niemann (1834–1861) demonstrated its use, which was developed by Josef Brettaner of Heidelberg and Karl Koller (1857–1944) working together in Vienna. Sigmund Freud was the first to suggest its use as a pain-killer, and more effective local anaesthesia was made possible with its use by 1884.

109 *Left to right: dental chisel, c.1770, 10 cm; hinged wooden nose-clamp operated by ivory screw, c.1865; separating file, cross-hatched ivory handle, c.1840. (I. Freeman & Son, Simon Kaye Ltd, London)*

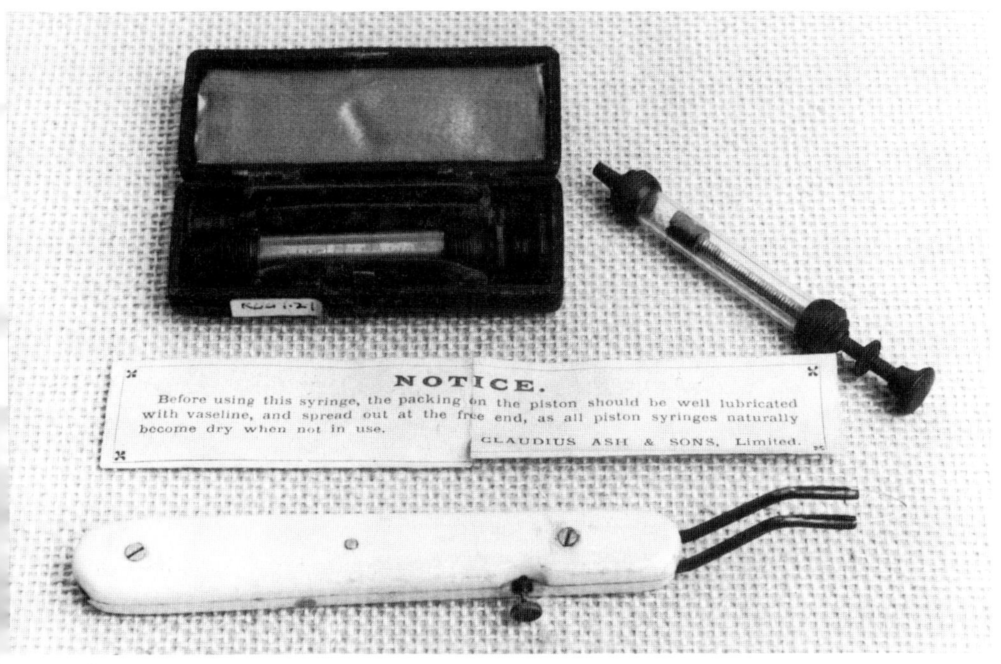

110 *Hypodermic syringe with vulcanite mounts, thread-packed piston, Ash, 1887, 5 cm; George Waite's electric cautery, as shown at the Great Exhibition of 1851, 12 cm. (Museum of the British Dental Association, London)*

William Stewart Halsted (1852–1922) of New York was the first dentist actually to try injecting cocaine, experimenting on himself, and by 1872 Pierre-Cyprien Oré (1828–89), Professor of Physiology at Bordeaux, had pioneered introvenous injections of chloral hydrate. Chloroform was sometimes used as a local anaesthetic in dentistry by putting saturated cotton on either side of the affected tooth; this, however, was only effective on account of the chloroform inhaled in the process. In the mid nineteenth century several methods of inducing cold in the area of a dental operation were tried, spraying with freezing mixtures and organic liquids, such as combined air and ethyl chloride. A pewter syringe was invented with a subsidiary cylinder at the side so that the mixture was only effected immediately before the ejection, but the successful use of ethyl chloride in local anaesthesia was not realized until 1891.

Other attempts at anaesthesia

Franz Anton Mesmer (1734–1815) experimented with magnetism in pain killing. He enjoyed considerable success and received support from the French Royal Family. Afterwards, he was denounced as a quack but his unwitting pioneering of hypnotism was later developed for use in medicine and dentistry.

The German L.B. Lentin first used electricity for relief of toothache in 1756, others having previously experimented with a magnet. At the Great Exhibition of 1851 George Waite exhibited an electric cautery for the relief of pain (pl. 110). Ash illustrated similar versions in the catalogues of 1858 and 1873. Joseph Snape of Liverpool undertook operations with the use of electricity between the years 1850 and 1875. His forceps and the patient were connected to a 'magneto-electric' machine, through which a galvanic current passed at the moment of extraction. Though it was thought very advanced it proved useless, as did a similar invention patented in America in 1858 by Jerome B. Francis of Philadelphia.

Anaesthesia became an accepted part of established surgical practice at a moment, in both Europe and America, when matters relating to the health of the people became more closely a matter of public control. Its acceptance would seem to have been inevitable and, in dentistry particularly, would appear to have presaged a closer relationship between dentist and patient. Not all patients, however, apparently welcomed its use. As late as 1913 E.F. Benson could write of one of his characters, 'But any woman with the slightest self-respect, when once convinced that it was better to have the tooth out, went to the dentist at the appointed hour, declined gas . . . opened her mouth and held the arms of the chair very firmly.'

XVII *Group of tooth-paste pot-lids illustrating: royal connections; self-advertisement; the inducement of a transatlantic recipe; and the high cost of the product. At the top is a Dutch example of good design and charming colour. (Private Collection, Dr Ben Z. Swanson, London)*

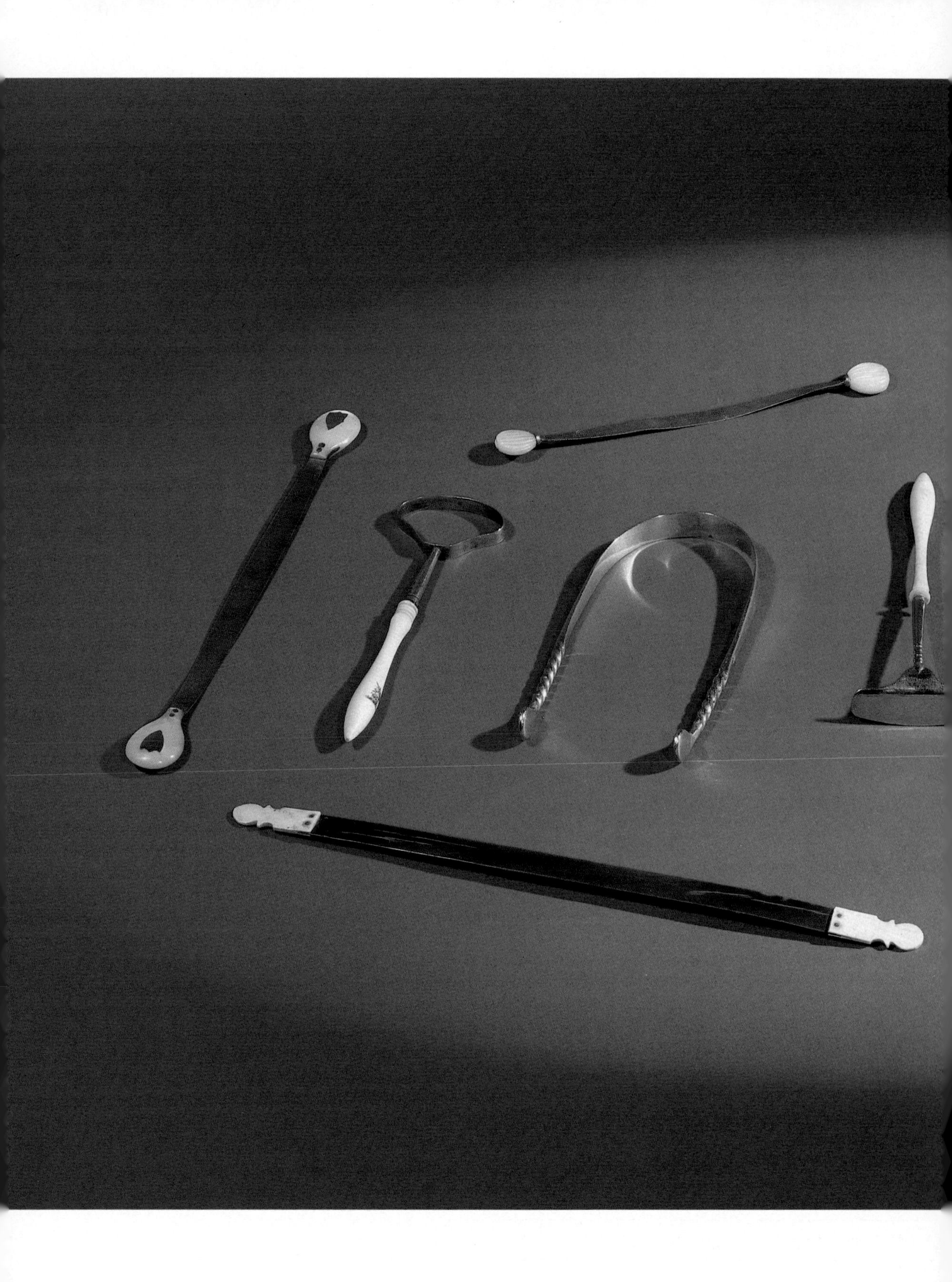

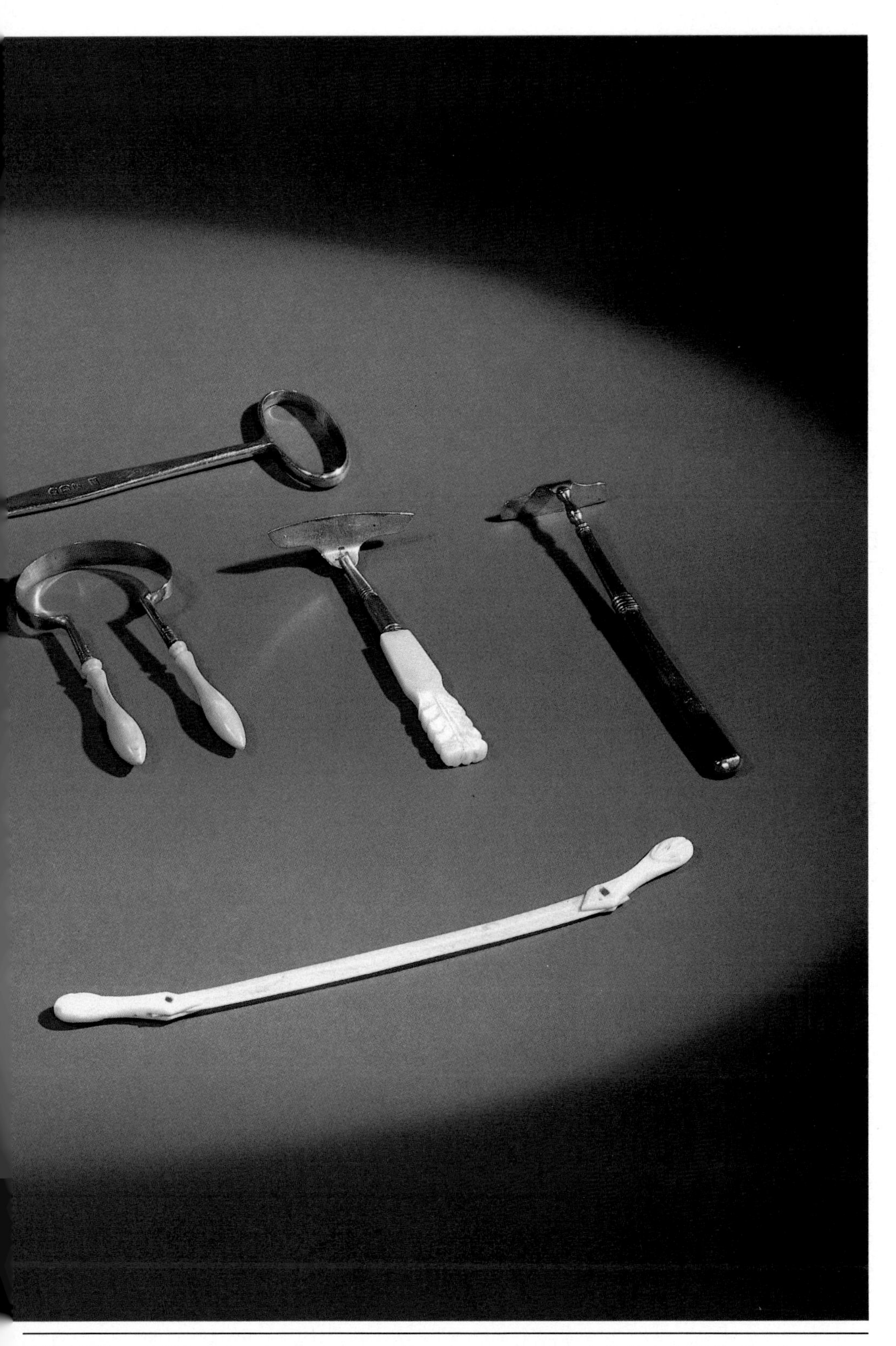

XVIII *18th- and 19th-century tongue-scrapers, silver, ivory and tortoiseshell. (Private Collection, London)*

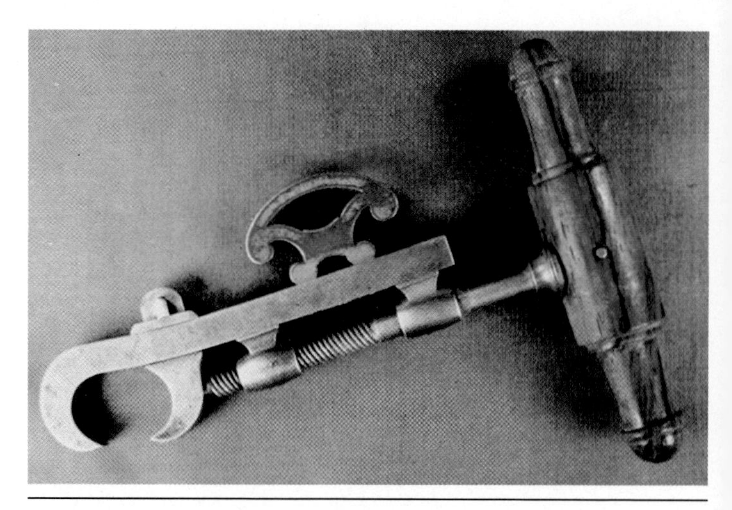

XX *Secateurs of Paul Gresset, as illustrated by Maury in 1841, 11.5 cm. (Musée Dentaire de Lyon)*

XIX *Early 18th-century wooden mouth-wedge. (Museum of Medicine of the USSR, Kiev)*

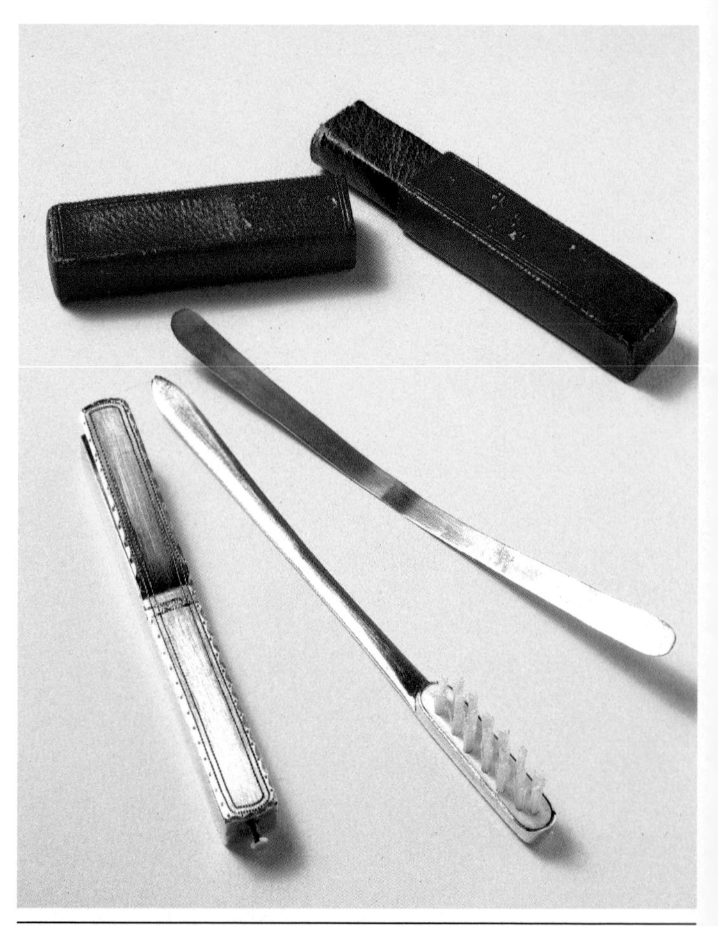

XXI *Red morocco travelling case containing silver tooth-brush, tongue-scraper and tooth-powder box, Birmingham, 1799. Joseph Taylor case, 13 cm. (Private Collection, Peter Gordon, London)*

6 Dental mirrors, scalers and miscellaneous instruments

Dental mirrors

It is interesting that overcoming the problem of obtaining an adequate view of the whole of a patient's mouth by means of a reflecting glass should not have occurred until the end of the eighteenth century. Richard Corson, in his book *Fashions in Eyeglasses*, is of the opinion that the very pretty little mirrors which resulted were the original quizzing-glasses of the *beau monde*, in which one might see all that was going on behind one without the vulgar necessity of turning round. This is possibly true of some of the rigid-stemmed examples, but those with a swivelling or hinged handle must certainly be classed as dental mirrors and, since there are many fixed-handled specimens included in large cases of dental instruments, one must query even this type as having had another use. For charm, delicacy and attraction, dental mirrors immediately appeal to the collector, but considering the very few mentioned or even illustrated in the dental treatises and makers' catalogues, one must presume they were not found indispensable. Obviously, they were not part of the general accoutrements of the tooth-drawers. Possibly they were the necessity of the fashionable dentist who sought to reassure his rich patients by the elegance of his tools, echoing an anonymous writer of the seventeenth century, who wrote that instruments were usually made of iron but, in the case of royals, gold 'and if there were a more costly metal then it would be used, because they remunerate so generously'. Certainly, to the profitable type of patient, royal or not, the appearance of the instrument was as important as its function.

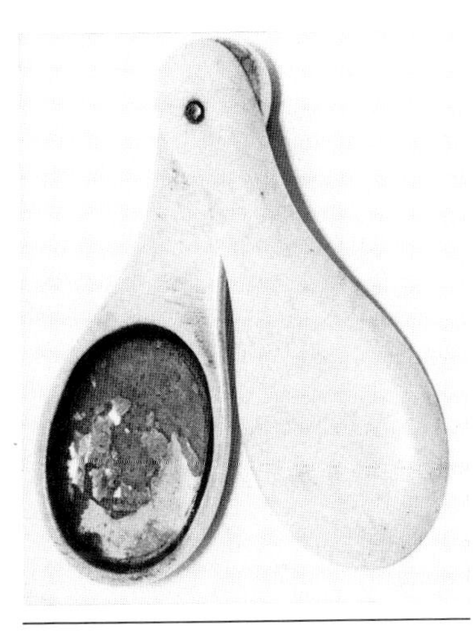

111 *Folding ivory mirror, c.1830, 8 cm. (Museum of the History of Science, Oxford)*

Between about 1780 and 1860 dental mirrors were made with an oval glass approximately 3 by 2.5 cm, framed in silver, silver-gilt and gold, sometimes chased, engraved and engine-turned. Alternatively they might be in tortoiseshell, ivory or mother-of-pearl. The most delightful contrived a combination of materials. The earlier examples were hinged at the point where the frame joined the handle, or the frame was held on either side by branches of the handle so that it swung like a cheval glass. By about 1830 one finds the frame attached to the handle by a ball-joint, although hinged examples were still made. An anonymous report, published in Salzburg in 1804, describes a double dental mirror invented by Bartholomew Ruspini (1728–1813), dentist to the Prince of Wales. 'The so-called instrument consists of two small elliptical mirrors. One is held between the teeth and the

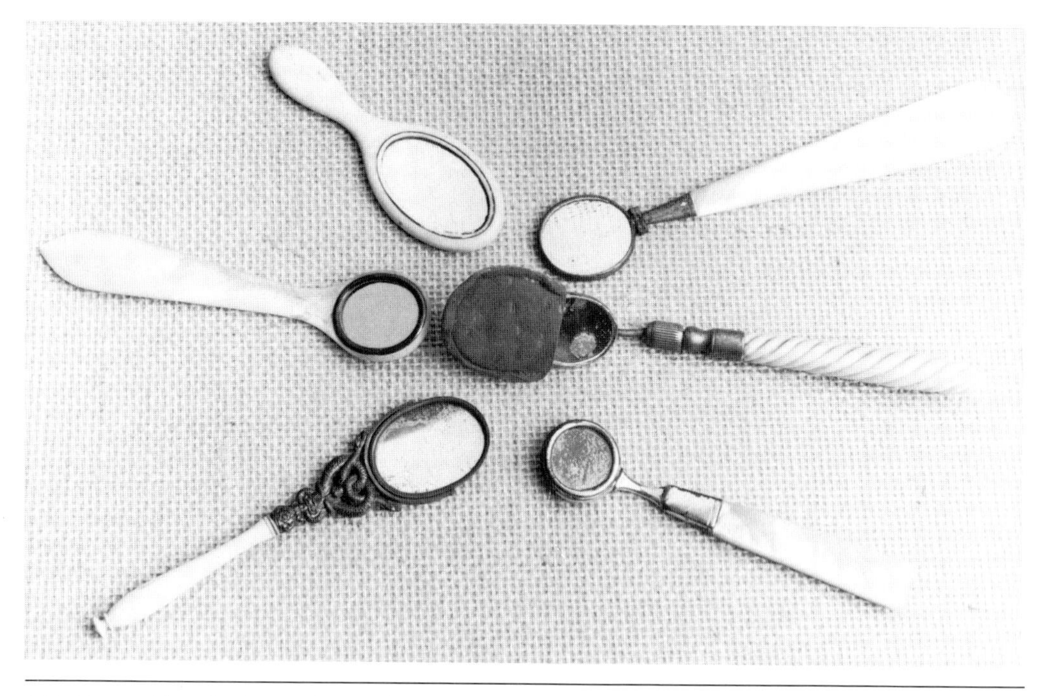

112 *Group of dental mirrors, ivory, silver and mother-of-pearl handles, first half 19th century, each approx. 10cm. (Museum of the British Dental Association, London)*

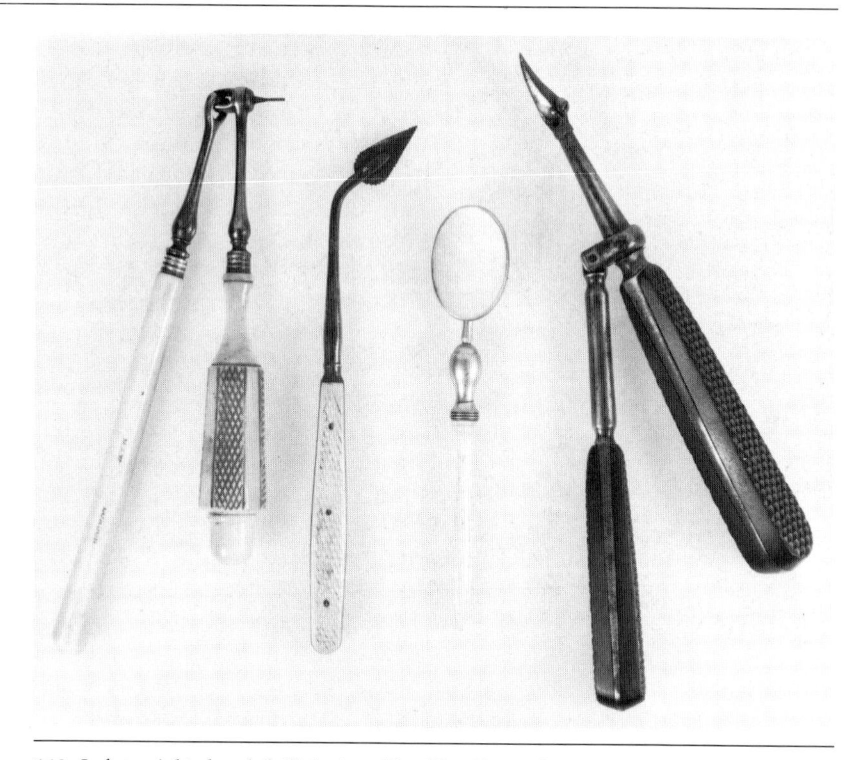

113 *Left to right: hand-drill designed by Claudius Ash, c.1850, 16cm; separating saw, c.1840; mirror with steel surface, c.1830; elevator in two parts, c.1845. (I. Freeman & Son, Simon Kaye Ltd, London)*

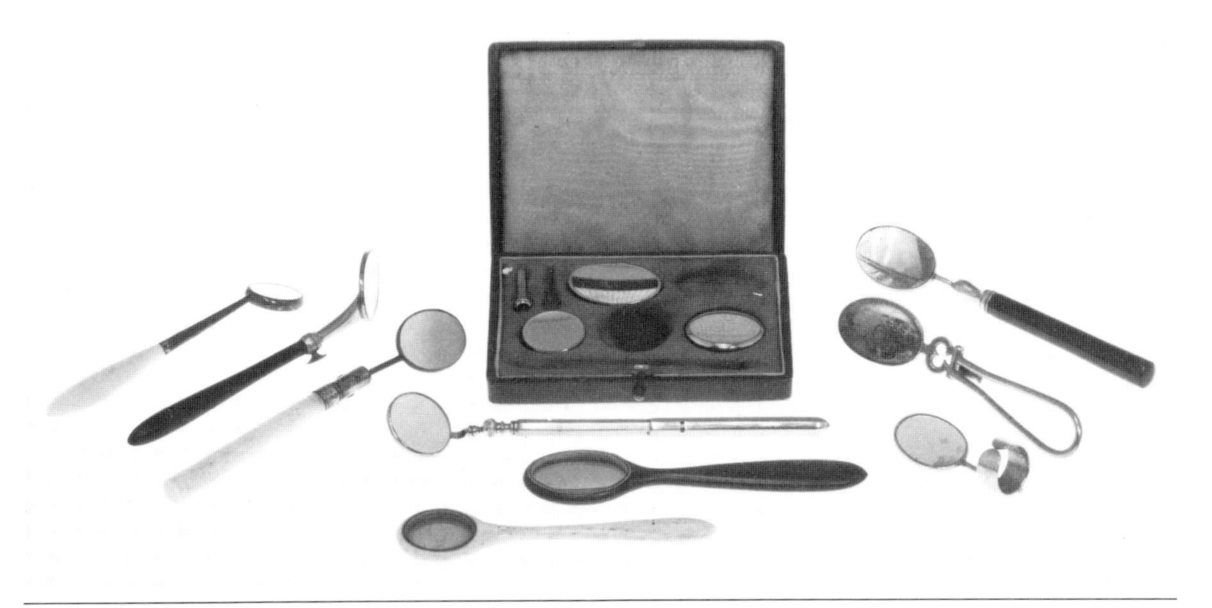

114 *Group of 19th-century dental mirrors. (Rijksuniversiteit, Utrecht)*

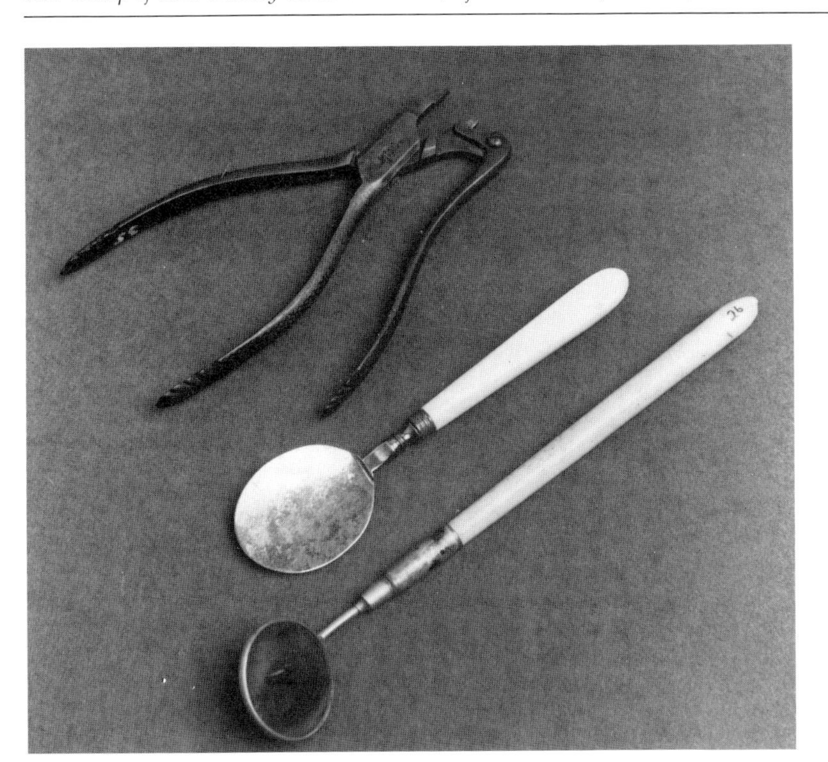

116 *Orthodontic pliers, Ash, c.1850, one of six pliers supplied to King's Troop Royal Horse Artillery; mirror with polished steel reflecting surface, as James Snell, c.1835; long-handled mirror, c.1850. (Royal Army Dental Corps Historical Museum, Aldershot)*

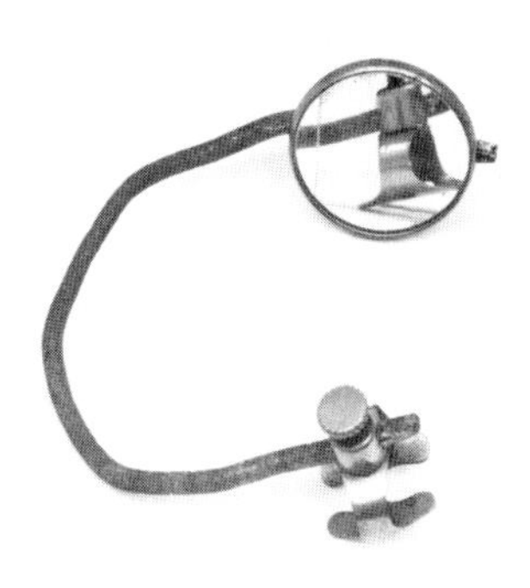

115 *Dental speculum of Dr V. Wunschheim, c.1850. (Museum of Swedish Dental Society, Stockholm)*

other in front of them. The item is completely new.' James Snell (?1795–1850), who wrote in detail on current practices, devised a mirror, in 1832, of polished steel, which he considered superior to the oval looking-glasses on a frame which were then in common use.

By the middle of the nineteenth century dental mirrors were rather less lavish. The handle grew longer and more practical, usually ivory of either cylindrical or polygonal shape, and the steel frame became quite plain. By the late 1880s mirrors appeared with the handle fixed at an angle to the frame, with the glass by this time usually circular.

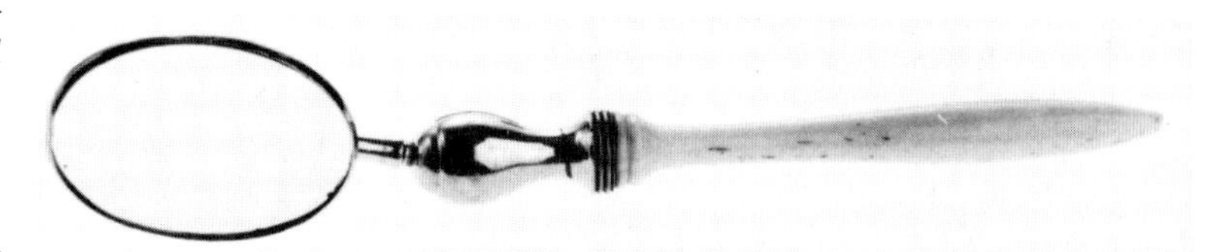

117 *Ivory-handled mirror, c.1830, 10cm. (University of Alberta Dental Museum)*

Scalers

The three different calcified tissues – enamel, dentine and cementum, in descending order of hardness – make up the structure of the teeth, and the early dentists felt confident, therefore, in removing tartar with a selection of fairly sharp instruments used with some force. Jacques Guillemeau (1550–1613), in 1597, warned the operator not to loosen teeth with the scraper and not to hurt the gums. He described tartar 'which as this increases, is not as yet obdurate or hard we may then with more facilitye remove the same'. In 1678 Antoni van Leeuwenhoek (1632–1723) researched the nature of tartar and demonstrated his discoveries to the Royal Society. John Hunter (1728–1793) advised scaling the teeth, together with scarification and an application of astringents, as treatment for pyorrhoea.

Scalers were popular in the Ancient World and in the Middle Ages but were not again in very general use until the eighteenth century. Some of the Roman instruments in pl. 119 are undoubtedly for scaling both the surfaces and the interstices of the teeth. Avicenna (980–1037) designed a collection of 14 scalers; he put his patient's head on his knee while he used them. Gerard of Cremona (1114–87) illustrated eight different scalers in the following century. Walter Ryff (1500–62), who published *Chirurgia Magna* in 1545, illustrating several dental instruments, included a series of 14 double-ended scalers with delicately turned and wrought ornamental sections in the centre.

By 1617 John Woodall (1556–1643) has little to say about scalers, which he calls gravers. 'And for Gravers they are used to take scales off, a hard substance which use to fix themselves to the teeth, causing them to become loose and stinke, or be blacke in the mouth, or to help to scrape or clense a bone in any other

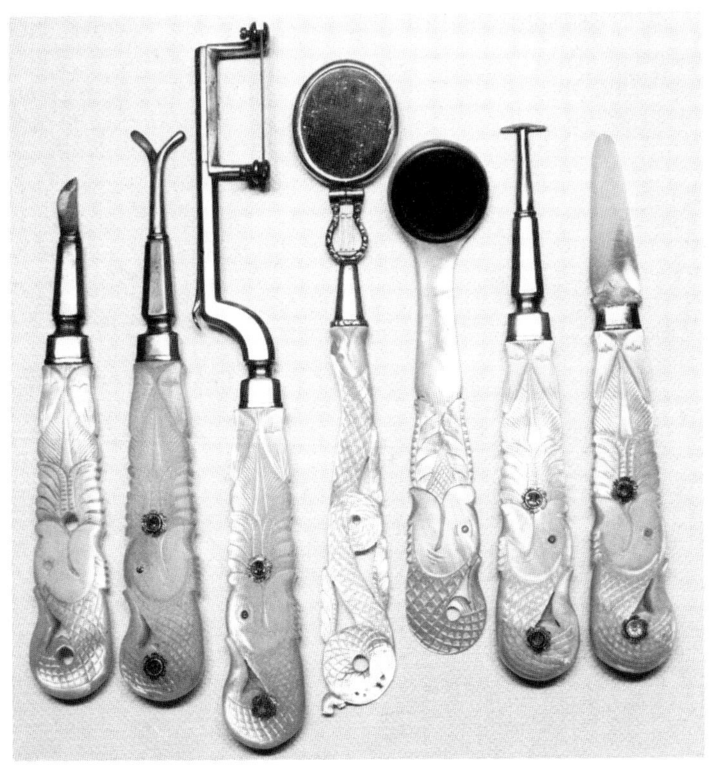

118 *Left to right: gum-lancet; plugger and burnisher; file-carrier; two mirrors; scaler; cheek-retractor. Handles of mother-of-pearl set with semi-precious stones. American, c.1840–50, largest 15cm. (Private Collection, Dr Gary Lemen, Sacramento, Cal.)*

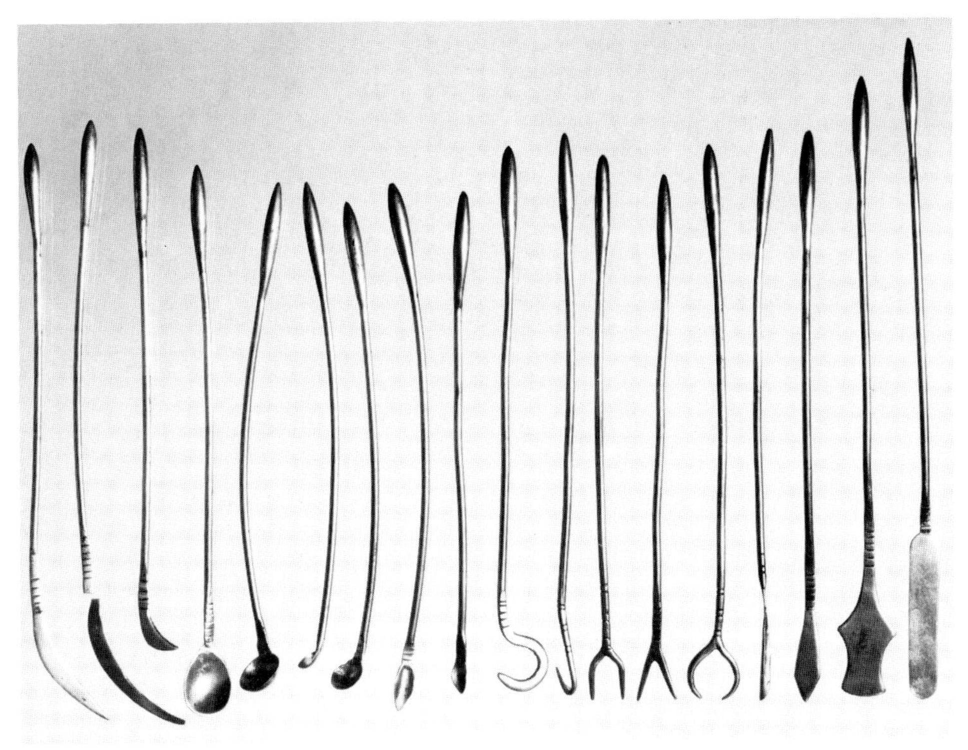

119 *Set of Roman silver dental instruments including scalers. (Central Museum, Mainz)*

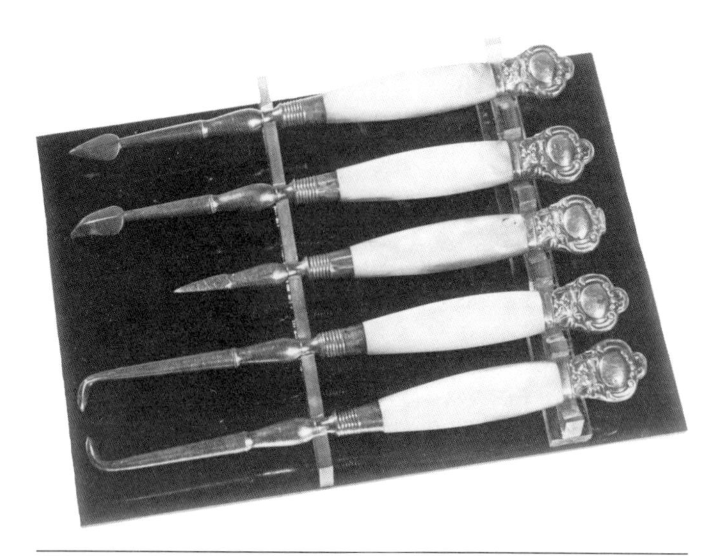

120 *Five scalers with mother-of-pearl and gilt handles, c.1820, 14 cm. (Odontological Museum of the Royal College of Surgeons, London)*

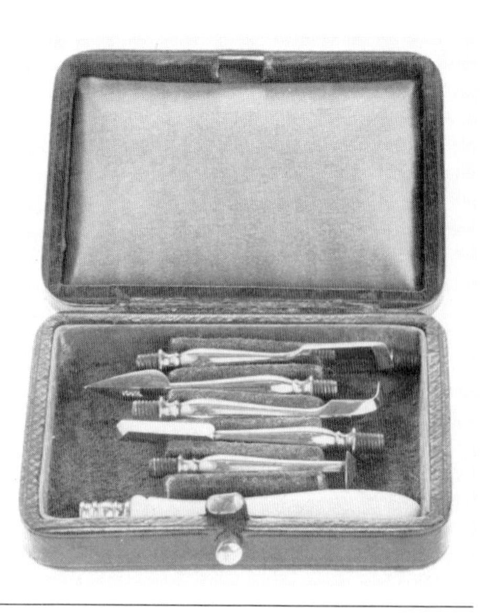

121 *Five scalers in leather case, ivory handle, c.1810. (University of Alberta Dental Museum, Edmonton)*

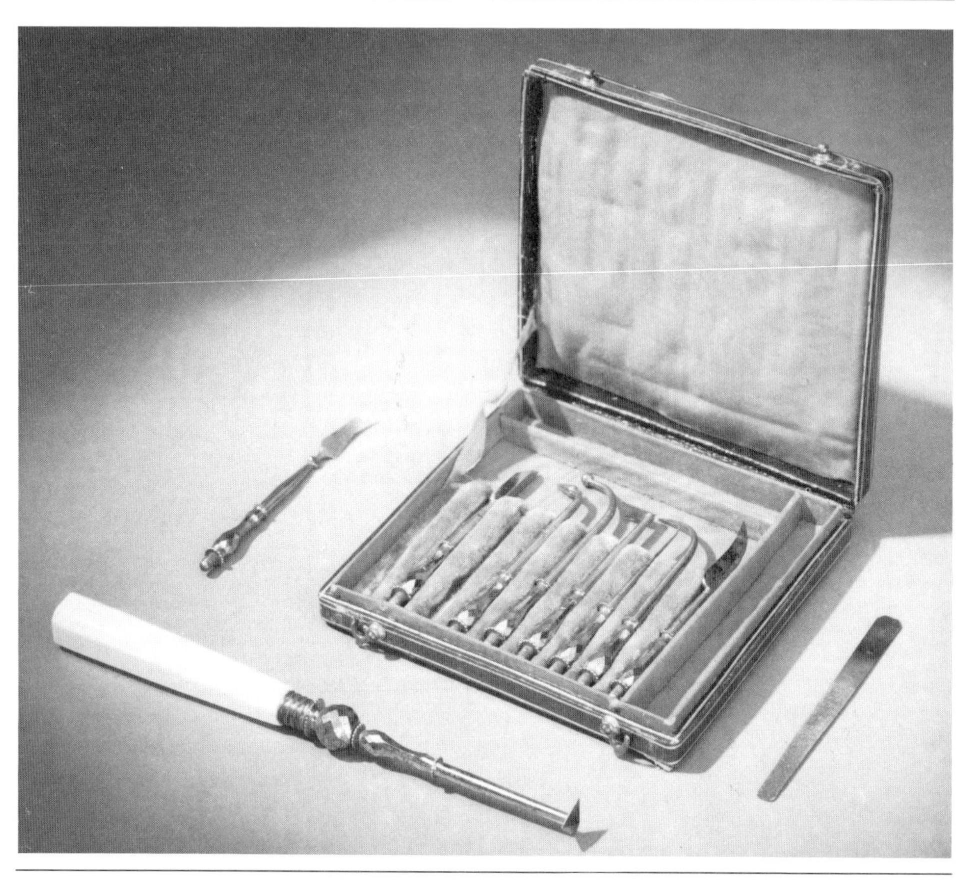

122 *Nine scalers with faceted steel-cut decoration, and a file, c.1820, assembled 10 cm. (I. Freeman & Son, Simon Kaye Ltd, London)*

part of the body as just occasion is offered.' Clearly a versatile instrument.

By the eighteenth century, with scaling becoming popular again, Pierre Fauchard (1678–1761) is more specific about the instruments. They are, he says, to be made of good steel so that they are sharp and scrape well. Gold and silver are not suitable as they are not hard enough. Pierre Dionis (1643–1718), speaking of scalers made of gold for kings and queens, can therefore be presumed to have been describing the handles. Fauchard only feels five types to be necessary: a rabbet chisel, a parrot's bill (curved at its point), a graver with three facets (as used by engravers), a small knife with a convex blade, and a hook like a Z. All these are sharp and will remove tartar from any place. They can be mounted on silver, ivory or some other material that accords with cleanliness and usefulness, but the handles must be round and not too heavy, since weight might endanger nimbleness. The ends should be finished with little caps, suitably fashioned, to embellish the instruments. They are to be kept sharp on a Levant or Lorraine stone, covered in a little oil. Fauchard's scalers are illustrated in Chapter 3 (pl. 80). Philip Pfaff (1716–80) and Lorenz Heister (1683–1758), who was very keen on oral hygiene, both illustrated several scalers.

Such scalers were for the professional. Throughout the eighteenth century and at the beginning of the nineteenth century those who cared for the state of their teeth would have had their own personal set of scalers. Small pocket cases made in shagreen, ivory, tortoiseshell and, a little later, red morocco and other leathers were made to contain a series of interchangeable scaler heads which screwed into a common handle; the lid of the case usually included a mirror covered by a piece of velvet. The common characteristic of these sets was elegance. The cases frequently had inlaid silver or brass shields to take the crest or monogram of the owner; they were lined in chamois leather or silk velvet which was often trimmed in gold galon. The handle which took the variety of heads might be of several types: prettily turned steel; ivory, either green or white, turned or cut in a spiral; cut and engraved mother-of-pearl or hardstone; silver or silver-gilt. The number of scaler-heads might vary between five and, possibly, twelve. The types which seem to have been common were: a triangular head, a right-angle, a carp's tongue both straight and curved, a long flat file, a sharp hatchet, a shovel shape with broad curved end, and an isosceles triangle.

From about 1830 onwards these beautifully fashioned sets were seldom made, and one finds more cases, of a more pedestrian nature, intended for use by the dentist. These, obviously, had a fixed handle for each instrument, usually octagonal and of ivory but occasionally of ebony or other material. They were cased in sets of five to ten or formed part of the large cases which the dentist of important patients might take with him to their houses (pl. 158).

Files

Albucasis (936–1013) felt the facial disfigurement caused by uneven teeth, particularly in women, was sufficient to justify treatment by filing them level, preferably over several days so that they might not fall out in the process. This was one of the uses for a file, which appears to have been a favourite instrument with the earlier operators. Celsus (25 B.C.–A.D. 50) used a file to arrest caries but principally for rounding off rough edges and corners likely to damage the tongue. Jacques Guillemeau, in 1597, describes the filing and cutting of protruding teeth (see below); and John Woodall, a little later, says, 'The small files are used to file a small snagg off a tooth, which offendeth the tongue or lipps.' John Scultetus of Ulm (1595–1645) mentions an angled raspatory, and René-Jacques Garengeot (1688–1759) also mentions files. Pierre Fauchard, a century later, again used the file to make uniform an uneven length of tooth but considered its more important use to be for separating the carious tooth from the healthy ones by filing between them. He recommended eight files of roughly three types: a straight shaft, a curved shaft, and one with a double right-angled bend to it. As has been seen above, a small file was often included as a scaling instrument.

Files were seldom double-sided and could be square-ended or pointed and had necessarily very fine cross-hatching. Some, probably those referred to as raspatories, had only a small surface of file, an oval centimetre at the end of the shaft. During the nineteenth century the number considered necessary declined, and a large case would only contain one or two of the type described above. Another design was introduced around 1840 and remained in use to the end of the century. This was made like a small bow-saw with a screw-in blade which might, in fact, have a toothed edge to effect a better separation (pl. 125).

Probes

It must be obvious that the probe has to be one of the most delicate of dental instruments. It is one mentioned by most writers on dentistry from the seventeenth century onwards but hardly thought worthy of illustration. A probe is a probe is a probe, apparently. Garengeot had a double-ended example, possibly the first; Fauchard mentions 'a little probe to discover caries', and he too used a double-ended example, each end curving in the opposite direction. Probes are included in the large dental cases, distinguishable from the pluggers or tampers by their greater refinement. The invention of the probe in its present form was claimed by C.F. Maury (1786–1840) in 1820.

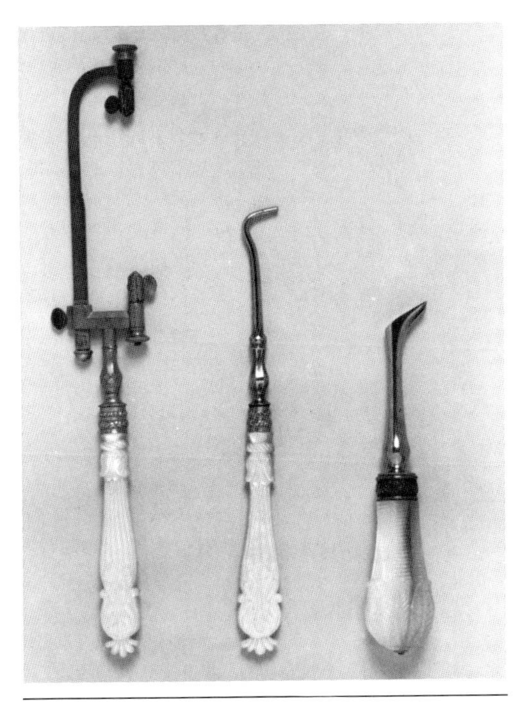

123 *Left to right: separating saw, Blanc, c.1860; plugger, c.1860; elevator, c.1780; all with mother-of-pearl handles, silver-gilt ferrules. (Musée Fauchard, Paris)*

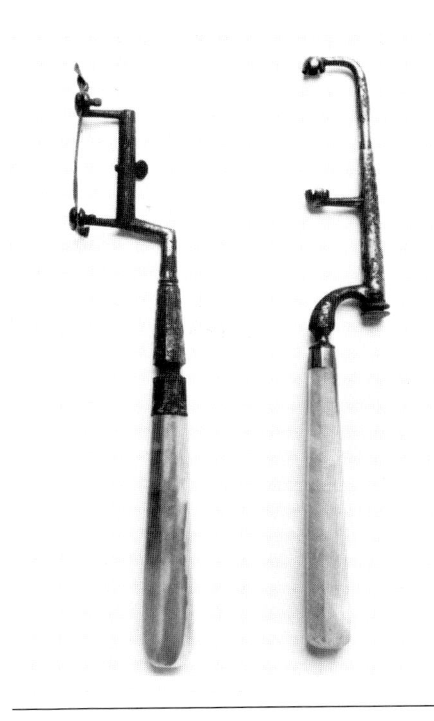

124 *Dental file-carriers, mother-of-pearl handles, c.1850, 17 cm and 18.5 cm. (Macaulay Museum of Dental History, Medical University of South Carolina)*

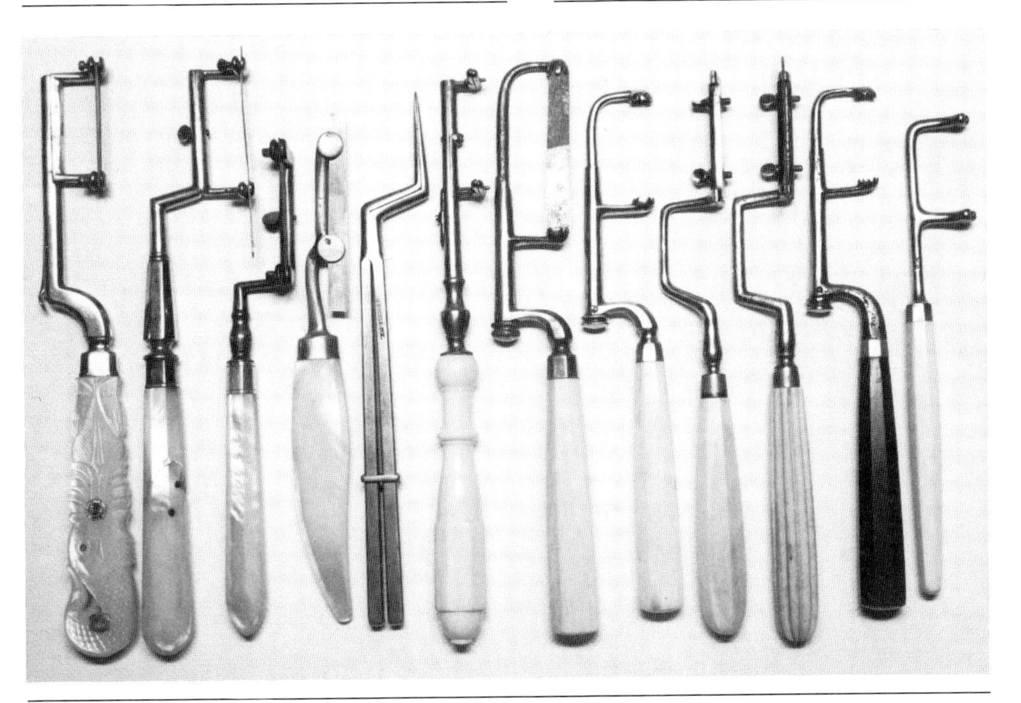

125 *Separating file-carriers, handles of mother-of-pearl, ivory, ebony and metal. American, c.1840–60. (Dr Gary Lemen, Sacramento, Cal.)*

Lancets and scarifiers

Dentistry could not expect to escape the ubiquitous practice of phlebotomy and, indeed, it was used for toothache, recovery from extraction, diseases of the gum, and to remove excess fluid. Lancets were needed for this and, in addition, for abscesses, and frequently, as has been seen in Chapter 2, to cut down between the gum and the root of the tooth to aid extraction. Hildegard of Bingen, who was, from 1147, Abbess of a convent in Bingen near Mainz, advocated lancing an abscess on the gum with a bramble if no lancet were available. John Woodall says, 'Phlemes have not only their uses in teeth drawing, but also to launch and cut the Gummes to let them bloud, or to cut oftentimes the superfluous flesh of the Gummes away, it being too rank, as in cases of the scurvy, the cure whereof (God willing) shall in another place be spoken of.' Charles Allen in 1687 suggests curing toothache by bleeding the gum or possibly the upper arm. He advises lancing the gum of teething infants down to the head of the emerging tooth, with two crosswise cuts. Joseph Hurlock, who published *A Practical Treatise upon Dentitian: or The Breeding of Teeth in Children* in 1742, recommended lancing the gums for most complaints, and the practice remained general until the nineteenth century.

Garengeot speaks of 'a curved gingival scalpel', presumably for extraction, and Fauchard illustrates a lancet, though speaks scathingly of those claiming to cure toothache by scarifying behind the ears. His lancet is the usual fine-pointed blade hinged to a tortoiseshell guard (pl. 126) and is interesting in that he recommends it to be wrapped in a spiral of fine linen to the tip, in order to protect the rest of the mouth and absorb any blood drawn. The swollen gum is to be incised as often and deeply as necessary. Depending on the part of the gum to be bled, straight or curved scissors may be more suitable; lunar-caustic in a silver holder (pl. 126) should then be applied. Osseous growths should be removed with a small chisel (pls. 109 and 127), the handle struck with a mallet, or sawn off with a saw-blade 'put into a handle like a knife'. Soft tumours could be removed with a curved bistoury, a scalpel with a blade only part of which had a cutting edge. An abscess should be lanced with a straight or gum-lancet, wrapped again in linen to the point, and the cavity then rinsed with a syringe, the tube long and curved.

Fauchard's gum-lancet had a crescent-shaped blade, thinner near the point and sharp on both edges at the point; this he used for detaching the gum from the root of the tooth. At the end of the eighteenth century and throughout the nineteenth century, a gum-lancet appeared in general use which had a hatchet-shaped end, protruding 0.5 cm; this had the advantage of not cutting more deeply than might be desirable. It was sometimes combined, opening from the same guard like a penknife, with the curved bistoury mentioned by Fauchard (pl. 126).

126 *Clockwise from top: curved bistoury, tortoiseshell guard, c.1800, 10cm; gum-lancet, pressed tortoiseshell handle, c.1860, 15.5cm; seamless silver caustic holder, 1873, 11cm; early single-bladed scarificator with scratch-engraved brass case, c.1740, 5cm; folding lancet in tortoiseshell guard, c.1810, 5.5cm. (I. Freeman & Son, Simon Kaye Ltd, London)*

127 *Two dental chisels, c.1780, 9cm and 11cm. (Museum of the History of Science, Oxford)*

A dental scarificator, both for phlebotomy and tooth-pulling, would have been of the single-bladed spring variety sometimes known as a 'schnappers'. This brass-cased instrument was operated by the finger on a trigger, which released the spring, bringing the triangular blade swiftly forwards (pl.126). A practice to obviate the use of the scarificator was that mentioned by Charles Allen: the 'Need of an instrument of Gold or Silver about a foot long, as big as a tobacco pipe and like a syringe'. This was to be applied to the gum where a wisdom tooth is growing. Its action was that of a partial vacuum raising the surface of the gum and repeated daily until the tooth emerged.

Obdurators

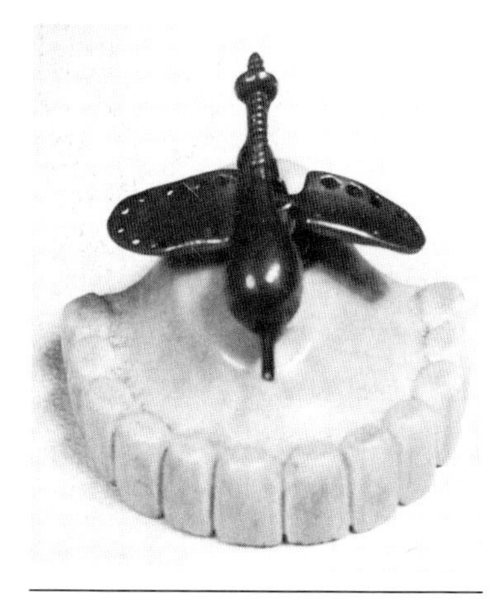

128 *Ivory obdurator, c.1750, similar to illustration by Pierre Fauchard, 1728. (Private Collection, Dr Gary Lemen, Sacramento, Cal.)*

When, *c.* 1495, a horrific outbreak of syphilis started across Europe, cases of palatal perforation became widely known. Ambroise Paré (1510–90) was the first to use leaves of gold or silver to close these defects of the palate; they were held in place by a small sponge pushed through the nose into the cavity. 'With the help of our art, they can regain the power of speech.' Franz Renner (d. 1577) of Nuremburg described, in 1557, a palatal obdurator made of sheets of leather glued together, though he said it could equally well be made of gold, silver or ivory. Later dentists made improvements, particularly Fauchard, who described five different types. In 1860 Norman W. Kingsley (1829–1913) perfected the gold obdurator and used artificial vellum or soft rubber for cases of cleft palate. However, the small likelihood of survival makes this item rather outside the scope of this book (pl. 128).

Orthodontics: secateurs and other cutting devices

The study of orthodontics, or the treatment of irregularities in teeth and jaw, is largely an American contribution to dentistry, and Norman W. Kingsley (see above) is considered to be the Father of Orthodontics, though the first book on the subject was written in 1858 by Charles Gaine, of Bath: *On Certain Irregularities of the Teeth with Cases Illustrative of a Novel Method of Successful Treatment*. Some small discoveries and treatments were attempted before this, which were conducive to orthodontic thought. When, in 1563, Bartholomeus Eustachius (1520–74) echoed Giovanni d'Arcoli in asserting that the secondary teeth have their own dental sac and do not originate from the roots of the milk teeth, he helped show that growth defects need not continue once the milk teeth are shed. It has been shown how Fauchard and others filed teeth to achieve uniformity of length, and Guillemeau, having done this, describes fastening any loose teeth – which by now there may well have been – to those

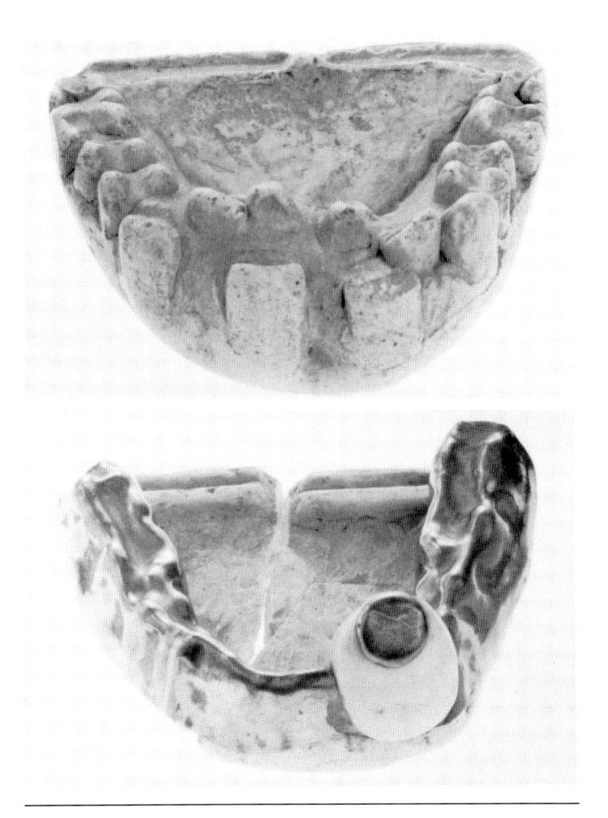

129 *Early orthodontic appliance, incised with date August 1872. (University of Alberta Dental Museum, Edmonton)*

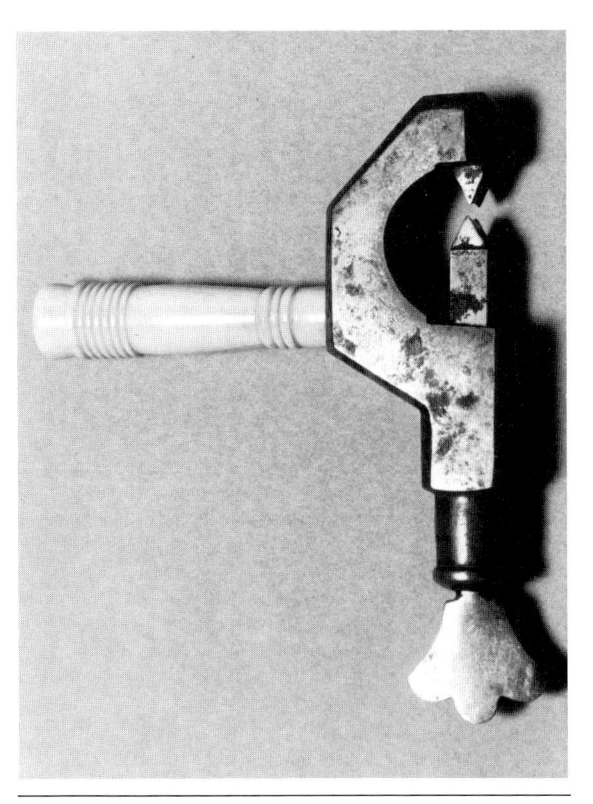

130 *Secateurs, ivory handle, c.1810. (Howard Dittrick Museum of Historical Medicine, Cleveland, Ohio)*

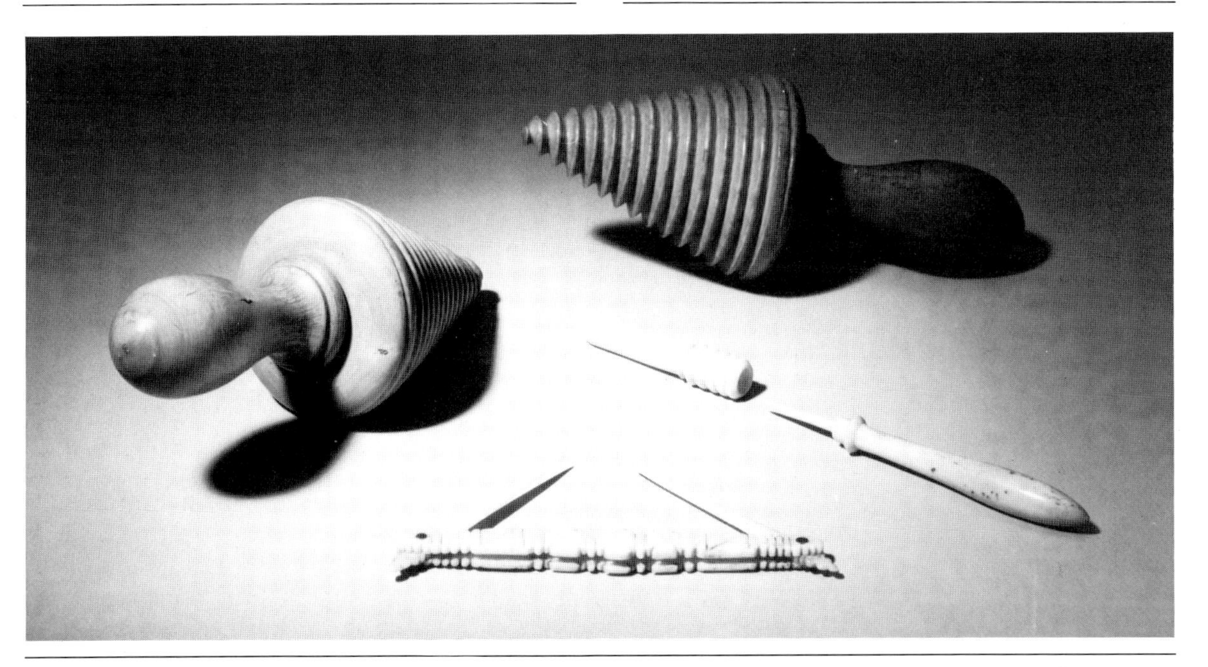

131 *Pair of boxwood spiral mouth-gags, c.1860, 12 cm; ivory toothpick, c.1840, 10 cm; double folding ivory toothpick, c.1860, 9 cm. (I. Freeman & Son, Simon Kaye Ltd, London)*

adjacent, with 'fyne goulden wyre of fyne Orientall goulde'. Etienne Bourdet (1722–89), in 1757, advised extraction to ease overcrowding and aid alignment, and extraction on opposite sides of the jaw to achieve symmetry. John Hunter was one of the first to study the ways in which continual pressure on a tooth can alter its direction of growth.

Even in the Middle Ages radical attempts to achieve the mouth beautiful were attempted by the actual cutting of uneven or protruding teeth. This was done with an instrument variously described as cutters, cutting-pincers, cutting-pliers or, by the French, secateurs. Fauchard had two kinds, one with the cutting edge at the side and one with it at the front. Both had strong convex handles with a spring between them. He attempted other forms of rudimentary orthodontic treatment with strips of lead or gold wire and occasionally adjusted the position of the teeth with the use of forceps or a pelican. Col. pl. XX shows Paul Gresset's secateurs which appeared in the 1841 edition of C.F. Maury's *L'Art du Dentiste*. It will be seen that the sturdy construction and screw-mechanism leave little hope for the tooth they attack; they are 'd'une très grande puissance', says Gresset. This particular instrument was intended for excision of the whole tooth at the neck and not for orthodontic use, but similar secateurs, though 'bien imparfait, d'un emploi souvent difficile' according to Gresset, were developed from his design to aid alignments.

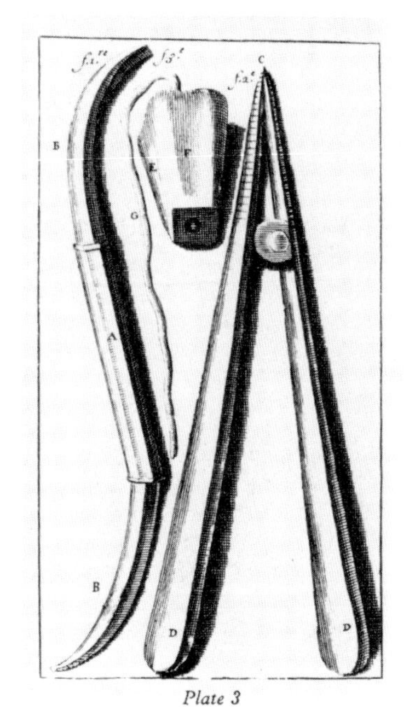

132 *Illustration from Pierre Fauchard's* Le Chirurgien Dentiste *(1728) showing three instruments for opening the mouth.*

Mouth-gags

Reluctance on the part of the patient was not the only reason for the variety of mouth-openers and mouth-gags devised. In dental practice, fear most frequently prompted their use; tetanus resulting in lockjaw, hysteria, insanity and catalepsy all made them necessary. Fabricius Hildanus (1560–1634) illustrates wooden wedges, shaped like little Chinese pillows, as mouth-props, and John Scultetus (1595–1645) had a mouth-gag with a screw-thread. Lorenz Heister (1683–1758), working as a military surgeon a century later, knew frequent cases of tetanus and shows several different mouth-openers and gags worked by a screw mechanism. Fauchard illustrates three instruments: an elevator, a speculum oris and a gag. The elevator is a double-ended instrument, each end a curved, faceted, sturdy piece of metal to be used as a lever. The speculum oris looks exactly like a glove-stretcher, the joint two-thirds of the way towards the points, which are corrugated on the outer surfaces; pressure on the handles forced the opposite ends apart. Sometimes, says Fauchard, it was necessary to extract a tooth in order to force-feed; this might be done by holding a punch against the tooth near the gum and striking it with a lump of lead. The mouth-gag he describes as a 'ribbed gag in the shape of a wedge' (pl. 132). It should be made of boxwood or service-tree and, the civilized

Fauchard adds, can be covered in 'fine clean linen each time it is used'. He sensibly has it threaded with a tape to prevent loss down the throat.

It can be seen that the screw-manipulated mouth-openers changed little over the years. A simple but ingenious device of a different type is the pair of boxwood gags on pl. 131. These are cut in a very strong and deliberate spiral and, once having been inserted in a gap in the teeth, would have acted both as openers and gags.

Masticators

For those with no teeth at all or for those whose artificial teeth did not allow for eating, it was necessary to use a masticator. Masticatory force was first measured by Giovanni Alfonso Borelli (1608–79) and described in *De Motu Animalium* in 1685. Masticators took the form of forceps, the jaws being shaped like two or three pairs of molars. Since they were still being advertised by Weiss in the last quarter of the nineteenth century, presumably there was still a demand for them (pls. 98 and 133). The catalogue entry reads,

> *This instrument works on the principle of the action of the teeth. Meat and other food which requires masticating is easily and quickly prepared for the digestion by the aid of the Masticator. The food when ready for eating is first cut up into small pieces, which are then crushed with the Masticator into a pulp easily swallowed . . . To avoid chilling the food, dip the blades from time to time into hot water.*

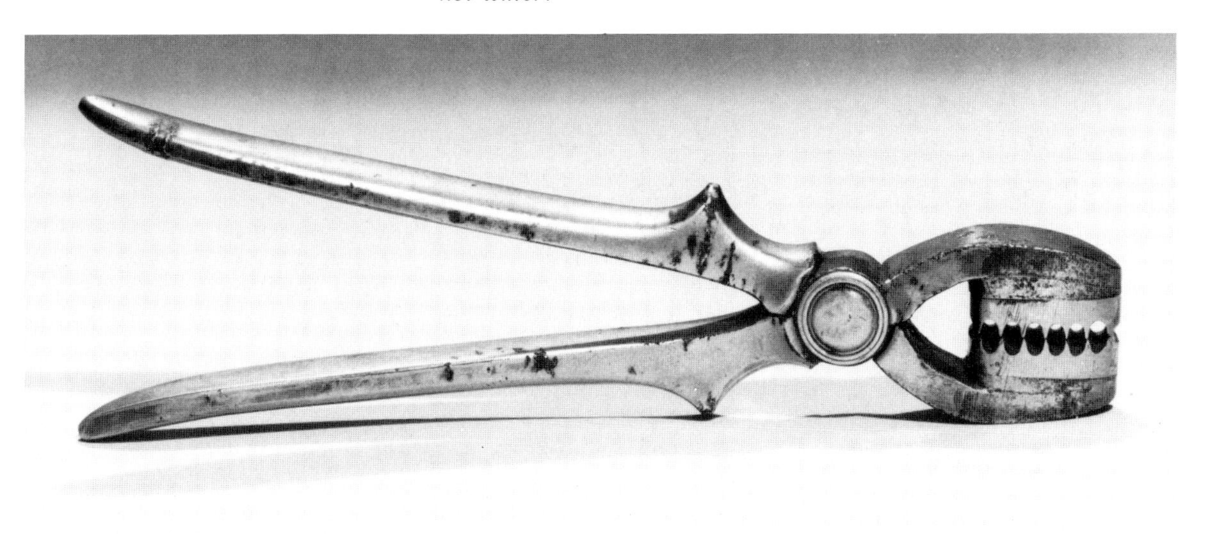

133 *Masticator, Weiss, c.1800, 16 cm. (Private Collection, the late Raymond Babtkis, New York)*

Chairs

Until Fauchard's day it was customary to place the patient's head between the operator's knees, and although royalty and the nobler patients would have been unlikely to accept this position, it will be seen that the history of dental chairs is relatively recent. Fauchard's recommendation was that the '. . . patient must be seated in an armchair which is steady and firm, suitable and comfortable, or with a soft pillow raised more or less according to the stature of the patient and particularly to that of the dentist'. The position was then described. 'In a word in an attitude which will be the least irksome as possible for the patient and at the same time the most convenient for the dentist.' Making the patient sit on the ground for an extraction is 'indecent and inconvenient'. Despite Fauchard's oft-quoted recommendation, it has to be noticed that the many over-reproduced pictures of extractions before his time all have the patient in a chair.

134 *Early dental chair, French, c.1810. On the right can be seen the slot into which the spittoon was fixed. (Private Collection, Dr Claude Rousseau, Paris)*

135 *Charitable dispensary chair, c.1880. (Museum of the British Dental Association, London)*

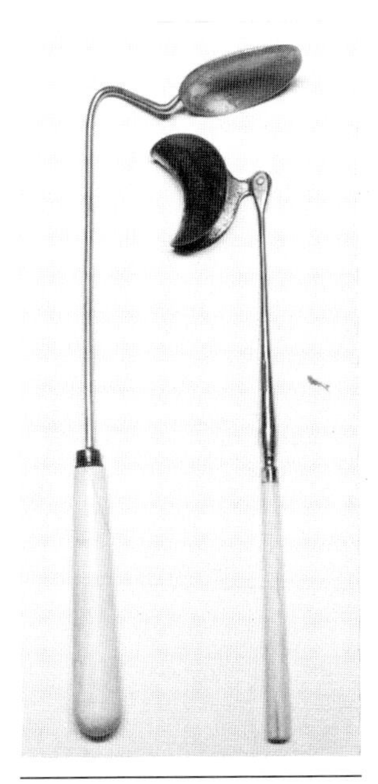

136 *Tongue-depressor, American, c.1860, and cheek-retractor, Chevalier, c.1860. The patient would hold one in each hand. (Private Collection, Dr Gary Lemen, Sacramento, Cal.)*

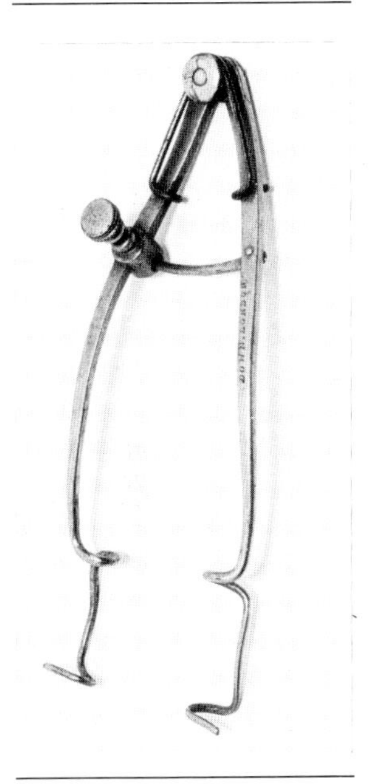

137 *Dental cotton-roll clamp, Down, c.1880. (Museum of the History of Science, Oxford)*

Describing a suitable chair is a far cry from designing one specially, and the known examples before the nineteenth century are rare. The Museum of the British Dental Association includes a curiously rustic example, said to have belonged to a sixteenth-century family of barbers who extracted teeth as a sideline. It has very crude tree-trunk arms and head-rest and might as easily be early nineteenth century from its design. On pl. 134 is a more elegant French chair of *c.* 1810.

James Snell (?1795–1850), in 1832, designed the first dental chair to be copied by others. It was an upholstered elbow chair with back adjusted by a ratchet and it incorporated a head-rest, a foot-rest, and a lamp, mirror and tray attached to the left-hand elbow. In America there was more impetus to improve the design and possibilities of the dental chair, and one prototype followed another. M.W. Hanchett produced a chair with head-rest in 1848 which allowed for a change in the height of the seat and back-rest. In 1849 the makers Jones, White & Co. of Philadelphia could advertise 'operating chairs of various patterns' having, two years previously, suggested head-rests adaptable to ordinary chairs for the travelling dentist. In 1859 they had chairs of black walnut, rosewood and mahogany and, after considerable dedicated perseverance and many designs later, they announced their first 'all metal' chair in 1871. It was supported on a quadruple pedestal onto which the chair screwed, revolving to adapt the height. The head-rest, back-rest and foot-rest were all adjustable, and the latter brought the feet off the ground, though not yet into the air.

In London the Owen chair, frequently made in walnut, was fashionable in the 1860s. It was adjusted by means of pulleys operated by a handle at the side. Special chairs for the charitable dental dispensaries, in which dentists gave their services free, were made during the last quarter of the nineteenth century (pl. 135). Very sturdy, almost indestructable in appearance, with a hard wooden seat and back, they were nevertheless adjustable and had a padded bolster head-rest.

In 1872 James Beall Morrison (1829–1917) introduced the first chair with compensating seat and back-rest, a substantial affair with decorative cast iron frame and a deep fringe round the seat. This chair provided the greatest vertical range so far achieved – 27 inches. A hydraulic chair was patented in 1851 but was not on the market until 1877. The following year, clients of S.S. White could have bought a pedal-lever chair which, by pumping, raised its height, or a swinging chair to tip one's patient backwards. In 1882 a design appeared which was curiously like a deck-chair, intended to be portable for the still-itinerant dentist. A plethora of new designs followed, bringing the dental chair to resemble many used today. Pedestal spittoon-stands, frequently very ornate and holding glass or metal spittoons, were used in the 1850s and '60s. The fountain spittoon, with turntable for instruments, appeared *c.* 1875, showing the increased wealth and stability of the practitioner.

7 Oral hygiene

Whiteness and evenness of teeth have always been admired, particularly in women. However, it is faintly surprising to find such a large number of early references to oral hygiene when one considers the number relating to rotting teeth and foetid breath. Presumably, as the first remedy for the latter two failed, one was all the more eager to report another possibility. The early treatments – for example, the sun-related snake-slough and earthworms – were probably rather more to relieve pain and inflammation than to stop the process of decay. Hippocrates suggested white wine, aniseed and myrrh for halitosis, with alum and nutgall for bleeding gums; Pliny, writing in the first century, advised the pervasive green frogs, burnt heel of ox, toads and worms; Diocles of Karystos, contemporary with Pliny, said, 'Every morning you should rub your gums and teeth with your bare fingers and with finely pulverised pennyroyal, inside and outside, and remove the adherent food particles.' In the Middle Ages superstition was added to some of the advice: when one saw the first swallow, one had to take running water into the mouth, rub the teeth with the middle finger of each hand, and one's teeth would be protected until the first swallow arrived the next year; in the Ukraine, one had to stand facing the moon, take some earth from under the right heel and rub the teeth with it. In Central Europe, rosemary leaves were chewed. Albucasis, the Arab surgeon of Cordoba (936–1013), was more realistic and advised a mouthwash of salt water. Guy de Chauliac (1300–68), who laid down many rules for the care and cleaning of the teeth, proposed alcohol, which was no doubt more popular.

By the late Middle Ages holy water was accepted without question as the best mouthwash, but the most easily obtainable, though probably less fashionable, was one's own urine, a remedy even recommended by Pierre Fauchard (1678–1761). 'There is a little difficulty at first in getting accustomed to it,' he said. It is used today, one understands, in the Far East.

Giovanni d'Arcoli (1412–84) was strong on hygiene, and he advised people to avoid indigestion and excessive movement after meals and anything sweet or likely to cause vomiting. The teeth were not to be used for crushing hard substances or to be set on edge, he said, and extremes of temperature in the mouth should be avoided. 'A diamond,' says Cervantes in *Don Quixote* (1605), 'is not as precious as a tooth.'

In 1682 Thomas Tryon (1634–1703), an early dietician, published *A Treatise of Meats*. This was the first work in English to include a section on the subject of teeth, pre-dating Charles Allen's work by three years. Tryon said that pain in the teeth was directly attributable to diet and hygiene and that applications of hot or cold liquids to unsound teeth were the direct cause of pain. He dismissed the mouthwashes and prescriptions which abounded as being to little purpose and suggested that physicians knew this to be so only too well. 'But when people come to them, they must give them something for their Money.' Much better, he thought, were fresh air and fresh water. The seventeenth-century recipe for whitening the teeth by wiping them clean with a wad of tobacco is unlikely to have found favour with him.

Equally bracing was a letter, written to his son in 1754, by Lord Chesterfield:

> *I hope you will take great care of your teeth, and that you will clean them well every morning with a sponge and tepid water with a few drops of arquebusade water dropped into it; besides washing your mouth carefully after every meal. I do insist upon your never using those sticks, or any other hard substance whatsoever, which always rub away the gums and destroy the varnish of the teeth.*

Christian Franz Paullini (1643–1712) wrote a book on oral hygiene which ran to five editions and was reprinted as late as 1847. The French dentist Robert Bunon (1702–48) published several works trying to interest the medical profession in dental matters and educating the public in preservation of the teeth. He established the theory that dental hygiene was necessary in infancy and that proper nourishment helped ensure good teeth. Fauchard had much good sense to impart on dental hygiene. He stressed the importance of thorough mastication and warned against sugar. 'It may be remarked that those who indulge in these seductive poisons [sweetmeats] are subject to disease of the teeth and lose them sooner than others.' Do not crack nuts or bite linen with the teeth, he warned, and remember that smoking and the contact of the pipe with the teeth is bad for them.

Patent mouthwashes and miracle tooth cleaners proliferated in the eighteenth century. A rather more scientific recipe containing hydrogen peroxide and lime-water appeared in 1808, but the mouths of the world had to wait until the end of the nineteenth century for antisepsis to overturn previously conceived notions of cleanliness.

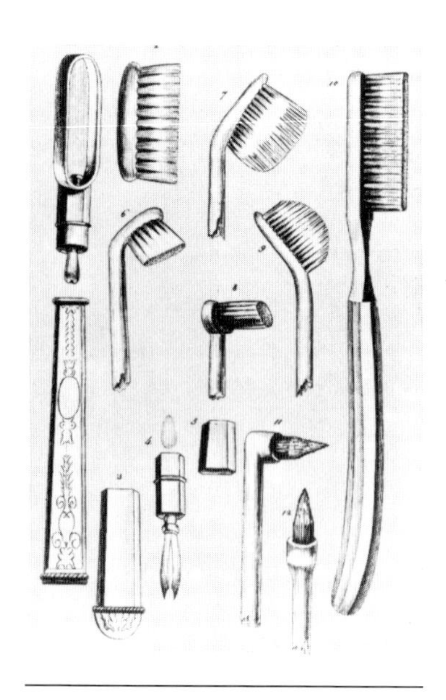

138 *Illustration from C.F. Maury's* Manuel de Dentiste *of 1820, showing a variety of tooth-brushes, including one reversible as, possibly, a pencil or, probably, a sponge-holder.*

Tooth-brushes

The first reference to a tooth-brush probably appears in the work of the Latin poet Ovid, in *Ars Amatoria*, when he advises a girl 'not to brush her teeth in the presence of her lover' – a far cry from 'would you care to use his tooth-brush?' As far as the modern world is concerned, tooth-brushes are thought to have been introduced to France from Spain *c.* 1590 by Antonio Perez. They were undoubtedly very crude bunches of horsehair or animal

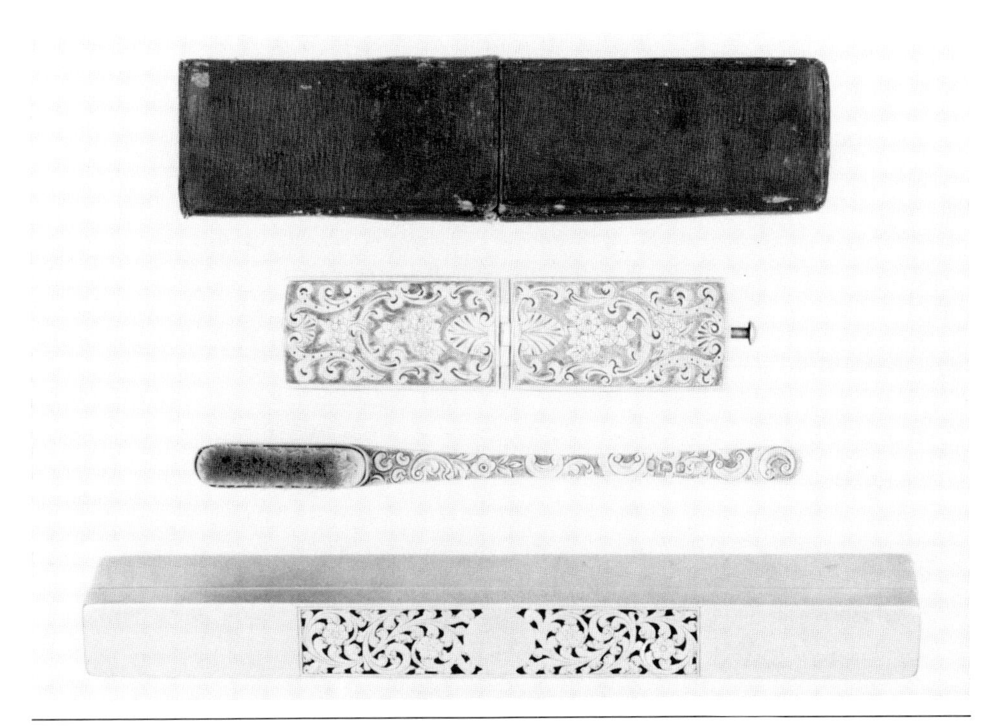

139 *Silver tooth-brush and tooth-powder box with red morocco case, 1802, Lockwood and Douglas. Silver tooth-brush case, 1834, T.W, 17 cm. (I. Freeman & Son, Simon Kaye Ltd, London)*

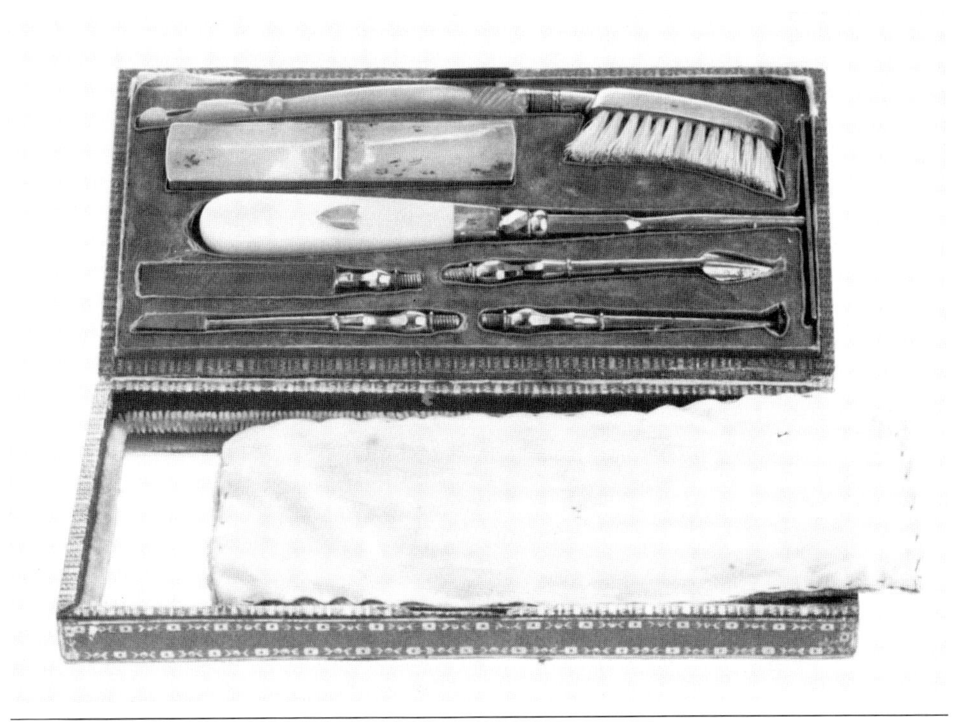

140 *Case of French items of dental toilet, silver and ivory, c.1819, including tooth-brush, powder-box, tongue-scraper and scalers. (University of Alberta Dental Museum, Edmonton)*

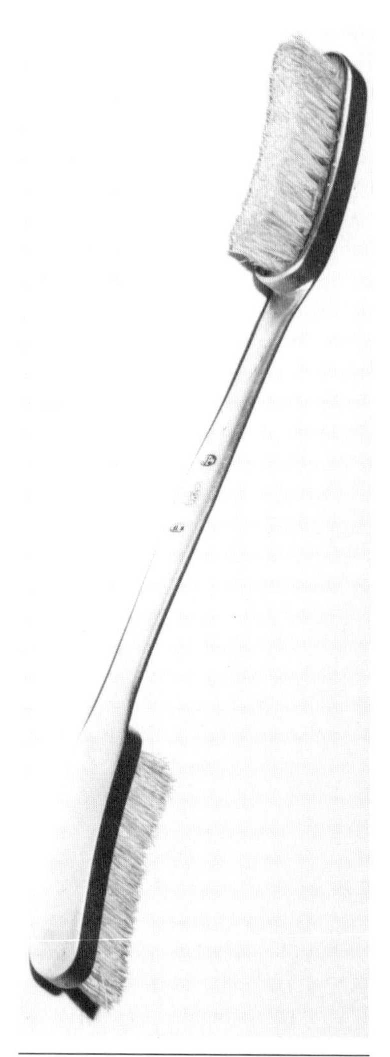

141 *Austrian silver double-ended tooth-brush, c.1820, 14cm. (E.P. Mallory & Son Ltd, Bath)*

bristle mounted in tubular handles in the manner of paint-brushes. They were not approved of by Fauchard, who preferred a sponge in tepid bran and water for cleaning the teeth. Bunon echoed his opinion in 1743. Sir Ralph Verney (1613–96) admitted that tooth-brushes were unknown to him; he had 'never seen any, nor know of what use they may be'. However, during the eighteenth century the tooth-brush, as we know it today, became more commonplace. In 1748 Edward Finch ordered six from the royal silversmith George Wickes; the novelist Tobias Smollett spoke of 'waiting women who . . . clean your toothbrushes'. Very handsome these tooth-brushes were, the handles silver or gilt, very occasionally gold, and varying in design with the importance of the owner. Sometimes provision was made for an interchangeable pad of bristles, which would be set either in wood or ivory. One silver-mounted tooth-brush at the Royal College of Surgeons in London has a circular brush of split cane. By the second half of the eighteenth century advertisements for tooth-brushes were appearing in the American press, often for the double-ended type (pl. 141), intended for both surfaces of the teeth.

There was much controversy in dental circles as to the methods of brushing, the length and closeness of the tufts and the relative hardness of the bristle. Thomas Beardmore (1740–85) recommended a tooth-brush similar to a paint-brush as giving 'a salutory stimulus'. In 1767 John Baker (1732–96), advertising his Albion-Essence and Anti-Scorbutic Dentifrice, gave excellent advice on dental hygiene: the brush was to be held vertically and, if it was not sufficient, then one must resort to the quill toothpick; children were to be trained early in daily tooth-brushing.

By 1800 the bristle brush had become the chief means of tooth cleaning. It was often more modest than its eighteenth-century forebear, with only the head being silver-mounted; the handle might be delicately turned ivory or mother-of-pearl. A tooth-brush was usually included in comprehensive travelling toilet cases: crested, monogrammed and substantial. Many small red morocco cases are found which include silver tooth-brush, tooth-powder box and tongue-scraper together (col. pl. XXI).

In 1843 Jean-Baptiste Gariot suggested that the choice of tooth-brush was a matter of the user's sex. 'Delicate females, who take a great care of their mouths, and whose teeth are easily cleaned, should use a soft brush. Men, who clean their teeth but seldom, require a hard one.' This suggests that tooth-brushing still had an *effete* image and accounts for the greater number of small and fragile brushes found. The all-ivory brush, resembling the modern type, was made during the second half of the nineteenth century; the handle is occasionally carved, engraved and inlaid. Pl. 139 shows a tooth-brush case, the lid perforated to keep the bristles dry.

Flossing silk was sold by S.S. White of Philadelphia from 1866.

Dentifrice, pots and boxes

142 *Group of tooth-paste pot-lids, each approx. 8 cm. (Private Collection, J. Saville Zamet, London)*

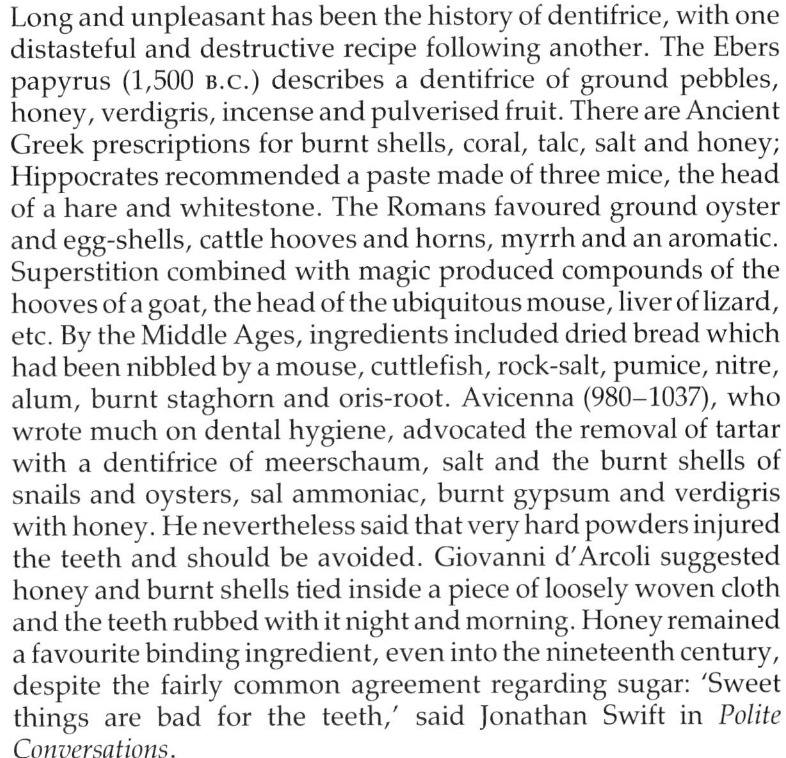

Long and unpleasant has been the history of dentifrice, with one distasteful and destructive recipe following another. The Ebers papyrus (1,500 B.C.) describes a dentifrice of ground pebbles, honey, verdigris, incense and pulverised fruit. There are Ancient Greek prescriptions for burnt shells, coral, talc, salt and honey; Hippocrates recommended a paste made of three mice, the head of a hare and whitestone. The Romans favoured ground oyster and egg-shells, cattle hooves and horns, myrrh and an aromatic. Superstition combined with magic produced compounds of the hooves of a goat, the head of the ubiquitous mouse, liver of lizard, etc. By the Middle Ages, ingredients included dried bread which had been nibbled by a mouse, cuttlefish, rock-salt, pumice, nitre, alum, burnt staghorn and oris-root. Avicenna (980–1037), who wrote much on dental hygiene, advocated the removal of tartar with a dentifrice of meerschaum, salt and the burnt shells of snails and oysters, sal ammoniac, burnt gypsum and verdigris with honey. He nevertheless said that very hard powders injured the teeth and should be avoided. Giovanni d'Arcoli suggested honey and burnt shells tied inside a piece of loosely woven cloth and the teeth rubbed with it night and morning. Honey remained a favourite binding ingredient, even into the nineteenth century, despite the fairly common agreement regarding sugar: 'Sweet things are bad for the teeth,' said Jonathan Swift in *Polite Conversations*.

Charles Allen, in 1687, gave as his recipe for a dentifrice so good that one would only need to use it once a week: magistery of pearls, powder of coral, dragon's blood and red rose water to bind. Fauchard gave several complicated formulae for tooth-paste and sold a great deal to his clients. He severely precluded from use any tooth-powders containing cuttlefish, powdered alabaster, brickdust, pumice or vitriol. In 1744 Thomas Greenough took the trouble to patent his Dental Tincture, which would not only clean and preserve the teeth but cure toothache; no doubt this is indicative of the immense jealousy and plagiarism that abounded. The patent lists no less than 26 ingredients, including several herbs and spices, spirit of laurel, alum, vinegar and henbane seeds; 'mix them all together and extract a tincture according to art'. The many acid cleaners used well up to this date accounted for a great deal of dental fatality.

By the second half of the eighteenth century one finds Thomas Beardmore inveighing against the quality of tooth-powders on sale. He conducted an interesting experiment with a single tooth held in a vice. By brushing it with a certain tooth-powder he found, after less than an hour, he had worn away the enamel on the part he had brushed. He then proceeded to repeat the experiment with other powders and found the 'effects varied only a little'.

Mr Paine, who opened a pharmacy in Rickmansworth in 1815, obviously tried to make his prescriptions very specific. For instance, the pyorrhoec Mrs Biggs was sent an astringent powder containing myrrh, cinchona bark and red coral; Miss Barker was sent an electuary which included oil of cloves and essence of bergamot to sweeten the breath. It was about this time that chalk and soap became commonly used ingredients for dentifrice.

Chewing mastic remained a very popular form of tooth cleaning from classical times to the twentieth century – shipments of resin from Chios in 1875 were estimated at 30,000 kilos – and powdered mastic was another common dentifrice component.

In the nineteenth century unbridled advertising of proprietary dentifrice promised wild hopes fulfilled, such as Hudson's Botanic Tooth-powder and Tincture, well known for its 'innocence', which would eradicate the scurvy and tartar from the gums; make the teeth, however yellow, beautifully white; fasten such as are loose; and if used constantly would entirely supersede the necessity of a dentist and 'preserve the teeth to the latest period of life'.

No known special containers for tooth-powders and pastes appeared before the end of the eighteenth century. Presumably the prescriptions were made up by the apothecary or dentist into a packet and transferred at home into whatever toilet container was most available and convenient. The simple remedies would have been mixed at home from the contents of the domestic medicine chest. Long silver tooth-powder boxes made their appearance *c.* 1780, often with two compartments, the lids hinged in the centre. The compartments may have been designed to accommodate two types of powder or, more possibly, to provide an opening the right size for the bristles of the brush. Tooth-pastes would have been transferred to one of the many glass-based, silver-topped toilet jars the tooth-cleaning classes would have owned.

In the early nineteenth century proprietary tooth-pastes were being sold in stoneware pots covered with oiled paper. With the enormous proliferation of such preparations in the 1840s, retailers began to realize the advantage of lids to the pots bearing, in underglazed print, not just their own names and those of their tooth-pastes, but eulogies bordering on fantasy. The more decorative examples had a design printed over the glaze, contributing to the variety of colour. In 1849 Pratt Ware started using a series of four underglaze transfers of different colours. Some of the simpler monochrome designs were merely stamped on, but there was a growing fashion for extravagant decoration, and that extravagance was only equalled by the floridity of the language used. Pictorial persuasion was incorporated, with flowers, fruit, oriental temples, bogus coats-of-arms and, most especially, royalty. Indeed, if Queen Victoria and her senior daughter-in-law had used all the tooth-pastes attributed to them, they might almost have had one for each day of the year. 'Beware of imitations' was a not infrequent message, and one the collector of pot-lids might take to heart as some reproductions have been made. Dating can be attempted by a study of typeface and, in some cases, by association of the elements in the design. One of the more rarely found pots is 'The Celebrated Alexandra Cherry Paste' which shows the Princess in her wedding headdress and veil, indicating it was first introduced after 10 March 1863 (col. pl. XVII and pl. 142).

Tongue-scrapers

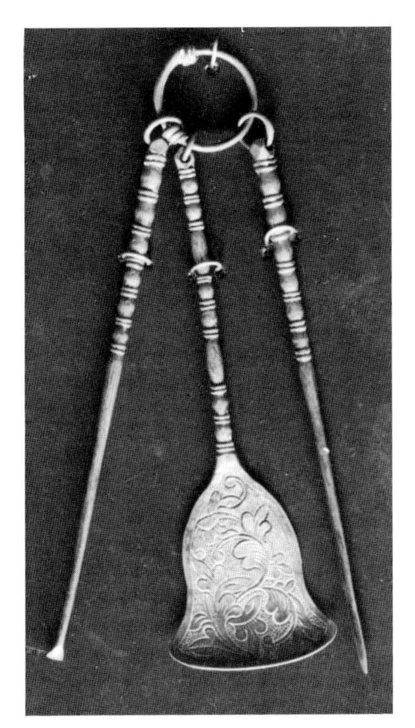

143 *Toothpick, earscoop and tongue-scraper on common ring, c.1680. (Museum of Dental History, Cologne)*

A set of Roman toilet items, each attached by a chain to a common ring and comprising a toothpick, an earscoop and a shovel-shaped tongue-scraper became a standard design well into the nineteenth century, suggesting that tongue-scraping was part of the toilet of the fastidious during the whole of the intervening time (pl. 143). Walter Ryff (1500–62) mentions a tongue-scraper and it is likely that his was of this shovel-shaped type. Modern research shows that the dorsum of the tongue is one of the main bases of micro-organisms in the mouth and is, therefore, a probable source of bacteria for dental plaque. Those tongue-scraping persons in the eighteenth century, who felt hospitality was lacking were the male guests able to walk away from the table, no doubt felt the benefit of this item of the toilet in the morning. An anonymous nineteenth-century writer was led to a type of tongue-scraping fortune-telling:

> *A furred tongue is very common in the case of people who smoke much. When the fur is white, thickish and tolerably uniform and moist, it usually indicates an open, active state of the fever, in which, though the symptoms may possibly be violent, there is little danger of any lurking mischief or of a malignant tendency. A yellowish hue of the fur is commonly indicative of disordered liver. A brown or black tongue is a bad sign usually indicating a low state of the system and a general condition of depression.*

The simplest tongue-scrapers were thin, flexible strips of silver, silver-gilt or gold, tortoiseshell or ivory, with two finials, and designed to be bent into a bow between thumb and index finger; these sometimes formed part of a set, with tooth-brush and powder-box (see above). Others were already bent into a half-hoop between one or two handles; or as widely-spaced sugar-tongs; or as a hoe, a blade set at right angles to the, usually ivory, handle, as an infant's 'pusher'. All these types appeared from *c.* 1770 onwards, the longest surviving being a half-hoop of tortoiseshell on an ivory handle which persisted to the end of the nineteenth century.

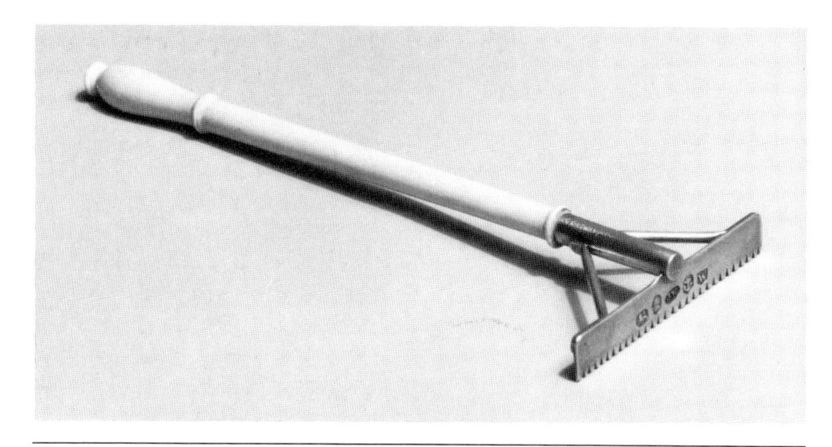

144 *Rare silver tongue-scraper, 1820, Joseph Willmore, with gently serrated blade and ivory handle, 8 cm. (I. Freeman & Son, Simon Kaye Ltd, London)*

145 *Silver-gilt tongue-depressor and tongue-scraper, Augsburg, c.1615, 16 cm. (Kunstgewerbemuseum, West Berlin)*

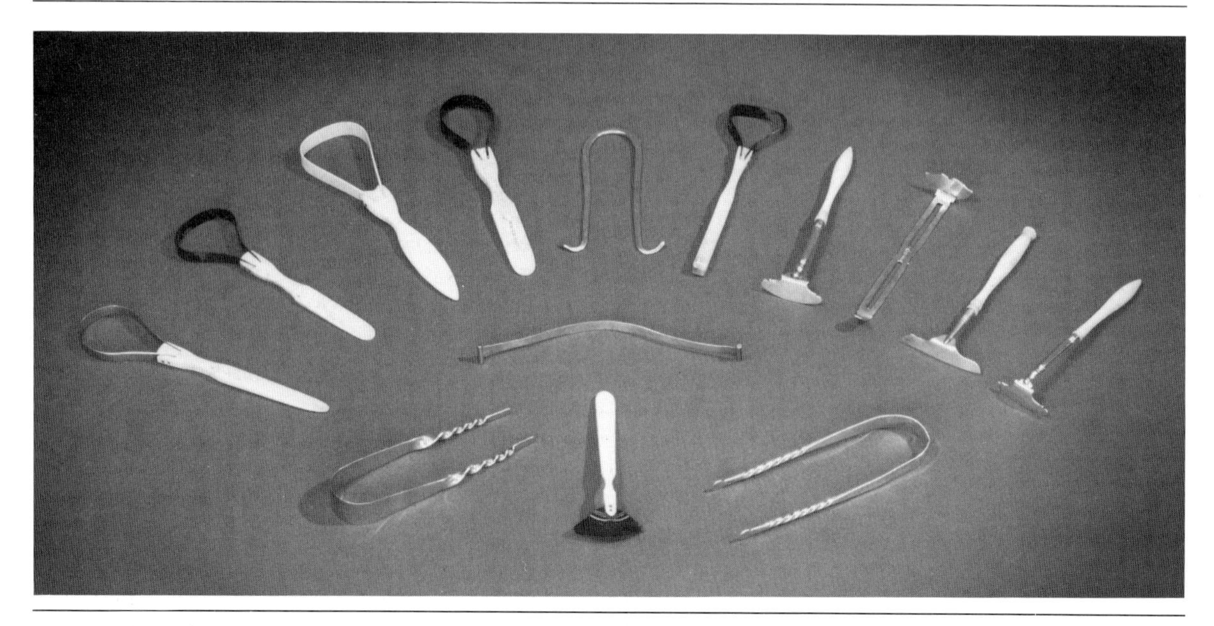

146 *A variety of tongue-scrapers in silver, ivory and tortoiseshell, c.1780–1870. (Private Collection, London)*

The present writer has been quite unable to discover any literary references to the tongue-scraper or its use, which is surprising given the number found.

Toothpicks and their cases

It is a reasonable assumption that primitive man picked his teeth, probably with thorns or slivers of wood and bone. Toothpicks manufactured for the purpose have been excavated from graves at Ur, dating from *c.* 500 B.C., and from other graves of a similar age and type. Most of them formed part of a set of metal utensils comprising a toothpick, tongue-scraper and earpick on a common ring (see above). Sets very like these were made well into the nineteenth century. The Talmud recommended a splinter of wood or a reed as a toothpick, which should be carried in the mouth between meals. The Ancient Greeks liked toothpicks made of wood from the mastic tree, quills, feathers and straws. These were used not just for the removal of impacted food between the teeth but as items of oral hygiene, part of the habit of (relative) cleanliness of a cultivated race. The same could be said of the Romans. Nero was known to have a silver toothpick whereas Pliny advised porcupine quill. There were special Roman slaves known as 'mastiche' who were required to clean the teeth with mastic sticks, probably pounded and frayed at one end. Omar Khayyam had a golden toothpick and the humbler Erasmus a quill from a chicken or a cockerel. Mohammed told his followers that a prayer preceded by use of the toothpick was worth 75 ordinary prayers.

In the Middle Ages the toothpick was a frequent subject of comment; a medieval book on table etiquette condemns picking the teeth with a knife, presumably a sufficiently common practice for notice. Giovanni d'Arcoli (1412–84) advises the use of a toothpick after meals, selecting a wood of an astringent nature, such as cypress, aloes, pine, rosemary or juniper. Fauchard warned against metal toothpicks, pins or the point of a knife as the hardness is harmful. He suggested a half-round toothpick from the root of marshmallow or lucerne, or a quill.

In 1576 it was said that Henry of Navarre spent 20 sous a month on toothpicks. Ben Johnson said, in *The Devil is an Ass*,

> *What diseases and putrefactions in the gummes are bred*
> *By those [toothpicks] are made of adultrate and false wood?*

In *The Winter's Tale* possession of a toothpick would appear to indicate nobility:

> *He seems to be more noble in being fantastical;*
> *A great man, I'll warrant:*
> *I know by the picking on's teeth.*

147 *Ivory toothpick case and toothpicks folding into fretted guard, c.1815. (Museum of Dental History, Cologne)*

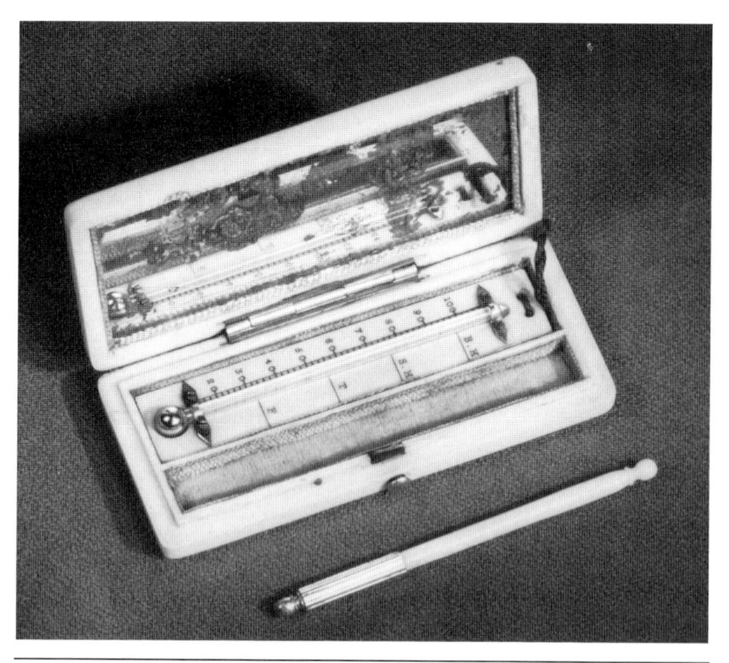

148 *Toothpick case of George IV, as pl. 149 (top left), but showing ivory toothpick with gold screw cap and thermometer by Alexander of Exeter, 1820, 9cm. (M. Ekstein Ltd, London)*

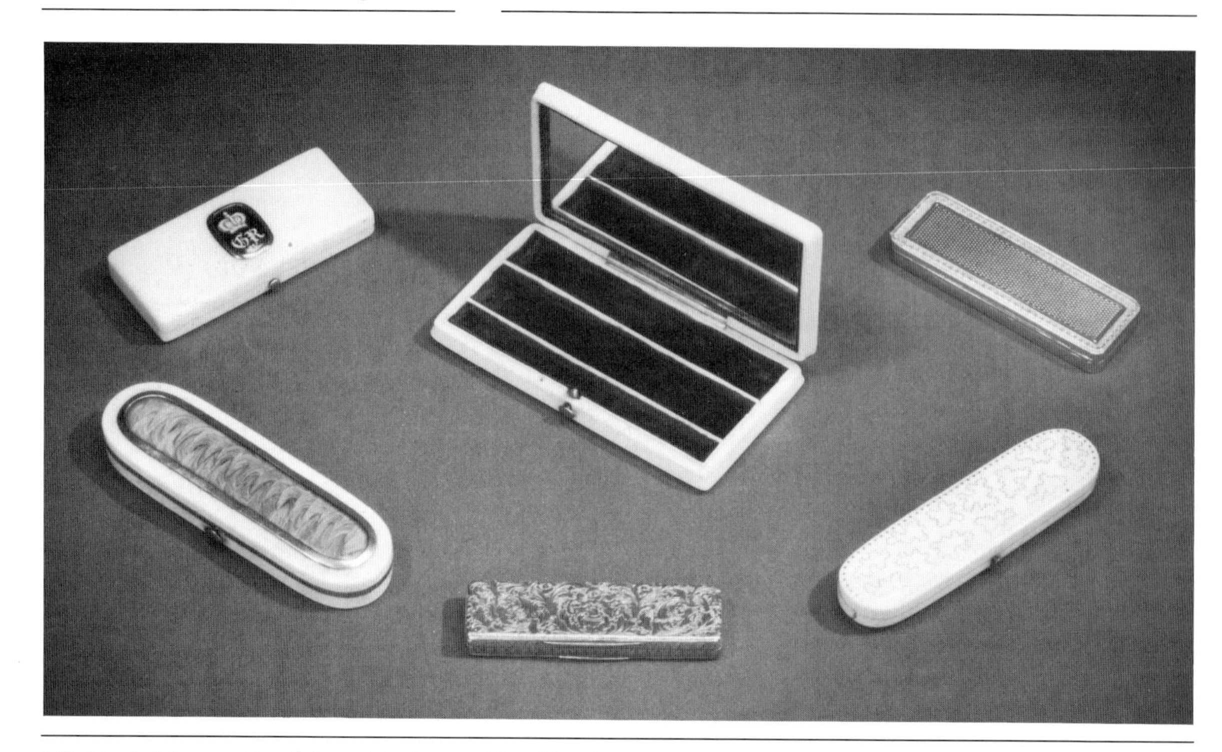

149 *Toothpick cases. Top, left to right: ivory with gold and enamel cypher of George IV, c.1820; ivory with three compartments, c.1810; French two-colour gold, c.1800. Bottom, left to right: gold-mounted ivory with inset panel of plaited hair, c.1810; gold, c.1810; ivory and gold picqué, c.1820. (M. Ekstein Ltd, London)*

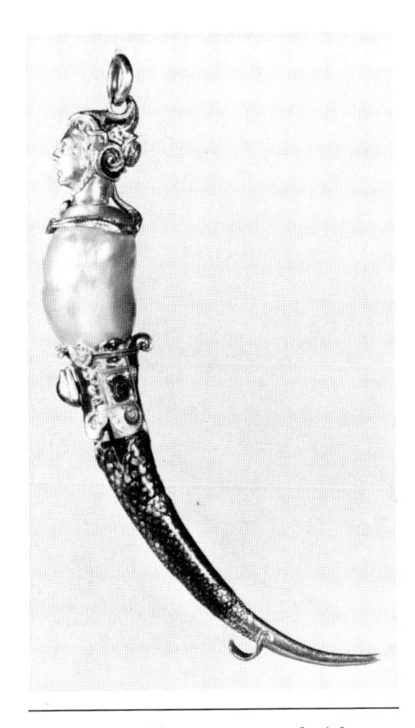

150 *Late 16th-century toothpick, probably Spanish, gold with green enamelled tail, baroque pearl and rubies, 15 cm. (British Museum, Waddesden Bequest, London)*

In Spain women carried toothpicks for self-defence. Flamenco dancers often kept theirs in their mouths while dancing, where it was thought they enhanced their grace. In France, *c.* 1600, toothpicks were served with dessert, stuck into the fruit, and during the following century they became an item of fashion and were seen to indicate that a bountiful and fleshy meal had been consumed, even if that were not the case. By 1797 Goethe could say of the French, 'During meals, their postulates are so exact and circumstantial that even the toothpicks are never forgotten.' It will be seen, then, that use of the toothpick had acquired a social purpose over and above the actual hygienic object, much as the gestures which accompany cigarette smoking have today. As toothpicks became personal and not expendable, so some were made of gold, silver and ivory, decorated and refined with prettily-turned finials; others were made – in greater quantity – of horn or bone. Once they had become necessary about the person they acquired a case for safe-keeping in the pocket or reticule. In the last half of the eighteenth century and in the nineteenth these long, thin, rectangular or elliptical cases, usually with a mirror on the inside of the lid, were made in every type of highly decorative material, often velvet lined. As an item of fashion they reflected the owner's taste and position, from plainer ivory and inlaid wooden examples to tortoiseshell, silver and gold, enamelled and jewel-set (pls. 148, 149 and 151).

In the nineteenth century more humdrum toothpicks, made of bone or ivory, were made to fold into a case like a penknife (pl. 147). Their use only declined as the genteel bourgeois behaviour of the end of the century strengthened.

151 *Ivory toothpick case, carved shipping scene within a gold-framed glass panel, c.1795, 8.8 cm, and containing a gold toothpick. (Phillips Ltd, London)*

Directory of instrument makers

Abbreviations used are as follows:

C.	Cutler
CH.	Chemist
D.	Druggist
D.I.M.	Dental instrument maker
M.I.M.	Mathematical instrument maker
OC.	Oculist
OP.	Optician
S.I.M.	Surgical instrument maker
T.M.	Truss maker
V.I.M.	Veterinary instrument maker

From the middle of the eighteenth century onwards, instruments and their cases appeared stamped with the maker's name. It is therefore desirable, as a dating principle, to have as much detailed information as possible about these makers. The lists which follow are largely those which appeared in *Antique Medical Instruments*, the cutlers and surgical instrument makers having included dental pieces in their work, as can be seen from the embellishments on their trade cards. Those names on the previous lists which applied solely to opticians, veterinary instrument makers, truss makers and others clearly not connected with dentistry have not been repeated. However, it will be seen that the lists have been expanded with the addition of many new names and much new material. I am grateful, once again, to all the county librarians whose records have further contributed towards compiling this list and to Dr Gary Lemen who has shared with me his list of American instrument makers.

United Kingdom instrument makers

Aitken	
1820	Established. Henry A. Aitken
1858	Known to have made percussion hammer introduced by Henry Vernon of the Great Northern Hospital
1861–76	Henry Aitken, 16 Railway Street, York
1886	Henry Aitken & Co.
1910	Henry Aitken & Co., 13 Micklegate (later renumbered 29), York
Alexander & Fowler	see Ewing
Allcard & Edgill	
1845–9	Allcard & Edgill, 6 Union Lane, Sheffield
1852	Allcard & Co., 6 Union Lane, Sheffield
Allen & Hanbury	
1715	Established London, E.2 as Bevan
1774	Samuel Mildred
1795	Mildred & Allen, 2 Plough Court
1797	Surgical instruments first mentioned in catalogue
1856	Allen & Hanbury
c. 1870	Moved to Wigmore Street
1878–9	Manufacture of instruments at Bethnal Green factory
c. 1972	Taken over by Escham Bros. & Walsh
Amesbury	
1843	Joseph Amesbury, 8 Berners Street, London

Archer & Co.	
(known 1817)	Strand, London
Armitage	
1843	John Armitage, 2 Hampton Street, Walworth Road, London
Arnold	(Post Office Directory 1883: 'by appointment to St Bartholomew's Hospital. Manufacturers of surgical instruments and general cutlery, trusses, elastic stockings, belts, bandages and bougies, catheters, artificial legs, arms, hands, eyes, etc. Veterinary instrument maker by appointment to the Royal Veterinary College, St Pancras'.)
1819	J. & S. Arnold (CH. and D.), 59 Barbican, London
1829	James Arnold (S.I.M.) } 35 West Smithfield, London
1837	James & John Arnold (S.I.M.) } 35 West Smithfield, London
1845	James Arnold (S.I.M.) } 35 West Smithfield, London
1857	James Arnold & Son (S.I.M.) } 35 West Smithfield, London
1866	Arnold & Sons (S.I.M.) } 35 West Smithfield, London
1928	Incorporated into John Bell & Croyden, 50–52 Wigmore Street, London
Ash	
1814	Ash & Son, Silversmith and Jeweller, 64 St James's Street, London
1835	C. Ash, 9 Broad Street, Golden Square, London
1840	C. Ash, 9 Broad Street, Golden Square. Manufacturers of mineral teeth.
1844	C. Ash & Sons, 9 Broad Street, Golden Square. Manufacturers of mineral teeth.
1846	C. Ash & Sons, 8 & 9 Broad Street, Golden Square. Manufacturers of mineral teeth.
1859	Claudius Ash & Sons, 6, 7, 8 & 9 Broad Street, Golden Square. Manufacturers of mineral teeth and dental material.
1875	C. Ash (D.I.M.), Factory in Kentish Town, London. Now Amalgamated Dental Co. Ltd, 26 Broadwick Street, London W.1
Atlee	
1847	T. Atlee & Co. (ether inhaler in Wellcome Collection)
Auchinleck	
1776	Gilbert Auchinleck (C.), Nether-bow, Edinburgh
Baker	
1765	Established
1894	Baker, 243 High Holborn, London
Ballard	
1843	Henry Ballard, 42 St John's Square, London
Barker	
1797	Geo. Barker (C.), Fargate, Sheffield
1817	Geo. Barker (C.), Hawley Croft, Sheffield
Barth	
19th century	Barth (D.I.M.)
Bartrop	
1843	Henry Bartrop, 33 Crawford Street, London
Battensby	
1821	John Battensby (C. and S.I.M.), Groat Market, Newcastle
1827	John Battensby (C., S.I.M. and T.M.), 15 Groat Market, Newcastle
1829	John Battensby (C., S.I.M. and T.M.), Middle Street, Newcastle
	No trace by 1883

Bayne	
1823	Charles Bayne (C.), High Street, Oxford
1846	Bayne & Chadwell (C.), 2 Grove Street, Oxford
1854	Bayne & Chadwell (C.), 112 High Street, Oxford
1867	Mrs Chadwell (C.), 112 High Street, Oxford
1872	Mrs Chadwell (C.), 30½ Cornmarket, Oxford
1880	Chadwell & Long (C. and S.I.M.), 30½ Cornmarket, Oxford
1884	Wemborn (late Chadwell) (C. and S.I.M.), 30½ Cornmarket, Oxford In business until 1912
Beauchamp	
c. 1820	Instruments at Royal College of Surgeons, London
Becker	
1802	Christian Becker (S.I.M.)
1856	Widow continued business until 1887, then became Mossinger
Bell (1)	
1798	Established (CH. and D.) Now John Bell & Croyden. See Arnold
Bell (2)	
1839	Thos. Bell (C.), 15 Cornmarket, Belfast
1850	Thos. Bell (C. and S.I.M.), 15 Cornmarket, Belfast Last mentioned 1880
Bernadoue (or variously Bernardeau)	
c. 1736	James Bernadoue, Russell Court, Drury Lane, London No trace by 1744
Best	
c. 1690	John Best
1750	John Best, Lombard Street, London. (Made Smellie's forceps, *c.* 1750. Trade card which showed D.I. known to date from 1690–1760.) No trace by 1843
Bickerstaff	
1678–*c.* 1700	Thos. Bickerstaff (C.), Princes Street, Drury Lane, London
Bigg	
1751	Established. Henry Bigg
1832–4	Sheldrake & Bigg, 29 Leicester Square, London
1842	Henry Bigg, 9 St Thomas's Street, Borough, London
1852	Bigg, St Thomas's Street, Southwark, London
1858	Heather Bigg, 29 Leicester Square, London
1858–9	Bigg & Millikin, 8 St Thomas's Street, London. (Apparently took over the Laundy business)
Blackwell	
1817	J. Blackwell
1826	Charles Blackwell, 3 Bedford Court, London
1843	William Blackwell, 3 Bedford Court, Covent Garden, London
Blair	
c. 1735	Thomas Blair (C.), Edinburgh
Louis Blaise & Co.	see Savigny

Blyde	
1841	Established. John Blyde Ltd, London see Down
Bodker	
1765	Henry Bodker (S.I.M.), Poultry, London
1768	Richard James Bodker (S.I.M.), Poultry, London
1770	Jane & Richard Bodker (S.I.M.), Poultry, London
1774	Richard Bodker (S.I.M.), Poultry, London
1777	Richard Bodker (S.I.M.), 2 Colman Street, London
Bond	Arthur Bond, Euston Road, London. Instrument at Royal College of Surgeons, London.
Boog	
1748	Robert Boog
1779	Andrew Boog, College Street, Edinburgh
1784	Alexander Boog
1800	Andrew & Alexander Boog, Netherbow, Edinburgh
1820–6	Andrew & Alexander Boog, 13 High Street, Edinburgh
1830	Thomas Boog (C. and S.I.M.), 105 High Street, Edinburgh No trace after 1859
Borthwick	
Early 19th century	B. Borthwick, College Street, Edinburgh
Borwick	
1791	Roger Borwick (C.), Sheffield
1817	Roger Borwick (C.), Bailey Lane, Sheffield
1825	Samuel Borwick (C.), Bailey Lane, Sheffield No trace after 1860
Botschan	
19th century	Joseph Botschan, 35 Worship Street, Finsbury, London
Bourne & Taylor	
Mid 19th century	Bourne & Taylor
Boyce	
1751–60	Samuel Boyce, Maiden Lane, London
Brace	
Early 19th century	Salisbury
Bradford	
Mid 19th century	136 Minories, London
Brady	
1855	Established as Henry Bowman Brady (CH.)
1857	Henry Bowman Brady (CH.), 40 Mosley Street, Newcastle
1869	Henry Bowman Brady (CH.), 29 Mosley Street, Newcastle
1879	Brady & Martin, 29 Mosley Street, Newcastle
1883	Brady & Martin (CH. and S.I.M.), 29 Mosley Street, Newcastle
Brailsford	
Early 18th century	John Brailsford, St Martin's Court, London
Brand	
Early 19th century	Brand

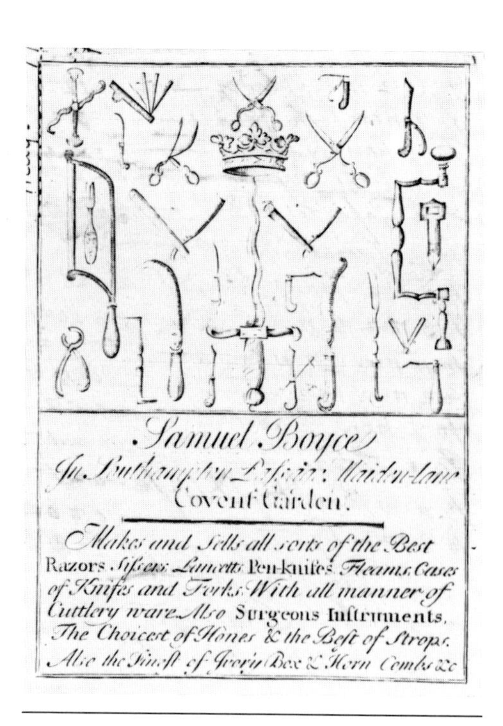

152 *Trade card. (British Museum, Ambrose Heal Collection, London)*

153 *Trade card. (British Museum, Ambrose Heal Collection, London)*

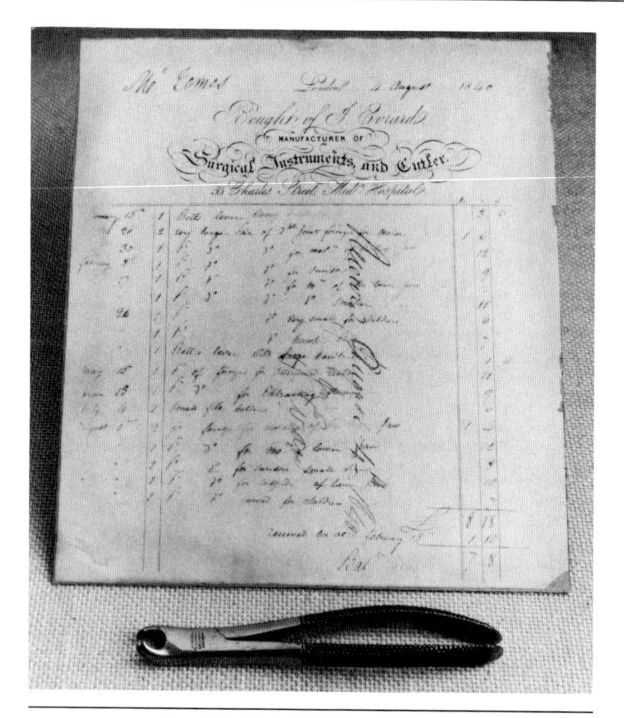
Mr Tomes London 4 August 1840

Bought of J. Evrard

Manufacturer of

Surgical Instruments, and Cutler.

154 *A bill from Evrard to Tomes, dated 4 August 1840, and below, one of the forceps he made for Tomes, possibly one of those mentioned in the bill. (Museum of the British Dental Association, London)*

155 *Trade card. (British Museum, Ambrose Heal Collection, London)*

Brennand	
1843	Pearson Brennand, 217 High Holborn, London
Brereton	
1830–70	Brereton
Brown (1)	
1822	John Brown, Wireworker, 2 Whitechapel Road, London
1852	John Brown (c.), 2 Townsend Road, London
1858	John Brown (c.), 17 Connaught Terrace, London
	No trace after 1861
Brown (2)	
1847	John Brown & Son (s.i.m. and c.), 68 Grey Street, Newcastle upon Tyne
1861	J. Brown (s.i.m.), 10 Upper Buxton Street, Newcastle upon Tyne
1863	Brown & Son (s.i.m.), 98 Grey Street, Newcastle upon Tyne
1865	Brown & Son (s.i.m.), 93 Grey Street, Newcastle upon Tyne
1870	Brown & Son (s.i.m.), 98 Grey Street, Newcastle upon Tyne
1875	J. Brown & Son (s.i.m.), 98 Grey Street, Newcastle upon Tyne
1877	No entry
Bruce	
1832–3	Henry Bruce (c. and s.i.m.), 66 Southbridge, Edinburgh
Bullen	
1858	Established. C.S. Bullen (s.i.m.), 89 Mount Pleasant, Liverpool
Butler	
c. 1681	Established. George Butler, Sheffield
c. 1810	George and James Butler (c.), 4 Trinity Street, Sheffield
1865	George and James Butler (c.), 105 Eyre Street, Sheffield
Capron	
19th century	Capron. Hernia bistoury found
Cargill	
1739	John Cargill, Lombard Street, London
1773	Peter Cargill, Lombard Street, London
1789	Peter Cargill (c.), Lombard Street, London
Carr	
1847	George Carr (c.), 25 Nun Street, Newcastle upon Tyne
	No entry after 1853
Carsberg	
1798	Established. Carsberg, 38 Great Windmill Street, London
Cartwright	
c. 1760–80	Paston Cartwright, Lombard Street, London
Chadwell	see Bayne
Chandler	
Late 18th century	Chandler
Charlwood	
1770	Yeeling Charlwood (c.), Russell Court, London. 'Successor to the late Mr Gordon, *c.* 1760'
	see Underwood

Chasson	
c. 1770	J. Chasson (C. and S.I.M.), Newgate Street, London
1789	Mary Chasson (C.), 68 Newgate Street, London
Clark	
1818	G. Clark (C.), 5 York Buildings, Bath
1828	G. Clark (C.), 16 Vineyards, Bath
1832	G. Clark (C.), 3 Bond Street Buildings, Bath
	No trace after 1832
Clarke	
c. 1861	J. Clarke, 225 Piccadilly, London
Cluley	
1813	Francis Cluley (S.I.M.), Westbar Green, Sheffield
1825	Francis Cluley (S.I.M.), 4 Surrey Street, Sheffield
	No trace after 1837
Cole	
c. 1760	Henry Cole, Strand, London
Collins (1)	
19th century	D. Collins & Son (D.I.M.)
Collins (2)	
c. 1840	Collins
Cooke	
1670	John Cooke
c. 1686	George Cooke
1698	George Cooke, Old Lombard Street, London
Coombes	
Before 1730	John Coombes, Cross Inn, Oxford
Corbett	
1820	Daniel Corbett, 34 Patrick Street, Cork
1844	Daniel Corbett, 1 Queen Street, Cork. Joseph Corbett, 11 Morrisson's Island, Cork
1856	Daniel Corbett, 17 South Mall, Cork. Joseph Corbett, 11 Morrisson's Quay, Cork
1893	Joseph Corbett, 11 Morrisson's Island, Cork. William Cochrane Corbett, 3 South Mall, Cork
	This family of dentists would appear to have been instrument makers as well, as there were no known cutlers of that name in Cork.
Corcoran	
Late 19th century	Corcoran, Dublin?
Corneck	
1768	James Corneck (C.), Cheapside, London
Courtney	
c. 1710	Richard Courtney, Hatton Gardens, London
Cox	see Savigny and Krohne & Seseman
Coxeter	
1836	Established
1843	J. Coxeter & Co., 23 Grafton Street, London
1863	J. Coxeter

1870	J. Coxeter & Son
1894	James Coxeter & Son, 4 & 6 Grafton Street, London
1923	Coxeter Ltd, London
Craddock	
1843	Geo. Craddock, 35 Leicester Square, London
Crawford	
1817	W. Crawford, 68 Charles Street, London
Crook	
c. 1750	John Crook, Great Turnstile, Holborn, London
Crookes	
1826	John Crookes (c.), Fetter Lane, London
Crooks	
1787	John Crooks, Razor Maker, Great Turnpike, Holborn, London
1826	John Crooks, 1 Back Church Lane, Whitechapel
Cruickshank	
1765	Cruickshank, London (made Pott's fistula knife)
Dadley	
1775	Thomas Dadley (c.), Bridge Street, Stratford-upon-Avon
1804	William Dadley (c.), Bridge Street, Stratford-upon-Avon
1846	John & Richard Dadley (c.), Bridge Street, Stratford-upon-Avon
Dalton	
1852	Dalton, 85 Quadrant, London
Davies	
Late 18th century	Davies (S.I.M.)
Dick	
1865	James Dick (c. and bandage maker), 28 St Enoch Wynd, Glasgow
1866	James Dick (c. and bandage maker), 92 Glassford Street, Glasgow
1871	James Dick (c. and bandage maker), 45 Renfield Street, Glasgow
1872	James Dick (c., bandage and artificial limbs maker), 45 Renfield Street, Glasgow
1874	James Dick (S.I.M.), 45 Renfield Street, Glasgow
1896	James Dick (S.I.M.), 107 West George Street, Glasgow
1921	Went out of business
Dixon	
1843	William Dixon, 2 Tonbridge Street, New Road, London
Donnell	
Mid 19th century	J.E. Donnell, 384 Strand, London
Down	
1874	Down Bros Ltd
1879	Millikin & Down, St Thomas Street, Borough, London
1894	Down Bros, 5–7 St Thomas Street, Borough, London
	Now Down Surgical Ltd, Mitcham, Surrey, incorporating Mayer & Phelps, Blyde & Gray
Druce	
Early 19th century	H. Druce
Dungworth	
1861	John Dungworth, 146 Broomhall Street, Sheffield

Dunsford	
c. 1780–1800	Dunsford
Durroch	
1788	Wm. F. Durroch established
1847	Wm. F. Durroch (S.I.M.), 2 New Street, London
1860	Wm. F. Durroch (S.I.M.), 28 St Thomas's Street, London
1862	Wm. F. Durroch (S.I.M.), 3 St Thomas's Street, London
	No trace after 1869. See Smith
Dyer	
1823	Wm. Dyer (C.), Old Town Street, Plymouth
1830	Wm. Dyer (C. and S.I.M.), 5 Old Town Street, Plymouth
1844	Daniel Dyer (C. and S.I.M.), 5 Old Town Street, Plymouth
1857	Daniel Dyer (C. and S.I.M.), 59 Old Town Street, Plymouth
1864	Alfred Dyer, (C. and S.I.M.), 59 Old Town Street, Plymouth
1873	Alfred Dyer, (C. and S.I.M.), 99 Old Town Street, Plymouth
1890	Daniel Dyer, 8 Whimpole Street, Plymouth and 13 Marlborough Street, Devonport
	In business until 1923
Eagland	
1826	Charles Eagland, 10 Poland Street, London
Einsle	
1843	Edward Einsle, 46 St Martin's Lane, London
Elam	
1843	Alfred Elam & Bros, 403 Oxford Street, London
Elliott	
1824	John Elliott (C. and S.I.M.), Spring Gardens, Clitheroe
1848	John Elliott (C. and S.I.M.), Church Brow, Clitheroe
1851	Robt. Elliott (S.I.M.), Church Brow, Clitheroe
1855	Robt. Elliott (S.I.M.), Waddington Lane, Clitheroe
	No trace after 1858
Ellis	
1843	Wm. Ellis, 3 Thanet Place, London
Ernst	
1863	Gustav Ernst, 19 Calthorpe Street, London
1869	Gustav Ernst, 80 Charlotte Street, London
Evans (1)	
1676	John Evans, Blacksmith
1783	David Evans (S.I.M.), 10 Old Change, London
1803	David Evans & Co. (S.I.M.), 10 Old Change, London
1811	John Evans & Co. (S.I.M.), 10 Old Change, London
1854	John Evans & Co. (S.I.M.), 10 Old Change, and 12 Old Fish Street, London
1855	John Evans & Co. (S.I.M.), 12 Old Fish Street, London
1867	Evans & Stevens (S.I.M.), 6 Dowgate Hill and 31 Stanford Street, London
1874	Evans & Wormall (S.I.M.), 31 Stanford Street, London
	'By Appt. to Army, Navy, and Indian Government'.
	Principal suppliers to the Navy. *c.* 1812 – instruments marked with crown
Evans (2)	
Late 18th century	Evans, Oswestry

Everill	see Savigny
Evrard	Jean-Marie Evrard (1808–82), born in Toulouse, became chief workman for Charrière in Paris before going to London
1837	Jean Evrard, 35 Charles Street, Middlesex Hospital, London
1865	Jean Evrard (principally D.I.M.), 34 Berners Street, London
Ewing	
Mid 19th century	Ewing, Liverpool
Fannin	
1829	Established. Fannin, 41 Grafton Street, Dublin
	Still in business
Ferguson	
1822	Daniel Ferguson (S.I.M.), 14 Castle Street, London
1826	Daniel Ferguson (S.I.M.), 44 West Smithfield Street, London
1828	Daniel Ferguson, (S.I.M.), 21 Giltspur Street, London
1851	Ferguson & Son, 21 Giltspur Street, London
1858	John Ferguson & Co., 21 Giltspur Street, London
	No trace after 1869
Ferris	
c. 1770	Established
1775	Till Adams
1783	Till Adams (D.), Union Street, Bristol
1787	Till Adams, Ann, Apothecaries, Union Street, Bristol
1812	Fry & Gibbs (D.), 3 Union Street, Bristol
1820	Fry Gibbs & Ferris (D.), 4 Union Street, Bristol
1826	Fry Gibbs & Ferris (D. and CH.), 4 Union Street, Bristol
1834	Ferris Brown & Capper (D. and CH.), 25 Union Street, Bristol and 1 Mall, Clifton
1837	Ferris Brown & Score (D. and CH.), 25 Union Street, Bristol and 1 Mall, Clifton
1842	Ferris & Score (D. and CH.), 4–5 Union Street, Bristol
1856	Ferris, Townsend, Lamotte & Bourne (D. and CH.), 4–5 Union Street, Bristol
1865	Ferris, Townsend, Bourne & Townsend (D. and CH.), 4–5 Union Street, Bristol
1869	Ferris, Bourne & Townsend (D. and CH.), 4–5 Union Street, Bristol
1893	Ferris & Co.
	Still in Business
Figgett	
1843	J.L. Figgett, 29 Trafalgar Street, Walworth
Fisher	
1805	John Fisher, 34 Wapping Street, London
1843	James Fisher, 7 Cannon Street Road, London
Fraser	
c. 1830	Fraser. (Not listed by the Post Office between 1840 and 1860)
Froggatt	
Mid 19th century	Froggatt
Fuller	
1832	John Fuller, Whitechapel Road, London
1843	John Fuller, 239 Whitechapel Road, London
	No trace after 1860.

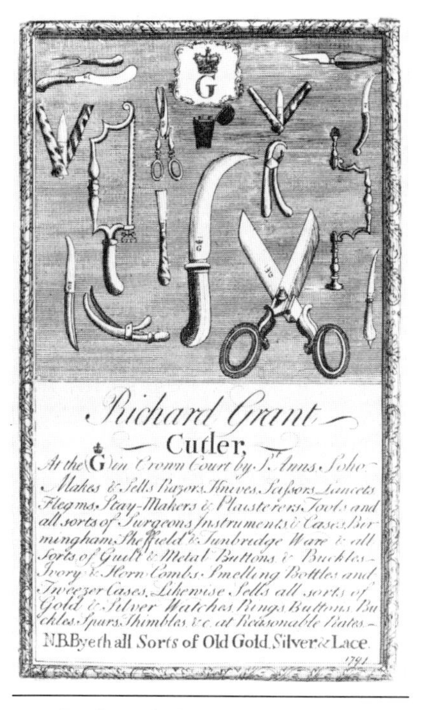

156 *Trade card. (British Museum, Ambrose Heal Collection, London)*

157 *Trade card. (British Museum, Ambrose Heal Collection, London)*

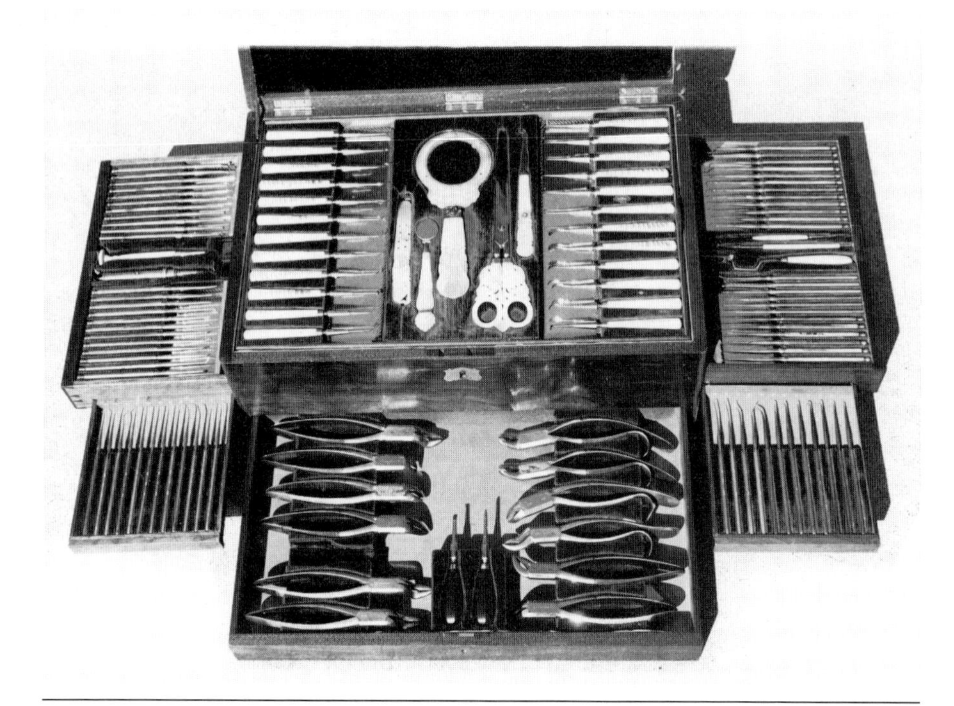

158 *Comprehensive set of instruments, handles variously mother-of-pearl, ivory, ebony, hardstone and metal. S.S. White, c.1865. Possibly made as an example of workmanship. (Private Collection, Dr Gary Lemen, Sacramento, Cal.)*

Gardner	
Mid 19th century	J. Gardner & Son, 32 Forrest Road, Edinburgh
Gay	
1817	John Gay (c.), 68 Kirkgate, Leeds
1822	John Gay (c. and s.i.m.), 68 Kirkgate, Leeds
1826	John Gay (c. and s.i.m.), 5 Kirkgate, Leeds
1839	John Gay (c. and s.i.m.), 10 Kirkgate, Leeds
1842	John Gay (c. and s.i.m.), 10 Kirkgate, Leeds
1845	John Gay (c. and s.i.m.), 132 Briggate, Leeds
1849	John Gay & Son (c. and s.i.m.), 132 Briggate, Leeds
1851	John R. Gay (c. and s.i.m.), 132 Briggate, Leeds
1878	Lavini & Gay (c. and s.i.m.), 132 Briggate, Leeds
1882	J.R. Gay (c. and s.i.m.), 132 Briggate, Leeds
	No trace after 1886
Gibbs	
c. 1740	Established. Gibbs
1756	Joseph Gibbs, 137 Bond Street, London
1772	James Gibbs, 137 Bond Street, London
1800	Gibbs & Lewis, 137 Bond Street, London
Gill (1)	
1825	John Gill (s.i.m.), 45 Salisbury Square, London
Gill (2)	
c. 1810	Thomas Gill (c.), 83 St James's Street, London
Gillett	
c. 1800	Gillett. At 'The Case of Knives' in St James's Market, London
Goodall	
1805	John Goodall, St Saviour's Churchyard, London
Gordon	
c. 1740	Established
c. 1770	Jacob Gordon, Russell Court, Drury Lane, London
c. 1825	Succeeded by H. Underwood
Graham	
c. 1800	Graham
Grant	
c. 1745	Established. Grant
1791	Richard Grant (c.), St Anne's, Soho, London
Gray (1)	
1849	Established. Joseph Gray, 154 Fitzwilliam Street, Sheffield
1864	Gray & Lawson, 51 New George Street, Sheffield
Gray (2)	
1841	Wm. Gray (c., s.i.m. and t.m.), 28 Market Street, Newcastle
	No trace after 1847
Gray & Selby	
1862–71	John Henry Gray (op.), Pelham Street, Nottingham
1874	Gray (Mrs Jane) & Selby (op. and s.i.m.), 27 Pelham Street, Nottingham
1876	Gray & Selby (s.i.m. and op.), 27 Pelham Street, Nottingham
	In business until 1936

Greer	
c. 1790	C. Greer, 10 Charing Cross, London
Grenier	
1698	Isaac Grenier
Grice	
c. 1800	Established. John Grice
1817	John Grice, 239 Whitechapel Road, London
1832	Grice & Fuller, Whitechapel, London
Grick	
Mid 19th century	Grick
Grover	
c. 1680	Samuel Grover, London Bridge, London
Guest	
Late 18th century	Guest. Pieces in Wellcome Collection, London
Hales	
1817	Henry Hales, 4 Manor Row, Tower Hill, London
Hall	
1817	Thomas Hall, 8 Charles Street, London
Hallam	
18th & 19th centuries	Hallam (D.I.M.)
Hammock	
1826	Charles Hammock, 53 Chiswell Street, London
Harnett	
19th century	J. & W. Harnett (D.I.M.)
Harris	
1825	Philip Harris – successor to S. Evans (CH.) – Bull Ring, Birmingham
1896	Philip Harris (CH.), 144–146 Edmund Street, Birmingham
Harvey (& Reynolds)	
1839	Thos. Harvey (CH. and D.), 5 Commercial Street, Leeds
1841	Thos. Harvey (CH. and D.), 13 Briggate, Leeds
1856	Harvey & Reynolds, (CH. and D.), 13 Briggate, Leeds
1861	Harvey, Reynolds & Fowler (CH. and D.), 10 Briggate, Leeds
1864	Haw & Reynolds (CH. and D.), Briggate, Leeds
1867	Haw, Reynolds & Co. (CH. and D.), Briggate, Leeds
1872	Haw, Reynolds & Co. (CH.), 14 Commercial Street, and Briggate, Leeds
1886	Reynolds & Branson
	Still in business today. (Makers of the first short clinical thermometer)
Haskoll	
1784	William Haskoll (Silversmith and C.), The Square, Winchester
1792	William Haskoll (C.), Winchester
	No trace after 1798
Hawkesley	
1865	Thomas Hawkesley, 357 Oxford Street, London
1925	Hawkesley & Son Ltd. Now Gelman Hawkesley, Shoreham, Sussex
Hemmings	
1843	Aug. F. Hemmings, 45 Chiswell Street, Finsbury, London

Hentsch	
1826	Fred. C. Hentsch, 18 Dukes Court, London
1843	Fred. C. Hentsch, 25 Bartlett Buildings, London
1894	Fred. Hentsch, 49 Greek Street, London
Higden	
Early 19th century	Higden, Edinburgh
Higham	
1843	Mrs Priscilla Higham, 48 Jermyn Street, London
Hill	
19th century	Hill (D.I.M.)
Hilliard (1)	
1834	Established. W.B. Hilliard & Sons, Buchanan Street, Glasgow
1856–7	W.B. Hilliard & Sons, 65 Renfield Street, Glasgow
1909	W.B. Hilliard & Sons, 157 Hope Street, Glasgow
1920	W.B. Hilliard & Sons, 123 Douglas Street, Glasgow
	(Made many instruments for Lister)
Hilliard (2)	
1834	H. & J.E. Hilliard, 57 Arcade, Glasgow
1837	Harry Hilliard, 28 Argyll Street, Glasgow
1842	Hilliard & Chapman, 28 Argyll Street, Glasgow
1848	Harry Hilliard, 28 Argyll Street, Glasgow
1851–64	Hilliard & Chapman, 28 Argyll Street, Glasgow
Hilliard (3)	
1832	Established. Hilliard
1850–51	H. & H. Hilliard (S.I.M.), 7 Nicolson Street, Edinburgh
	Now trading as Ross & Hilliard
Hills	
c. 1825	Monson Hills
1853	Henry J. Hills, 46 King Street, Borough, London
Hobbs, Robert & Swayne	
1628	Hobbs, Robert & Swayne. Makers of Prujean Collection
Hockin	
19th century	Hockin
Hodge	
Early 19th century	J. Hodge
Hooper	
19th century	Hooper, Pall Mall. Makers of anaesthesia apparatus
Hughes	
1843	Francis Hughes & Co., 247 High Holborn, London
Hunter	
1843	Hunter Mason & Co., 44 Webberrow, Blackfriars, London
c. 1865	Hunter & Zac, 44 Webberrow, Blackfriars, London
Hutchinson	
1825*	Wm. Hutchinson & Son, Razor Makers, 10 Pinstone Street, Sheffield
1833	Wm. Hutchinson & Son, Razor Makers (S.I.M. and V.I.M.), 10 Pinstone Street, Sheffield
1841	Wm. & Henry Hutchinson (S.I.M. and V.I.M.), 76 Norfolk Street, Sheffield

1859	Wm. Hutchinson & Co. (S.I.M. and V.I.M.), 78 Norfolk Street, Sheffield
1871	Wm. & Henry Hutchinson & Co. (S.I.M. and V.I.M.), 36 Duke Street, Sheffield
1879	Wm. & Henry Hutchinson & Co. (S.I.M. and V.I.M.), 36 Matilda Street, Sheffield
	Now see Skidmore (1922)
	*Said to be 'founded 30 years before Simpson was born' (1811), presumably, therefore, 1781. During the American Civil War a ship bound for America was wrecked and found later to have large numbers of surgical instruments marked 'W.H. Hutchinson'.
Jackson	
1821–2	James Jackson (C.), 30 Bell Yard, Lincoln's Inn, London
Jamieson	
Early 19th century	Jamieson
Jarvis	
Early 19th century	Jarvis
Jessop	
1774	Established. Wm. Jessop & Sons, Sheffield
1818	Wm. Jessop & Sons, Spring Street, Sheffield
Johnson	
1818	Geo. Johnson & Son, Furnivall Street, Sheffield
1856	Geo. Johnson & Son, 13 Porter Street, Sheffield
Johnstone	
c. 1860	Johnstone, Near Long Acre, London
Kettlebutter	
1636	Registered. Richard Kettlebutter
1694	Mentioned
Kidston	
1850	W. Kidston & Co., 18 Bishopsgate Street, London
Krohne & Seseman	
c. 1860	Established. Krohne & Seseman by Mr Grice
1878	First Catalogue. 8 Duke Street, Manchester Square, London, and 241 Whitechapel Road, London
1926	Bought by Alfred Cox (Surgical) Ltd. Now trading in that name. See Savigny
Lane	
c. 1730	James Lane, Fleet Street, London
Laundy	
1783	Sam. Laundy (S.I.M.), 12 St Thomas's Street, Borough, London
c. 1790	S. Laundy (S.I.M.), 12 St Thomas's Street, Borough, London
1802	J. Laundy (S.I.M.), 12 St Thomas's Street, Borough, London
1802	Laundy & Son (S.I.M.), 12 St Thomas's Street, Borough, London
1803	J. Laundy & Son (S.I.M.), 12 St Thomas's Street, Borough, London
1811	Joseph Laundy (S.I.M.), 12 St Thomas's Street, Borough, London
1814	Laundy & Son (S.I.M.), 12 St Thomas's Street, Borough, London. (No trace at this address after 1820)
1805	S. Laundy & Son (S.I.M.), 9 St Thomas's Street, Borough, London
1813	Joseph Laundy (S.I.M.), 9 St Thomas's Street, Borough, London
1816	Joseph Laundy & Son (S.I.M.), 9 St Thomas's Street, Borough, London

1819	Joseph Laundy (S.I.M.), 9 St Thomas's Street, Borough, London Business ceased in this name *c.* 1843. Afterwards, 1844, H. Bigg, 9 St Thomas's Street, Borough, London. See Bigg
Laurie	
1826	John Laurie, 2 St Bartholomew's Close, London
Lawley	
1866	Wm. Lawley, 78 Farringdon Street, London see Milliken
Leavers	
1817	T. Leavers, 28 Charles Street, Hatton Garden, London
Lindsey	
Mid 19th century	Lindsey
Lings	
Mid 19th century	Lings
Logan	
Early 19th century	Logan
Looker	
1790	James Looker (C.), 86 Lombard Street, London
c. 1820	Henry Looker (C.), Poultry, London
Loyd	
19th century	Loyd (D.I.M.)
Lumley	
c. 1800	Lumley
McFay	
19th century	McFay (D.I.M.)
Machin	
c. 1820	Machin & Co.
Mackenzie	
1835	Donald Mackenzie (C.), 48 Nicholson Street, Edinburgh
1839	Donald Mackenzie (C. and S.I.M.), 48 Nicholson Street, Edinburgh
1850	Donald Mackenzie (C. and S.I.M.), 48 Nicholson Street, Edinburgh, and 58 South Bridge Street, Edinburgh No trace after 1876
MacLeod	
1813	John MacLeod (C. and S.I.M.), 17 College Street, Edinburgh
1818	John MacLeod (C. and S.I.M.), 2 College Street, Edinburgh
1836	John MacLeod (C. and S.I.M.), 3 College Street, Edinburgh No trace after 1837 in this name, but then:
1838	James Simpson, 3 College Street, Edinburgh
1844	James Simpson, 80 South Bridge, Edinburgh
McLellan	
1805	Wm. McLellan, St Martin-le-Grand, London
1852	Wm. McLellan, 3 Twiner Street, London
McQueen	
1847	Robt. McQueen (C. and S.I.M.), 52 Grainger Street, Newcastle
1873	Robt. McQueen (C., S.I.M. and OC.), 52 Grainger Street, Newcastle

Mappin	
1818	J. Mappin, 3 Whitecroft, Sheffield
c. 1850	J. Mappin, Bull Street, Birmingham
	Later J. Mappin (S.I.M.), 17 Motcomb Street, London
	Now Mappin & Webb Ltd
Marr	
1878	David Marr, 27 Little Queen Street, London. (Made many of Lister's instruments)
Mather	
1848	Wm. Mather (CH. and D.), 105 Chester Road, Manchester
1858	Wm. Mather (CH. and D.), 109–111 Chester Road, Manchester
1868	Wm. Mather (D. and S.I.M.), 14 Bath Street, London, and 109 Chester Road, Manchester
1877–8	Wm. Mather (D. and S.I.M.), Dyer Street, Manchester
Mathews	
1846	Wm. Mathews, 10 Portugal Street, London
1851	Wm. Mathews, 8 Portugal Street, London
1865	W. Mathews & Co., 8 Portugal Street, London
1878	Mathews, London
1894	Mathews Bros, 10 New Oxford Street, London
Maw	
1807	Established as Hornby & Maw, Fenchurch Street, London
1814	Hornby & Maw, Plaster Factory, Whitecross Street, London
1826	Geo. Maw & Son, Aldermanbury, London
1828	J. & S. Maw, 11 Aldersgate Street, London
1830	First Catalogue (illustrated by Cox, J.F. Lewis and Turner)
1860	S. Maw & Son
1868	Second Catalogue
1870	S. Maw, Son & Thompson
1901	S. Maw, Son & Sons
Mayer	
1864	Jos. Mayer (S.I.M.), 51 Great Portland Street, London
1869	Mayer-Meltzer (S.I.M.), 59 Great Portland Street, London
1874	Mayer-Meltzer (S.I.M.), 71 Great Portland Street, London
	(Factory at 83a Dean Street, London) After, see Down
Mayer-Meltzer	see Mayer
Mayer & Phelps	
1863	Established. See Down
Mechi & Bazin	
c. 1862	London
Medlalow	
19th century	Medlalow
Meesham	
1855	T. Meesham (C.), Market Place, Salisbury
1865	Meesham & Son (C.), Oatmeal Row, Market Place, Salisbury
1875	Henry Meesham & Co. (C.), 19 Market Place, Salisbury

Migden	
Late 18th century	Migden. Instrument in Wellcome Collection, London
Millikin	
1822	J. Millikin (S.I.M.), 301 Strand, London
1826	Millikin & Wright (C. and S.I.M.), 301 Strand, London
1846	John Millikin, 161 Strand, London
1860	Millikin & Lawley, 161 Strand, London
1860–61	Millikin (late Bigg & Millikin), 9 St Thomas's Street, London
1863	Millikin (late Bigg & Millikin), 33 St Thomas's Street, London
1865	John Millikin (late Bigg & Millikin), 12 Southwark Street, London
1875	John Millikin, 3 St Thomas's Street, London (see Bigg)
Montague	J.H. Montague, see Savigny
Mountaine	
c. 1750	Established. Richard Mountaine (C. and silversmith), (1729–1808), High Street, Portsmouth
1798	William Mountaine (C.), High Street, Portsmouth
Moyes	
c. 1825	Moyes
Mundy	
19th century	Mundy
Norie (or **Norrie**)	
1801	W.A. Norie (C.), 77 Hutcheson Street, Glasgow
1813	W.A. Norie (C.), 618 Argyll Street, Glasgow
1821	W.A. Norie (C. and S.I.M.), 5 Argyll Street, Glasgow
1824	W.A. Norie (C. and S.I.M.), 94 Glassford Street, Glasgow
1826	W.A. Norie (C. and S.I.M.), 12 Glassford Street, Glasgow
1833	Mrs W.A. Norie (C. and S.I.M.), 12 Glassford Street, Glasgow
1839	L. Norie (C. and S.I.M.), 12 Glassford Street, Glasgow
1840	Mrs Norie (C. and S.I.M.), 12 Glassford Street, Glasgow
1841	W.A. Norie (C. and S.I.M.), 12 Glassford Street, Glasgow
	No later trace
Nowill	
1700	Thomas Nowill (C.), Sheffield
1788	Nowill & Kippax (C.), 27 High Street, Sheffield
c. 1800	Hague & Nowill (C.), 7 Meadow Street, Sheffield
1861	John Nowill & Sons (C.), 115 Scotland Street, Sheffield
Oliver & Ogle	
1818	Oliver & Ogle, Sycamore Street, Sheffield
1825	Oliver & Webster, 12 Sycamore Street, Sheffield
1830	V. & Wm. Webster, Sycamore Street, Sheffield
	No trace after 1835
Orok	
1774	John Orok (C.), Head of Barrenger's Close, Edinburgh
	No trace after 1778
Paget	
1822	Established. Richard Paget
1826	Richard Paget, 184 Piccadilly, London

Palmer	
Mid 19th century	Palmer
Patten	
c. 1750–80	Henry Patten, Middle Row, Holborn, London
Paul	
19th century	Paul (D.I.M.), London
Peacock	
1867	Aaron Peacock (M.I.M.), 10 Clarence Street, Newcastle
1929	Peacock (S.I.M.), Newcastle
	Still in business
Pearce	see Cuzner
Pepys	
	John Pepys (C.), St Helen's Bishopsgate, London. (d. 1760)
	Wm. Hasledine Pepys (nephew) (C. and S.I.M.), Poultry, London. (b. 1748, d. 1805)
	Wm. Hasledine Pepys F.R.S. (son) (C., S.I.M. and CH.), Poultry, London. (b. 1775, d. 1856)
	Robt. Edmond Pepys (son) (S.I.M.), Poultry, London. (b. 1819, d. 1883)
	Continued in business until 1863 when Poultry was pulled down
Perkins	
1826	Jonathan Perkins, 15 Portland Street, London
Philp, Whicker & Blaise	see Savigny
Plum (1)	
	Plum. In business for himself before entering Weiss, *c.* 1830
Plum (2)	
1822	R. Plum (C.), 4 Dolphin Street, Bristol
1826	R. Plum (C. and S.I.M.), 4 Dolphin Street, Bristol
1841	G. Plum (C. and S.I.M.), 3 Dolphin Street, Bristol, and 262 Strand, London
1851	G. Plum (C. and S.I.M.), 3 Dolphin Street, Bristol, and 448 Oxford Street, London
1880	G. Plum (C. and S.I.M.), 6 Dolphin Street, Bristol
	Went out of business 1932
Plum (3)	
1854–1939	Robt. Plum (C. and S.I.M.), 3 St Augustine's Parade, Bristol
Pratt	
1852	J.F. Pratt (S.I.M. and D.I.M.), 10 Chase Street, Middlesex Hospital, London
1855	J.F. Pratt (S.I.M. and D.I.M.), 420 Oxford Street, London
Price	
Late 18th–mid 19th century	Price
Prockter	
1826	Henry James Prockter, 12 Barton Street, London
Prout	
Late 19th century	Prout, 229 Strand, London
Pryor	
1826	Thomas Pryor, 67 Minories, London Now Pryor & Howard Ltd, London

Quiney	
19th century	Quiney
Quixall	
c. 1800	Quixall
Raeburn	
1805	George Raeburn, 22 Little Queen Street, London
Rauschke	
19th century	Rauschke, Leeds. (Late Mayer & Meltzer)
Read (1)	
1826	John Read (V.I.M.), Bridge Street, Newington Causeway, London (Inventor of the stomach pump)
1829	John Read (S.I.M.), 35 Regent Circus, London
1848	Richard Read (S.I.M.), 35 Regent Circus, London
Read (2)	
1670	James Read, Sword Cutler, Blind Quay, Dublin
1718	James Read, granted freedom of Dublin
1735	James Read, Warden of Cutlers Guild (d. 1744)
1745	John Read (C.)
1746	John Read (C.), Crane Lane, Dublin. Also 4 Parliament Street (front door), Crane Lane (back door)
1776	Thomas Read (C.), Crane Lane, Dublin. Also 4 Parliament Street (front door), Crane Lane (back door).
1800–1900	(S.I.M.)
Reay & Robinson	
1829	Thomas Reay
1837	Reay & Robinson, 87 Church Street, Liverpool
1851	Partnership ended, thereafter Thos. Reay
Remm	
Early 19th century	Remm
Revell	
19th century	Revell (D.I.M.)
Reynolds	
c. 1840	Reynolds, Liverpool
Rhodes	
1818	Rhodes & Son, Wicker, Sheffield
1868	W.C. & J. Rhodes, Castle Hill, Sheffield
Richardson (1)	
1832	John Richardson (C. and S.I.M.), 92 South Bridge, Edinburgh
Richardson (2)	
c. 1750	John Richardson, Prescot Street, London
Richardson (3)	
1800	Thos. Richardson (C.), 31 Maguire Street, Liverpool
1805	Thos. Richardson (C.), 121 Dale Street, Liverpool
1807	Thos. Richardson (C.), Post Office Place, Liverpool
1810	Thos. Richardson (C. and S.I.M.), Post Office Place, Liverpool
1825	Wm. & Thos. Richardson (C.), 74 Church Street, Liverpool
1827	Thos. Richardson (C. and S.I.M.), Post Office Place, Liverpool
1829	Thos. Richardson Jun. (C.), 72 Church Street, Liverpool

1832	Richardson Sen. (c. and s.i.m.), 72 Lord Street, Liverpool
1832	Richardson Jun. (c.), 70 Church Street, Liverpool
1841	Thos. Richardson Jun. (c. and s.i.m.), 70 Church Street, Liverpool
1862	Thos. Richardson, Jun. (c. and s.i.m.), 18 South Street, Waterloo, Liverpool
	No trace after 1862
Rigby	
19th century	Rigby (d.i.m.)
Risley	
1826	Wm. Risley, 18 Roy Street, London
Roberts (1)	
1844	Benjamin Roberts, Surgeon-Dentist, 15 North Parade, Bradford
1844	Benjamin Roberts (c. and t.m.), 6 Darley Street, Bradford
1849	Benjamin Roberts, (c. and t.m.), 5 Darley Street, Bradford
1849	Benjamin Roberts, Dentist, 42 Darley Street, Bradford
1861	Benjamin Roberts, Surgeon-Dentist, 8 Little Horton Lane, Bradford
Roberts (2)	
c. 1800	Moses Roberts, New Street, Covent Garden, London
Robinson	
1826	John Robinson, 19 Kingsland Road, London
Rodgers	
c. 1820	J. Rodgers & Sons, London
Rooke	
c. 1800	Rooke
Rose	
19th century	Rose (d.i.m.)
Rudford	
c. 1850	Rudford, Manchester
Ryley	
1826	J.W. Ryley, 4 Duke Street, London
Salt	
1773	Wm. Salt (c.), Cock Street, Wolverhampton
1781	Wm. Salt (c. and Toy Dealer), Cock Street, Wolverhampton
1822	Richard Salt (c.), 4 Dale End, Wolverhampton
1828	Sarah Salt (c.), 4 Dale End, Wolverhampton
1830	Sarah Salt & Son, 4 Dale End, Wolverhampton
	Thomas P. Salt
	Salt & Son
	Edward W. Salt
	Salt & Son Ltd, Orthopaedic Appliances
Saunders	
19th century	Saunders
Savigny	
c. 1720	Paul Savigny, succeeded to business of late Widow How (c.), Halbert & Crown, St Martin's Churchyard, London
1726	John Tessier Savigny (s.i.m. and Razor Maker), Acorn and Crown, Gerrard Street, London
1784	John Henry Savigny (s.i.m.), 129 Pall Mall, London

1794	John Henry Savigny (S.I.M.), 28 King Street, London
1798	First Catalogue issued
1810	Savigny, Everill & Mason (S.I.M.), 67 St James's Street, ('removed from Pall Mall and King Street'), London
c. 1850	Everill, Philp & Whicker (late Savigny & Co.)
1855	Philp, Whicker & Blaise, 67 St James's Street, London
1856	Whicker & Blaise (S.I.M.), 67 St James's Street, London
1868	Louis Blaise & Co. (late Savigny & Co.)
1872	Louis Blaise & Co., 67 St James's Street, and 276 Westminster Bridge, London
1885	C. Wright & Co. (from Louis Blaise & Co., late Savigny & Co.), 108 New Bond Street, London
1896	Alfred Cox (late partner of C. Wright & Co., from Louis Blaise, late Savigny & Co.), 108 New Bond Street, London
1896	J.H. Montague (late partner of C. Wright, etc.), 101 New Bond Street, London
Sawyer	
19th century	Sawyer
Schmidt & Robinson	
19th century	Schmidt & Robinson, 267 Strand, London
Scudamore	
c. 1700	Scudamore, Spiceal Street, London
Settle	
19th century	Settle
Sharp	
1851	James Sharp (S.I.M.), 26 Market Street, Newcastle No trace after 1866
Sheldrake	
1790	Timothy Sheldrake (T.M.), 483 Strand, London
1796	Timothy Sheldrake, 50 Strand, London
1805	Timothy Sheldrake, 50 Strand, London William Sheldrake, 483 Strand, London
1820	Timothy Sheldrake, 10 Adams Street, London William Sheldrake, 483 Strand, London
1823	William Sheldrake, 483 Strand, London
	see Bigg
Simpson (1)	
1788	Robt. Simpson (C.), 9 Clerkenwell Green, London
1803	Simpson & Smith (C.), 16 Strand, London
1822	Simpson & Smith (C.), 55 Strand, London
1863	Henry Simpson, 55 Strand, London
Simpson (2)	see MacLeod
Skidmore	
1851	Wm. Skidmore (S.I.M.), awarded prize at Great Exhibition, 1851
1898	Wm. Skidmore & Co. Ltd, Sheffield
	see Hutchinson
Smale	
19th century	Smale

Smith (1)
1826 Benjamin Smith, 68 Cromer Street, London

Smith (2)
1803 Wm. Smith, 4 St Saviour's Churchyard, London
1831 Wm. Smith, (s.i.m.), New Street, London
see Durroch

Snidall
1818 James Snidall, 52 Pond Street, Sheffield

Sparling
c. 1780 Sparling (c.), Corner of Norris Street, Haymarket, London

Spurr
1818 Peter Spurr, Arundel Street, Sheffield

Staniforth
1864 G.H. Staniforth (c.), 10 Church Street, Cardiff
1885 G.H. Staniforth (c.), 5 Church Street, Cardiff
1889 G.H. Staniforth (c.), 6 Church Street, Cardiff
Still in Business at Staling Road, Penarth

Stanton
1738 Edward Stanton, Lombard Street, London
No trace after 1744

Stevens
c. 1830 J. Stevens (s.i.m.), 159 Gower Street, London
Later Stevens & Pratt

Stevenson
1822 John Stevenson (c.)

Still (1)
1799 Alexander Still (c. and s.i.m.), Infirmary Street, Edinburgh
1835 Alexander Still (c. and s.i.m.), 3 Infirmary Street, Edinburgh

Still (2)
1817 Charles Still (t.m.), 9 Leicester Street, London

Stirling (1)
1828 Robt. Stirling (c.), 19 New Vennal, Glasgow
1834 Robt. Stirling (c. and s.i.m.), 19 New Vennal, Glasgow
1836 Robt. Stirling (c. and s.i.m.), 12 London Street, Glasgow
1837 Mrs Robt. Stirling (c. and s.i.m.), 12 London Street, Glasgow
1839 Robt. Stirling & Co. (c. and s.i.m.), 12 London Street, Glasgow
1854 Robt. Stirling & Co. (c. and s.i.m.), 3 Saltmarket, Glasgow
No trace after 1858

Stirling (2)
1851 James Stirling (c. and s.i.m.), 88 Gallowgate, Glasgow
No trace after 1860

Stirling (3)
1856 Wm. Stirling (c. and s.i.m.), 44 Trougate, Glasgow
1858 Wm. Stirling (c.), 44 Trougate, Glasgow
No trace after 1892

Stodart	
1787	J. Stodart (C. and S.I.M.), 401 Strand, London
1791	James Stodart (C), 401 Strand, London
1805	J. Stodart (C.), 401 Strand, London
1826	David & Samuel Stodart, 401 Strand, London
1839	David Stodart, 401 Strand, London
Strange	
1815	Wm. Strange (S.I.M.), 17 Cloisters Street, St Bartholomew's Hospital, London
1820	Wm. Strange (S.I.M.), 44 West Smithfield, London
1826	Taken over by Ferguson
Stubbs	
c. 1860	Stubbs (D.I.M.), Birmingham
1897	Edwin Stubbs (CH. and DR.), Warwick Road, Acocks Green, Birmingham
Swain	
c. 1735	Thomas Swain, Bedford Street, London. (Made Chapman's obstetrical forceps)
Tax	
1705	Thomas Tax (S.I.M.), Lombard Street, London
Thistlewaite	
c. 1850	S. Thistlewaite, Manchester
1890	Place & Thistlewaite (S.I.M.), 4 Palatine Buildings, Manchester
1893	Place & Thistlewaite (S.I.M.), 31 Market Street, Manchester
	Still in business 1940
Thompson	
1817	James Thompson, 42 Great Windmill Street, London
1826	James Thompson, 38 Great Windmill Street, London
1843	J. Thompson, 38 Great Windmill Street, London
	see Maw
Thompson & O'Neill	
1833	S. Thompson, 6 Henry Street, Dublin
c. 1860	Thompson & O'Neill
Tully	
1806	Geo. Tully (C.), 24 Maryport Street, Bristol
1808	Philip Tully (C.), Somerset Street, Bristol
1813	George Tully (C.), 24 Maryport Street, Bristol
1813	Philip Tully (C.), Gay Street, Bristol
1816	George Tully (C.), 4 Dolphin Street, Bristol
1818	Philip Tully (C.), 17 St James Place, Bristol
	No trace of George Tully after 1821. No trace of Philip Tully after 1828
Tymperon	
c. 1735–70	Edward Tymperon, Russell Court, Drury Lane, London
Underwood	
c. 1820	H. Underwood (late Charlwood), 56 Haymarket, and Russell Court, Drury Lane, London
	see Yeeling Charlwood

Walker	
Early 19th century	F. Walker, 16 Moorgate Street, London
Walsh	
1839	Jonathan Walsh, 12 St Bartholomew's Street, London
Walters	
19th century	F. Walters & Co., 12 Palace Road, Lambeth
Warren	
1826	James Warren, 20 & 21 Chenies Mews, Bedford Square, London
1887	Warren & Rudgley
Watts	
c. 1800	Watts
Weale	
c. 1740	Richard Weale, Cannon Street, London
Weedon	
1789	Thomas Weedon (c.), 18 Little Eastcheap, London
c. 1830	Weedon (c.), 41 Hart Street, Bloomsbury, London
	(Pieces known until *c.* 1856)
Weiss	
1787	Established. John Weiss (c.), 42 Strand, London
1811	John Weiss (c.), 33 Strand, London
1823	John Weiss (c.), 62 Strand, London
1830	John Weiss & Son, 62 Strand, London
1831	First Catalogue
1843	Second Catalogue, 62 Strand and King William Street, London
1863	Third Catalogue
1883	John Weiss & Sons, 62 Strand, & 287 Oxford Street, London
1889	J. Weiss & Sons, 287 Oxford Street, London
1894	J. Weiss & Sons, 287 Oxford Street, London (formerly 62 Strand)
	Now 17 Wigmore Street, London
Well	
c. 1800	B.B. Well, 431 Strand, London
Wenborn	
19th century	Wenborn (c. and s.i.m.), 30a Cornmarket, Oxford
	see Bayne
Westbrook	
1817	H. & J. Westbrook (s.i.m.), 92 Broad Street, London
Westbury	
1852	Established. Robt. Westbury (s.i.m. and t.m.), 15 Old Millgate, Manchester
1861	Robt. Westbury (t.m.), 26 Old Millgate, Manchester
1865	Robt. Westbury (s.i.m. and t.m.), 26 Old Millgate, Manchester
	In business until 1920
Whitford	
1798	John Whitford (c.), 2 Little Cloisters, Smithfield, London
1814	John Whitford, (s.i.m.), 47 West Smithfield, London
1822	Elizabeth Whitford (s.i.m.), 47 West Smithfield, London
1823	Whitford & Co. (c.), 2 Porter Street, London
	No trace thereafter

Whyte	
Mid 19th century	John Whyte, 58 Upper Sackville Street, Dublin
Wight	
c. 1790	Wight
Wightman	
19th century	Joseph Wightman
Wing	
19th century	Wing (D.I.M.)
Wolloms	
c. 1850	Wolloms, 14 Mortimer Street, Cavendish Square, London
Wood (1)	
1799	Joseph Wood, Spurriergate, York
1831	Joseph Wood & Son
1845	Joseph Wood
1850	Invented York razor
1871	Joseph Wood & Co
1935	Closed business
Wood (2)	
1833	J. & W. Wood (C. and S.I.M.), 109 Piccadilly, Manchester
1836	J. & W. Wood (C. and S.I.M.), 72 King Street House, and Grove Street, Manchester
1840	J. & W. Wood (C. and S.I.M.), 72 King Street House, and 4 Ardwick Place, Manchester
1845	J. & W. Wood (C. and S.I.M.), 74 King Street, and 79 Market Street, Manchester
1850	J. & W. Wood (C. and S.I.M.), 74 King Street, Manchester
1861	J. & W. Wood (C., S.I.M. and T.M.), 74 King Street, Manchester
1881	William Wood & Son
	In business until 1929
Wood (3)	
1868	Wm. Wood (S.I.M.), 95 Lord Street, Liverpool
	No trace after 1875
Wood (4)	
1864	John Wood (S.I.M.), 81 Church Street, Liverpool
1878	John Wood (S.I.M., OP. and T.M.), 81 Church Street, Liverpool
1885	John Wood (C. and S.I.M.), 81 Church Street, Liverpool
	No trace after 1916
Woolhouse	
1818	John Woolhouse, 27 Smith Street, Sheffield Sam Woolhouse, Orchard Street, Sheffield
Woolley	
1836	James Woolley (CH.), 58 King Street, Manchester
1841	James Woolley (CH. and D.), 58 King Street, Manchester
1851	James Woolley (CH. and D.), 69 Market Street, Manchester
1871	James Woolley & Sons (D.), 69 Market Street, Manchester
1881	James Woolley, Sons & Co. (D. and CH.), 69 Market Street, Manchester
	Last entry in this name in 1963

Wotherspoon	
1816	Geo. Wotherspoon (c.), 17 New Vennal, Glasgow
1824	Geo. Wotherspoon (c.), 7 Blackfriars Street, Glasgow
1825	Geo. Wotherspoon (c.), 17 New Vennal, Glasgow
	No trace after 1828
Wright (1)	see Savigny
Wright (2)	
1794	John Wright (c.), 7 Ships Alley, London
1809	Wm. Wright (c. and T.M.), 7 Ships Alley, London
1825	Henry Wright (S.I.M.), 13 London Road, Southwark, London
1832	Henry Wright (S.I.M.), 32 London Road, London
1843	Henry Wright (S.I.M.), 18 London Road, London
	No trace after 1867
Wright (3)	
1782	William Wright (c.), Morrison's Close, Edinburgh
1784	Wm. Wright (c.), Blackfriars Wynd, Edinburgh
1795	Wm. Wright (c.), Blairs Street, Edinburgh
1809	Wright & Son (c.), Horse Wynd, Edinburgh
1815	Wright & Son. (c.), 31 West College Street, Edinburgh
1820	William Wright (c.), 26 Potterrow, Edinburgh
1827	William Wright (c.), 18 Middletons Entry, Edinburgh
Wyke	
1758	John Wyke (Watchmaker and S.I.M.)
c. 1780	John Wyke and Thomas Green
1786	John Wyke died
	(Supplied tools to Josiah Wedgwood and James Watt)
Young (1)	
1777	Established, now Young, Son & Marlow Ltd
Young (2)	
1784	Young, Edinburgh
1803	Archibald Young (c.), Leith Wynd, Edinburgh
1808	Archibald Young (c.), Leith Walk, Edinburgh
1809	Archibald Young (c.), Reid's Nursery, Edinburgh
1811	Archibald Young (c.), Ronaldson's Buildings, Edinburgh
1817	Archibald Young Sen. (c.), Ronaldson's Buildings, Edinburgh
1818	Archibald Young Jun. (S.I.M.), 19 College Street, Edinburgh
1819–21	Archibald Young Sen. (c.), 50 Rose Street, Edinburgh
	No trace after 1821
1823	Archibald Young Jun. (S.I.M.), 58 Bridge Street, Edinburgh
1835	Archibald Young Jun. (S.I.M.), 79 Princes Street, Edinburgh
1847	Archibald Young assisted Simpson in early experiments; he submitted to full ether anaesthesia and allowed naked flame to be applied to his mouth
1861	Archibald Young, (S.I.M.), 58 North Bridge Street, Edinburgh
1879	Archibald Young, (S.I.M.), 58 North Bridge Street, and 57 Forest Road, Edinburgh
1887	Archibald Young (S.I.M.), 57–61 Forest Road, Edinburgh
	Now Archibald Young & Son, 57–61 Forest Road, Edinburgh

European instrument makers

Anton	Germany
Aubry	Paris
Becker	Holland
Beligne	France
Benois	France
Bernard	France
Bichlie	Sweden. Carl Friedrich Bichlie (1799–?). Studied in Stockholm, dentist to the King of Sweden. Made his own instruments
Billard	Paris. Louis Alexandre Billard (1798–1877). Earliest specialist D.I.M. in Paris. Started *c.* 1860
Birck	Germany
Blanc	France
Bogner	Strasbourg, 18th century
Bohme	Germany
Bonneels	Belgium
Bosch	Strasbourg
Boullay	Paris. 'Coutelier de l'Ecole Royale', rue de l'Ecole de Médecine 1, Paris
Boze	Russia
Brager	France
Brevette	France
Canali	Italy
Carter	France
Chardin	France
Charrière	France. Joseph François Bernard Charrière (1803–76). *c.* 1826 established as S.I.M., Paris. 1860 firm became Collin
Chiron	France
Clasen	Belgium
Collin	France
Conrad	Strasbourg
Cotsani	Italy
Creuzand	France
Delamotte	France
Denis	Belgium
Detert	Germany
Dewitt & Herg	Germany
Eberle-Manheim	Paris
Elser	France
Eppendorf	Germany
Esterlus	Germany
Faure	Holland

Ferras	Toulouse
Fischer	Hungary
Franck-Valery	France
Galante	France
Gasselin	France
Gauet	France
Gauvin	France
Gentile	France
Gerber	Russia
Germain	France
Gilbert	France
Glitschka	Belgium
Goldschmidt	Germany
Graiff	France
Grangeret	France. 1795 S.I.M. to French Navy. 1805 S.I.M. to Napoleon. No trace after 1815
Gribel	Germany
Grotewahl	Germany
Gueride	France
Guerin	France
Gugenbutter	Germany
Hajek	Eastern European
Hammer & Vorsak	Germany
Hansen	Denmark
Haran	France
Haufland	Germany
Hebert	France
Henry	France. 'Coutelier de la Chambre des Pairs', wrote *Precis Descriptif sur les Instruments de Chirurgie*, Paris, 1825. Sometimes marked instruments Sir Henry
Hersan	France
Hertel	Germany
Herzhause	Germany
Heynemann	Germany
Hunzinger	Germany
Jetter & Scheering	Germany
Jolivet	France
Joyant	France
Jung	Germany
Keller	Germany
Kraus	Germany

Lassere	France
Laurent	France
Lautenslager & Lautenslager	Germany
Leiter	Austria
Lemaitre	France
Lemale	France
Lepine	France
Leplanquais	France
Lesueur	France
Lichtenberger	Strasbourg
Lipowsky-Fischer	Germany
Loewenstein	Germany
Lollini	Italy
Lollins Frat	Italy
Lowe	Germany
Luer	France
Luent Freres	France
Lutter	Germany
Magnet	Germany
Malliard	Austria
Mariand	France
Mathieu	France
Maug	Germany
Menier	France
Mette	Sweden
Meyer-Ketsting	Germany
Michault	France
Moeke	Germany
Molinari	Spain
Moison	France
Moll	France
Morette	France
Mossinger	Holland
Mouniot	Nantes
Muller	Germany
Nachet	France
Neupart	Germany
Neuhold	Vienna
Noel	Paris
Nyrop	Denmark

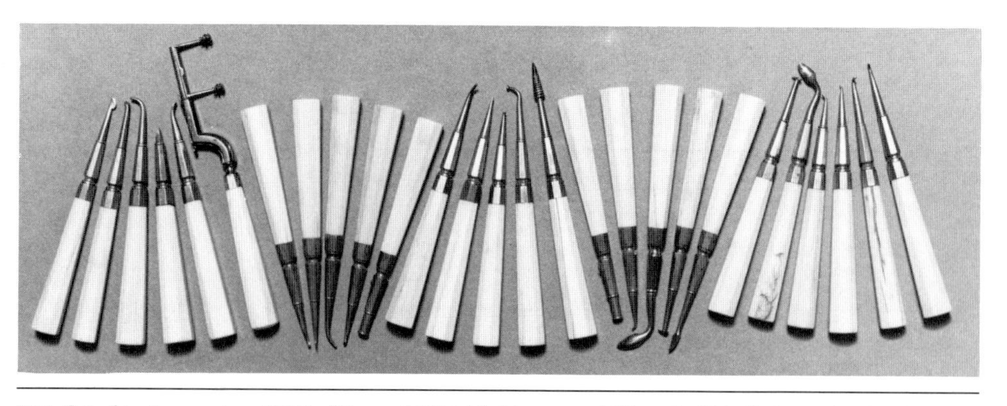

159 *Set of instruments, c.1825. (Howard Dittrick Museum of Historical Medicine, Cleveland, Ohio)*

Odelga	Germany
Odoux	France
Perret	France (Catalogue of 1771)
Personne	France
Pohl	Holland
Raillot	France
Ratery	France
Reiner	Austria
Renault	France
Reymond Frères et Cie	Geneva, D.I.M.
Rizzoli	Italy
Robert & Collin	France
Rohrbeck	Germany
Romelin	France
Sabaj, Neck	Austria
Samson	France
Saverio	Naples
Schaedel	Germany
Schaffer	Switzerland
Schaube	Russia
Schmid-Luniger	Germany
Schmidt	Germany
Schutz, A.	Germany
Seerig	Germany (Catalogue of 1838)
Serendal	France
Simal	France
Sirhenry	France (see Henry)
Siries	Italy
Songy	France

Soubrillard	France
Sourget	France
Sousa-Ferreira, de	Portugal
Soyez	France
Stille	Sweden
Suderie	France
Varnout & Galante	France
Verdin	France
Walter-Biondetti	Switzerland
Weber	France
Windler	Germany
Wulfing-Luer	France
Wunsche	Germany

160 *Case of instruments of Juan Alexand Brambilla (1728–1800). (Museum of the History of Science, Florence)*

North American instrument makers

Aloe	St Louis
Arnold	
1841	Dally & Arnold, Baltimore
1847	Francis Arnold. Instruments stamped F. Arnold
c. 1860	F. Arnold & Son
c. 1865	F. Arnold & Sons
	In business until 1880s
Bagot	
1850	E. Bagot, New York
	E. Bagot & Son
Biddle	
c. 1878	John Biddle, New York. Instruments stamped J. Biddle
	In business until 1880s
Boehun	Rochester
Boekal	Philadelphia
(Bonnerave	Argentina)
Buffalo	
1867	Buffalo Dental Manufacturing Co., Buffalo
Bushnell	
Caswell Hasard & Co.	New York
Chamberlain	
c. 1840	N.B. Chamberlain, Boston Makers of Morton apparatus
Chevalier	
1833	Chevalier, New York. Established at least by this date. Earlier instruments stamped Chevalier
1858	J.D. Chevalier & Sons, New York
Cleveland Dental Manufacturing Co.	Cleveland
Codman-Shurtleff	
1851	Codman-Shurtleff, Boston
Crocker	Cincinnati
Davis & Lawrence	New York and Montreal
Ford	New York
Frye	Portland
Gardiner	Minneapolis
De Garmo	New York
Gemrig	Philadelphia
Goulding	
1847	William R. Goulding, New York (Sometimes Gould but believed to be the same firm)
Haenstein	New York
Hernstein	New York

Hood & Reynolds	
1874	Hood & Reynolds
1897	John Hood & Co.
1903	John Hood Company
Johnson & Lund	
1859	Johnson & Lund, Philadelphia
	In business until 1934
Johnston Brothers	
1869	Johnston Brothers, New York
1881	see S.S. White
Kastner	
Kern	
1830	Horatio G. Kern, New York
	Instruments stamped H.G. Kern
	In business until 1889
Kolbe	D.W. Kolbe, Philadelphia
Krug Sheerer Corp.	New York
Kurmerle	J.F. Kurmerle, Philadelphia
Kurn	Philadelphia
Kuy-Scheerer	New York
Lane	New York
Leach & Green	Boston
Lentz	Philadelphia
Leslie	
1856	Established as Mississippi Valley Dental Depot, St Louis, Miss. Instruments stamped Leslie
1865	A.M. Leslie & Co., St Louis
1883	St Louis Dental Manufacturing Co.
Lufkin Rule Co.	?Michigan
Otto	New York
Otto & Reynders	New York
Penfield	Philadelphia
Plumb	D.B. Plumb & Co., Georgia
Pratt	Boston
Queen	Philadelphia
Reynders	New York
Rochester Surgical Appliances Co.	Rochester
Sharp & Smith	Chicago
Shepard & Dudley	New York
Sherrard-Duffy	New York
Snow	Syracuse

Snowden	
1856	Snowden, Baltimore
1860	Snowden & Cowden
Spencer	See Toland
Sutton & Raynor	
1854	Sutton & Raynor, New York
Taylor	New York
Tiemann	New York
Toland Dental Depot	
c. 1850	Toland Dental Depot, Cincinnati
	Instruments stamped J.T. Toland or H.R. Sherwood or (Dr) J.M. Bronn } until 1856
1863	Spencer & Moore
1874	Spencer and Crocker, later Samuel A. Crocker & Co.
Traux Greene & Co.	Chicago
White	
1844	Dr Samuel S. White, 273 Race Street, Philadelphia
1845	Jones, White & Co.
1849	Jones, White & Co., 120 Mulberry Street
1851	Jones, White & McCurdy
1852	Jones, White & McCurdy, 116 Mulberry Street
1859	Jones and White
1861	Samuel S. White
1868	S.S.W. trade mark adopted
1881	S.S. White Dental Manufacturing Co., Philadelphia
White (Branch Offices) (1)	
1850	Jones, White & Co., 23 Tremont Row, Boston
1851	Jones, White & McCurdy
1857	Jones & White
1861	Samuel S. White
1881	S.S. White Dental Manufacturing Co., Boston
White (Branch Offices) (2)	
1858	Jones, White & McCurdy, 102 Randolph Street, Chicago
1859	Jones & White
1861	Samuel S. White
1869	Samuel S. White, 121–123 State Street, Chicago
1881	S.S. White Dental Manufacturing Co., Chicago
White (Branch Offices) (3)	
1852	Jones, White & McCurdy, Fulton Street, Brooklyn
1859	Jones & White
1861	Samuel S. White
1881	S.S. White Dental Manufacturing Co., Brooklyn
White (Branch Offices) (4)	
1846	Jones, White & Co., 263 Broadway, New York
1851	Jones, White & McCurdy
1857	Jones, White & McCurdy, 335 Broadway, New York

1859	Jones & White
1860	Jones & White, 658 Broadway, New York
1861	Samuel S. White
1881	S.S. White Dental Manufacturing Co., New York
Wightman	
c. 1845	Joseph Wightman, probably of Boston. Made some of Morton's apparatus
Yarnall	Philadelphia

161 *Dentist's showcase with sample dentures. French, c.1860. (Arthur Middleton Ltd, London)*

Chronological chart

of principal surgeons, dentists and scientists

DATE OF BIRTH	UNITED KINGDOM	FRANCE	GERMANY	ITALY	SPAIN
936					ALBUCASIS
1114				GERARD OF CREMONA	
1280	JOHN OF GADDESDEN				
1300		GUY DE CHAULIAC			
1412				GIOVANNI D'ARCOLI	
1460				GIOVANNI DA VIGO	
1498		JACQUES HOULLIER			
1500	JOHN VICARY *c* 1500	ANDREAS DELLA CROCE			
1510		AMBROISE PARE			
1518					FRANCISCO MARTINEZ
1520				BARTHOLOMEUS EUSTACHIUS	
1523				GABRIELE FALLOPIUS	
1537				GIROLAMUS FABRIZZI FABRICIUS AB AQUAPENDENTE	
1540			FRANZ RENNER *c* 1540		
1550	PETER LOWE	JACQUES GUILLEMEAU			ANTONIO PEREZ *c* 1550
1556	JOHN WOODALL				
1590				GABRIELE FERRARA *c* 1590	
1595			JOHN SCULTETUS		
1608				GIOVANNI BORELLI	
1626			JOSEPH SCHMIDT *c* 1626 JOHANNES STOCKER		
1632					
1634	THOMAS TRYON				
1641					
1643		PIERRE DIONIS		CHRISTIAN FRANZ PAULLINI	
1650	CHARLES ALLEN *c* 1650				
1660		NICHOLAS ANDRY			
1678		PIERRE FAUCHARD			
1683			LORENZ HEISTER		
1688		RENE-JACQUES GARENGEOT			
1697	ALEXANDER MONRO				
1700	JOSEPH HURLOCK *c* 1700				
1702		ROBERT BUNON			
1711		LOUIS LECLUSE			
1712	FOTHERGILL				
1714		ALEXIS DUCHATEAU			
1715	PEZE PILLEAU				
1716			PHILIP PFAFF		
1722		ETIENNE BOURDET			
1728	JOHN HUNTER			BARTOLOMEO RUSPINI	
1730				MAURO SOLDO *c* 1730	
1732					
1733	JOSEPH PRIESTLEY				
1734					
1735	JAMES SPENCE *c* 1735				
1737					
1738				ANTONIO CAMPANI	
1740	THOMAS BEARDMORE JOHN AITKEN *c* 1740				
1742					
1748	JOHN CHANNING				
1749	BENJAMIN BELL		JOHANN JACOB BUCKING		
1753		NICHOLAS DUBOIS DE CHEMANT	JUSTUS CHRISTIAN LODER		
1756					
1758		J. R. DUVAL			
1759			JOHANN JACOB SERRE		

● *Countries listed include modern geographical areas*

SWITZERLAND	AUSTRIA	HOLLAND	BELGIUM	HUNGARY	UNITED STATES
			JAN YPERMAN *c* 1280		
		ANTONI VAN LEEWENHOEK			
		CORNELIUS SOLINGEN			
		ANTON NUCK			
	JUAN ALEXAND BRAMBILLA				
					JOHN BAKER (U.K)
					PAUL REVERE
	ADAM ANTON BRUNNER				
					ROBERT WOOFENDALE (U.K.)
					JAMES GARDETTE

DATE OF BIRTH	UNITED KINGDOM	FRANCE	GERMANY	ITALY	SPAIN
1760	THOMAS BEDDOES		THOMAS KNAUR *c* 1760 AUGUST GOTTLIEB RICHTER		
1763					
1766		DOMINIQUE LARREY			
1767	ROBERT CLARKE				
1768				GIUSEPPANGELO FONZI	
1770		JEAN-BAPTISTE GARIOT			
1771			CALMAN JACOB LINDERER		
1776	JOSEPH FOX				
1778	CYRUS FAY				
1780		LOUIS-NICHOLAS REQUART			
1783			FRIEDRICH SĚRTURNER		
1785					
1786		C. F. MAURY			
1789	SAMUEL CARTWRIGHT				
1790		AUGUST O. TAVEAU *c* 1790			
1791	MICHAEL FARADAY	CHARLES G. PRAVAZ			
1792	THOMAS BELL FRANCIS BOOTT				
1794	ROBERT LISTON				
1795	JAMES SNELL ALEXANDER NASMYTH J. CHITTY CLENDON JOHN GRAY *c* 1795				
1796			WILLIAM F. HAHN		
1797		EUGENE SOUBEIRON			
1798					
1800	JACOB BELL *c* 1800 HENRY HILL HICKMAN	PIERRE J. LEFOULON			
1802	EDWARD W. MURPHY				
1804	GEORGE WAITE				
1805					
1809	EDWIN TRUEMAN		JOSEPH LINDERER		
1810					
1811	JAMES YOUNG SIMPSON				
1812	GEORGE F. HARRINGTON				
1813	JOHN SNOW				
1814	FRANCIS SIBSON				
1815	JOHN TOMES				
1816	JAMES ROBINSON				
1817	ROBERT L. ELLIS ALEXANDER WOOD				
1818					
1819					
1820	JONATHAN TAFT				
1823					
1825	SAMUEL J. SALTER				
1826		EUGENE D'ESTANQUE			
1827	JOSEPH LISTER				
1828	ALFRED COLEMAN	PIERRE-CYPRIEN ORÈ	FERDINAND A. JUNCKER		
1829	NORMAN W. KINGSLEY				
1834					
1836					
1838	ARTHUR E. SAMPSON				
1840	THOMAS SKINNER *c* 1840				
1844	JOHN MURRAY				
1850	LAMBERT H. ORMSBY				
1852					
1857	FREDERICK W. HEWITT				

SWITZERLAND	AUSTRIA	HOLLAND	BELGIUM	HUNGARY	UNITED STATES
					JOHN GREENWOOD
					JOSIAH FOSTER FLAGG
					SAMUEL GUTHRIE
					ROBERT C. SKINNER *c*1785
					LEVI SPEAR PARMLY
					JOHN HARRIS
					JOHN LEWIS *c*1800
					CHARLES THOMAS JACKSON
					OLIVER W. HOLMES
					SIMON P. HULLIHEN
					GARDNER Q. COTTON
					HORACE WELLS
					CRAWFORD W. LONG
					AMOS WESTCOTT
				FRIEDRICH TURNOVSKY	
					WILLIAM T. G. MORTON
					CHARLES MERRY
					ARTHUR ROBERT *c*1820
					THOMAS W. EVANS
					MAHLON LOOMIS
					JAMES B. MORRISON
	ALBERT NIEMANN				
GUSTAVE JUILLARD					GREEN V. BLACK
					SANFORD C. BARNAM
					WILLIAM S. HALSTED
	KARL KOLLER				

Bibliography

Allen, Charles. *Curious Observations on the Teeth,* 1687. Reprinted John Beale, London, 1924

D'Allemagne, Henry. *Decorative Antique Ironwork.* Dover Publications, London, 1968

Bremner, M.D.K. *The Story of Dentistry.* Dental Items of Interest Publishing Co. Ltd, New York, 1939

Cahn, Lester R. 'British Influence on American Dentistry', *British Dental Journal,* 133, 1972

Castiglioni, Arturo. *History of Medicine.* Transl. E.B. Krumbhaar. Alfred A. Knopf, New York, 1947

Christen, Arden G. & **Swanson,** Ben Z. 'Oral Hygiene', *Journal of the American Dental Association,* 96, 1978

Colyer, Sir Frank. *John Hunter and Odontology.* Claudius Ash, London, 1913

Colyer, Sir Frank. *Old Instruments Used for Extracting Teeth.* Staples Press, London, 1952

Cope, Sir Zachary. *Sir John Tomes* (Some Famous General Practitioners). Pitman, London, 1961

De Bono, Edward. *Eureka: A History of Invention.* Thames & Hudson, London, 1974

Dechaume, Michel & **Huard,** Pierre. *Histoire Illustrée de l'Art Dentaire.* Les Editions Roger Dacosta, Paris, 1977

Duncum, Barbara. *The Development of Inhalation Anaesthesia.* O.U.P. for Wellcome History of Medicine Museum, London, 1946

Fairly, Peter. *The Conquest of Pain.* Michael Joseph, London, 1978

Fauchard, Pierre. *The Surgeon-Dentist.* Transl. Lilian Lindsay. Butterworth & Co., London, 1946

Green, Roger & **Lewis,** David. *The Advertising Art of Printed Pot Lids, Old Bottles & Treasure Hunting.* Bridgnorth, 1979

Guerini, Vincenzo. *A History of Dentistry.* Lea & Febiger, Philadelphia & New York, 1909

Guthrie, Douglas. *A History of Medicine.* Thomas Nelson, London, 1945

Heilman, Hans J. 'The Development of Rotary Instruments', *McGill Dental Review*

Hoffmann-Axthelm, Walter. *History of Dentistry.* Quintessence Publishing Co., Chicago, 1981

Kanner, Leo. *Folklore of the Teeth.* Macmillan Company, New York, 1928

Keane, H.C. (ed.). *A Century of Service to Dentistry.* S.S. White Dental Manufacturing Co., Philadelphia, 1944

Lesky, Erna. *The Vienna Medical School of the 19th Century.* Johns Hopkins University Press, Baltimore, 1976

Lindsay, Lilian. *A Short History of Medicine.* John Bale, Sons & Danielsson Ltd, London, 1933

Lindsay, Lilian. 'Worms in the Teeth', *British Dental Journal,* 50, 1929

Longfield-Jones, G.M. 'A Set of Silver Dental Instruments from the New Milton Collection', *Medical History,* 28, 1984

Lufkin, Arthur Ward. *A History of Dentistry.* Henry Kimpton, London, 1948

Munch, J. 'Drills, Drilling Equipment & Instruments', *Stoma,* 19, Heidelberg, 1966

Ring, Malvin E. 'Paul Revere, Dentist', *New York State Dental Journal,* 42, Dec. 1976

Samson, Edward. *The Immortal Tooth.* John Lane, The Bodley Head, London, 1939

Smith, Maurice. *A Short History of Dentistry.* Allen Wingate, London, 1958

Thomas, K. Bryn. *The Development of Anaesthetic Apparatus.* Blackwell Scientific Publications, Oxford, 1975

Townend, B.R. 'Oral Magic, Folklore & Tradition' (6 articles), *The Dental Magazine* and *Oral Topics,* London, 1938

Tweddell, Denys. 'Caring for the Teeth 150 Years Ago', *Rickmansworth Historian,* 34, 1978

Underwood, E. Ashworth & **Singer,** Charles. *A Short History of Medicine.* Clarendon Press, Oxford, 1962

Wilson, R. Lucock. *The Story of Dentistry.* Unilever Ltd, Liverpool, 1954

Woodall, John. *The Surgeon's Mate.* Ed. John Kirkup. Kingsmead Press, Bath, 1978

Woodcroft, Bennet. *Index of Patentees of Inventions, 1617–1852.* Evelyn Adams Mackay, London, 1969

Woodforde, John. *The Strange Story of False Teeth.* Routledge & Kegan Paul, London, 1968

Further reading*

John Aitken *Surgical Essays*, 1771
Albucasis *Chirurgicorum Omnium*, 1532
Charles Allen *Curious Observations on the Teeth*, 1685
Giovanni d'Arcoli *Practica*, 1460
Benjamin Bell *A System of Surgery*, 1782
Thomas Bell *Anatomy, Physiology and Diseases of the Teeth*, 1829
Michael Blum *Artzney Buchlein*, 1530
Etienne Bourdet *Researches and Observations*, 1757
Juan Alexand Brambilla *Instrumentarium Chirurgicorum Viennense*, 1781
Antonio Campani *Odontologia Ossia Trattato Sopra i Denti*, 1786
John Channing *Artificial Teeth Made of Calves' Bones*, 1778
Guy de Chauliac *Chirurgia Magna*, 1478
Andreas della Croce *Chirurgiae*, 1573
Dupont *L'Operateur Charitable*, 1633
J.R. Duval *Le Dentiste de la Jeunesse*, 1817
Eugene d'Estanque *L'Union Medicale*, 1864
Bartholomeus Eustachius *Libellus de Dentibus*, 1563
Fabricius ab Aquapendente *Pentateuchos Chirurgicum*, 1604
Pierre Fauchard *Le Chirurgien Dentiste*, 1728
John of Gaddesden *Rosa Medicinae*, c. 1350
Charles Gaine *On Certain Irregularities of the Teeth with Cases Illustrative of a Novel Method of Successful Treatment*, 1858
René-Jacques Garengeot *Traité des Opérations de Chirurgie*, 1725
Jean-Baptiste Gariot *Traité des Maladies de la Bouche*, 1805
John Gray *Dental Practice*, 1837
Jacques Guillemeau *Oeuvres de Chirurgie*, 1598
Lorenz Heister *General System of Surgery*, 1753
Henry, *Précis Descriptif sur les Instruments de Chirurgie*, 1825
Jacques Houllier *Chirurgia*, 1555
John Hunter *Natural History of the Human Teeth*, 1771
— *Pathology of the Teeth*, 1778
Joseph Hurlock *Practical Treatise upon Dentitian*, 1742
Thomas Knaur *Selectus Instrumentorum Chirurgicorum*, 1796
Charles Larforgue *L'Art du Dentiste*, 1802
Ferdinand Joseph Leber *Preselectiones Anatomicae*, 1790

Louis Lecluse *Nouveaux Elemens d'Odontologie*, 1754
Calmann Jacob and Joseph Linderer *Handbook of Dentistry*, 1837
Justus Christian Loder *Anatomical Tables*, 1794
Peter Lowe *Discourse of the Whole Art of Surgery*, 1612
Francisco Martinez *Coloquia Breve*, 1557
C.F. Maury *L'Art du Dentiste*, 1841
Alexander Monro *Medical Essays and Observations*, 1742
Ambroise Paré *Instrumenta Chirurgiae*, 1564
Philip Pfaff *Abhandlung von den Zahnen*, 1756
August Gottlieb Richter *Rudiments of the Art of Surgery*, c. 1798
de la Roche and Petit-Radel *Encyclopedie Méthodique de Chirurgie*, 1790
Walter Ryff *Chirurgia Magna*, 1545
Joseph Schmidt *Speculum Chirurgicum*, 1656
John Scultetus of Ulm *The Chyrurgeons Store-House*, 1674
Johann Jacob Joseph Serre *Essay on the Anatomy and Physiology of the Teeth*, 1817
Robert Cartland Skinner *Treatise on the Human Teeth*, 1801
James Snell *Practical Guide to Operations on the Teeth*, 1831
Mauro Soldo *Descrizione degl'Instrumenti*, 1766
Cornelius Solingen *Manuale Operatien der Chirurgie*, 1684
John Tomes *On the Construction and Application of Forceps for Extracting Teeth*, 1841
Giovanni da Vigo *Practica*, 1516
John Woodall *The Surgeon's Mate*, 1617

*Books available for inspection in some libraries and museums.

Photographic acknowledgements

Those by whose courtesy the illustrations have been published are:

American Dental Association, Chicago, Ill.
Archaeological Museum, Tarquinia

British Museum (Sir Ambrose Heal Collection, Waddesden Bequest)
British Library, London

Central Museum, Mainz
Condé Museum, Chantilly (Photographie Giraudon)

M. Ekstein Ltd, London

I. Freeman & Son, Simon Kaye Ltd, London

Peter Goodwin, London

Hartford Dental Society, Connecticut

Howard Dittrick Museum of Historical Medicine, Cleveland, Ohio

Kunstgewerbemuseum, West Berlin

Loyd Trustees, National Gallery, London

Macaulay Museum of Dental History, Medical University of South Carolina
E.P. Mallory & Son Ltd, Bath
Massachusetts General Hospital, Boston
Arthur Middleton Ltd, London
Musée Dentaire, Lyon
Musée Fauchard, Paris
Musée de l'Histoire de la Médecine de Paris (Cliché Assistance Publique)
Musée du Val-de-Grâce, Paris
Museum of the Baltimore College of Dental Surgery
Museum of the British Dental Association, London
Museum of the History of Dentistry, Cologne
Museum of the History of Science, Florence
Museum of the History of Medicine, Vienna
Museum of the History of Science, Geneva
Museum of the History of Science, Oxford
Museum of London
Museum of Medicine of the USSR, Kiev
Museum of the Swedish Dental Society, Stockholm

New York Academy of Medicine

Odontological Museum of the Royal College of Surgeons, London

Phillips Ltd, London
Private collections in London, Paris and the United States, including those of the late Raymond Babtkis, New York; Rosalind Berman, Cheltenham, Pa; Peter Gordon, London; Dr Gary Lemen, Sacramento, Cal; Dr Claude Rousseau, Paris; Dr Ben Z. Swanson, London; J. Saville Zamet, London.
Punch Library, London

Royal Army Dental Corps Historical Museum, Aldershot

Science Museum, London (Wellcome Collection)
Semmelweis Museum, Budapest
Sotheby & Co, London

Trinity College, Cambridge

University of Alberta Dental Museum, Edmonton
University Museum, Utrecht

Dean and Chapter, Wells Cathedral

162 *Illustration by George Cruickshank.*

Index of proper names

Note: numbers in italics refer to the illustrations
D.I.M. denotes Dental Instrument Maker

Index of subject

Note: numbers in italics refer to the illustrations